Preface

Once again the North/South Liaison Committee is proud to publish the Directory of Libraries and Information Services in Ireland, which is now in its fifth edition. The Directory is a tangible result of the co-operation between the Library Association of Ireland and the Northern Ireland Branch of the Library Association. It is thirteen years since the first edition of the Directory was published and it has grown in size and reputation with each edition.

The Committee on Library Co-operation in Ireland (COLICO) Directory of Professional Associations and Organisations is included in this edition of the Directory as it has been since the second edition. Other familiar features are the three indexes (Name, Subject, and Database, Software & Systems) which have been substantially revised for this new edition. This edition contains an additional 65 entries from the previous edition and also includes the E-mail and World Wide Web addresses of organisations where available. Another new feature, which indicates the technological changes which have taken place since the last edition, is the provision of Telnet addresses for remote login to many library catalogues.

This Directory is a result of the hard work and dedication of many people and the committee is extremely grateful to them all, including the libraries and information services who responded to the questionnaires. The committee would particularly like to thank Angela Cotter who edited the Directory, overseeing and working on everything throughout the whole process of producing the Directory. The committee is also grateful to Crónán Devlin for his work on the indexes. Thanks must also go to Kevin Quinn, Brendan Teeling, Margaret Mooney, Breda Deely and Fintan Costello. For the COLICO Directory the committee is very grateful to Eva Berkery and Orla Fitzpatrick.

The committee is pleased to acknowledge the financial support of Ryco Library Supplies and Swets United Kingdom, Ltd. and thanks are also due to Dublin Public Libraries for the access they provided to their desktop publishing facilities.

Julian Warner

Chairman
North/South Liaison Committee

June 1996

If calling a number in Northern Ireland from the Republic of Ireland place the digits 08 in front of the number given in the Directory. For example if the number given in the Directory is (01232) 12345 dial 08 01232 12345.

If calling a number in the Republic of Ireland from Northern Ireland place the digits 00 353 in front of the number given in the Directory and remove the 0 of the trunk code. For example if the number given in the Directory is (01) 123 4567 dial 00 353 1 123 4567.

The information contained within this Directory is as received from the Libraries and Information Services listed - April 1996.

DIRECTORY OF ̄ ̄ ̄ ̄ ̄ ̄ES AND INFORMATIO̲N̲ ̲ ̲ ̲VICES IN IRELAND

5th edition

Editor: Angela Cotter B.A.(Mod.), M.L.I.S.

Index compiled by Crónán Devlin, B.A., M.Lib.

The Library Association of Ireland
and
The Library Association (Northern Ireland Branch)
1996

First published 1983.
2nd Edition 1988.
3rd Edition 1990.
4th Edition 1993.
5th Edition 1996.

027· 0025 / 862983

ISBN 0-946037-33-7 (LAI)
ISBN 0-906066-11-5 (LANI)

CONTENTS

Preface

NATIONAL AND GOVERNMENT LIBRARIES

AERONAUTICAL LIBRARY 1
Irish Aviation Authority,
Aviation House,
Hawkins Street,
Dublin 2
Tel: Dublin (01) 603 1156/603 1155
Fax: Dublin (01) 679 3349

Technical Librarian	Frances Griffin
No. of Staff	1
Opening Hours	09.15 - 17.30 (Mon. - Fri.).
Services Offered	The Library caters for the needs of staff in the Irish Aviation Authority. Not open to the public, except by special request.
Special Collections	ICAO; ECAC; International Register of Civil Aircraft; Aircraft Flight Manuals.
Subject Specialisation	Aeronautics; Civil Aviation; Airworthiness; Certification.
Bookstock	6,300 volumes.
Periodicals	20 titles.
Catalogue	Card index.
Classification	By Aircraft type, registration, ICAO/ECAC subject.
Computer Equipment	The library is connected to the Irish Aviation Authority Local Area Network Computer System, which has a CD-ROM, File Server. The machine in the Library is a full multi-media machine with CD-ROM. Database, Windows.
Other Equipment	2 Microform Readers/Printers; Photocopier; Fax.

BORD FAILTE 2
76, Lower Baggot Street,
Dublin 2.
Tel: Dublin (01) 602 4000
Fax: Dublin (01) 602 4100
E-mail: p_byrne@failte.travel.ie

BORD FAILTE continued

Librarian	Pauline Byrne
No. of Staff	1
Opening Hours	10.00 - 12.30, 14.00 - 16.30 (except Monday).
Services Offered	Research for 3rd level students studying Tourism subjects.
Special Collections	Ireland of the Welcomes - Volumes 1 - 44, (1952 - present); Irish Travel - Volumes 1 - 21, (1925 - 1946 complete, 1950 - 1952 incomplete).
Bookstock	3,000 volumes - available on loan to staff only.
Periodicals	Will photocopy.
A/V Stock	30,000 audio-visual slides - for hire to staff and professional users.

3   **BORD IASCAIGH MHARA**
(Irish Sea Fisheries Board)
P.O. Box 12,
Crofton Road,
Dun Laoghaire,
Co. Dublin.
Tel: Dublin (01) 284 1544
Fax: Dublin (01) 284 1123
Telex: 93237

Librarian	Aoife Geraghty/Michael Lamb
No. of Staff	2 (1 Professional, 1 Non-professional).
Opening Hours	09.30 - 12.30 14.00 - 16.45 (Mon. - Fri., by appointment).
Services Offered	Subject Searches; On-line Searching; Phone-Fax-Letter Service; Photocopying; Accessions List; Fish-vet for Windows.
Special Collections	B.I.M. publications.
Subject Specialisation	Fisheries.
Bookstock	Will lend to other libraries on BLLD ILL.
Periodicals	350 current titles - not available for loan or ILL; will photocopy.
A/V Stock	35 audiocassettes; 1 compact disk - not available for loan or ILL; BIM video -

Catalogue	available for loan and ILL.
	Computerised.
Classification	Dewey.
Computer Equipment	2 Microcomputers; Software; CAIRS;
	Wordperfect; Transend; Compact Disk;
	Spicers Centre for Europe Database.
Other Equipment	Microform readers; Photocopier;
	TV/video.

BORD NA GAELIGE   4
7, Cearnóg Mhuiríean,
Baile Átha Cliath 2.
Tel: Átha Cliath (01) 676 3222
Fax: Átha Cliath (01) 661 6564

Librarian	Antoine Ó Coileaín
No. of Staff	30
Opening Hours	09.30 - 13.30, 14.30 - 17.30.
Services Offered	Bord na Gaelige is the state body responsible for the promotion of Irish as an everyday community language. Its aims are to provide to Ministers, Government Departments, State Bodies and other organisations on all aspects of Irish, to grant-aid organisations where appropriate and to devise projects for the promotion of Irish.
	Is é Bord na Gaelige an bord stáit atá freagrach as an Ghaeilge achur chun cinn mar ghnáth-theanga pobail. Is iad aidhmeanna an bhoird ná comhairle a thabhairt d'Airí Rialtais, Ranna Stáit agus Eagrais Stáit, eagraíochtaí stáit agus eile a spreagadh chunan Ghaeilge a usáid, eagraíochtaí a mhaoiniú nuair is cuí agus beardais a thionsenaimh agus a maradh chun leasa na Gaeilge.

5   CENTRAL STATISTICS OFFICE
     [Entry as 1993 edition - no update received]
     St. Stephen's Green House,
     Earlsfort Terrace,
     Dublin 2.
     Tel: Dublin (01) 676 7531
     Fax: Dublin (01) 668 2221

Librarian	Catherine Dempsey
No. of Staff	2 (Non-professional).
Opening Hours	09.30 - 12.45, 14.30 - 16.45 (Mon. - Fri.).
Services Offered	Photocopying; ILL (to Government Departments and Libraries).
Special Collections	Statistical publications of CSO and International Organisations; Annual reports of Government Departments and State-sponsored bodies; publications of ESRI, NESC, Statistical and Social Enquiry Society etc.
Subject Specialisation	Statistics.
Bookstock	20,000 volumes - available for loan and ILL, to be returned before 1 Month.
Periodicals	20,000 titles - available for loan, ILL and photocopy.
Other Equipment	Photocopier.

6   CENTRE FOR MANAGEMENT AND ORGANISATION
     DEVELOPMENT
     Department of Finance,
     Lansdowne House,
     Lansdowne Road,
     Dublin 4.
     Tel: Dublin (01) 676 7571 ext. 5035
     Fax: Dublin (01) 668 5506

Contact	Annette Keane, Training Officer
Services Offered	Primarily for use by the training staff of the Centre.
Subject Specialisation	Public administration; management development; management skills and techniques; training and development.
Bookstock	350 volumes, not available for ILL.
Periodicals	15 current titles.

(The Irish Forestry Board)
Sidmonton Place,
Bray,
Co. Wicklow.
Tel: Bray (01) 286 7751
Fax: Bray (01) 286 8126

Librarian	Angela Hogan
No. of Staff	1 (Non-professional)
Opening Hours	09.15 - 17.30 (Mon. - Fri.).
Services Offered	Available to staff only. Public allowed access by prior arrangement. Book loans; ILL; SDI service; Current Awareness Bulletin; On-line and CD-ROM searches.
Special Collections	CAB abstracts on CD-ROM; FAO Forestry, British Forestry Commission material; US Department of Agriculture (USDA) Forest Service Reports.
Subject Specialisation	Forestry
Bookstock	3,500 volumes - available for loan (to staff only) and ILL.
Periodicals	200 titles - not available for loan or ILL; will photocopy.
A/V Stock	7 compact disks; 4 video-cassettes - not available for loan or ILL; 7 video-cassettes - available for purchase.
Catalogue	Computerised - Inmagic.
Classification	Dewey (19th edition).
Computer Equipment	Dell Pentium and printer; Inmagic, Windows; CD-Rom - Tree CD; dBase III, Open Access; CD-ROM player.
Other Equipment	Microform reader/printer; Photocopier; Spiral Binder; Letraset Machine; Heat Sealer; Use of Laser Printer.

DEPARTMENT OF AGRICULTURE, FOOD AND FORESTRY   **8**
Agriculture House,
Kildare Street,
Dublin 2.
Tel: Dublin (01) 607 2803/678 9011 ext. 2163
Fax: Dublin (01) 661 6263

8   DEPARTMENT OF AGRICULTURE, FOOD AND FORESTRY continued

Librarian	Mary Doyle
No. of Staff	5 (2 Professional, 3 Non-professional).
Branches	CEREAL TESTING STATION, Backweston, Leixlip, Co. Kildare; Tel: (01) 628 0426, Fax: (01) 628 0634. VETERINARY RESEARCH LABORATORY, Abbotstown, Castleknock, Dublin 15; Tel: (01) 678 9011 ext. 1002, Fax: (01) 820 4260; (Eileen Gavin, Librarian).
Opening Hours	10.00 - 12.30, 14.30 - 17.00.
Services Offered	Loans, including ILL, and information provision to staff of the Department. Access to others by arrangement with the Librarian.
Special Collections	FAO publications.
Bookstock	c.100,000 volumes - available for loan (3 weeks) and ILL.
Periodicals	1,100 titles - not available for loan or ILL; will photocopy.
A/V Stock	7 compact disks (some multi-disk sets) - not available for loan or ILL; 15 video-cassettes - available for loan.
Catalogue	Computerised, older material on card catalogue.
Classification	In-house, older material UDC abridged.
Computer Equipment	PCs (not yet networked) using CARDBOX-PLUS as the main software package; 2 CD-ROM towers; Databases include in-house database on the Irish food and agricultural industry; CD-ROMs include CAB, AGRICOLA, AGRIS, FSTA, OJCD (EU legislation), COMEXT (EU trade statistics); Diskette - Current Contents.
Other Equipment	1 Microform Reader/Printer; Photocopier.

**9   DEPARTMENT OF AGRICULTURE FOR NORTHERN IRELAND
Room 615,
Dundonald House,**

Upper Newtownards Road,
Belfast BT4 3SB
Tel: Belfast (01232) 524401
Fax: Belfast (01232) 525546

Librarian	Noel Menary
No. of Staff	7 (3 Professional, 4 Non-professional).
Opening Hours	09.00 - 17.00 (Mon. - Fri.).
Services Offered	Photocopying; ILL; Translations; On-line searches; ISBN/ISSN allocation to DANI Publications.
Special Collections	Agriculture; Fisheries; Food; Forestry; Health and Safety; Public Administration; British and EU Legislation.
Bookstock	52,000 volumes - all available for loan and ILL, except core reference material.
Periodicals	700 titles - all available for loan and ILL; will photocopy
A/V Stock	40 audio-cassettes, 160 video-cassettes - available for loan and ILL.
Catalogue	Automated - Soutron Library System.
Classification	DC20.
Computer Equipment	Soutron Library System networked on 7 PCs, 2 printers, CD-ROM drive, Modem.
Other Equipment	1 Microform Reader/Printer; 1 Xerox Photocopier; 1 Unibind binder.

DEPARTMENT OF ECONOMIC DEVELOPMENT   10
Netherleigh,
Massey Avenue,
Belfast BT4 2JP
Tel: Belfast (01232) 529900 ext. 29374/29375
Fax: Belfast (01232) 529550

Librarian	Diane Elliott
No. of Staff	5 (1 Professional, 4 Non-professional).
Opening Hours	09.00 - 17.00 (Mon. - Fri.).
Services Offered	To Department of Economic Development Staff: Photocopying facilities; ILL; On-line searches; CD-ROM facilities.
Special Collections	Economics; Commerce; Industrial Development; Employment and Training; Industrial Relations; Public Administration; Energy.

10 DEPARTMENT OF ECONOMIC DEVELOPMENT
continued

Bookstock	22,000 volumes - all available for loan and ILL, except core reference material.
Periodicals	420 titles - available for loan, ILL; will photocopy.
A/V Stock	10 compact disks - not available for loan or ILL.
Catalogue	Author/title; classified; subject index (card).
Classification	Dewey 20.
Computer Equipment	PCs (not yet networked); CD-ROM facility; Heritage system bought (not yet functional).

11 DEPARTMENT OF EDUCATION
Marlborough Street,
Dublin 1.
Tel: Dublin (01) 873 4700 ext. 2767
Fax: Dublin (01) 8786712

Higher Executive Officer	Margaret Curley
No. of Staff	2.5 (Non-professional).
Opening Hours	09.15 - 12.45, 14.00 - 17.30 (Mon. - Thurs.); (Fri. - 17.15).
Services Offered	Teachers and researchers admitted by appointment (letter of introduction and telephone call in advance appreciated); photocopying; ILL.
Special Collections	Reports and pamphlets on Irish Education; Newspaper cuttings on Irish Education, 1975 onwards; OECD, UNESCO and Council of Europe publications on Education.
Subject Specialisation	Education.
Bookstock	8,000 volumes - 95% available for loan (strictly within the Department) and ILL.
Periodicals	300 titles - available for loan (strictly within the Department) and ILL; will photocopy.
Catalogue	Card catalogue.
Classification	UDC.

| Computer Equipment | Zenith computer; computerisation in progress; electronic mail being installed. |
| Other Equipment | Photocopier. |

DEPARTMENT OF ENTERPRISE AND EMPLOYMENT   12
**Kildare Street,
Dublin 2.
Tel: Dublin (01) 661 4444 ext. 2132 - 2136
Fax: Dublin (01) 676 2654**

Librarian	Carol Flynn
No. of Staff	4 (Non-professional).
Opening Hours	09.15 - 17.30 (Mon. - Fri.).
Services Offered	Mainly internal service with interdepartmental by arrangement.
Bookstock	600 volumes (approx.) - available on loan to Government libraries only.
Periodicals	30 titles - available for loan to Government libraries only.
Computer Equipment	Financial Times Info by FT Profile; Business Eye; CD-ROMs: CELEX and SCAD; Local Area Network; introducing E-mail on Internet.
Other Equipment	Photocopier; Fax and Telex.

DEPARTMENT OF FINANCE   13
**Government Buildings,
Upper Merrion Street,
Dublin 2.
Tel: Dublin (01) 676 7571 ext. 5679/5683
Fax: Dublin (01) 678 5272**

Librarian	Mary Kavanagh/Bláithín Ní Giolla Rua
No. of Staff	2 (Professional - 1 full-time, 1 part-time).
Opening Hours	09.30 - 16.00 (Mon. - Fri.).
Services Offered	A small and specialised library, for Officials within the Department of Finance, not the public.
Special Collections	OECD, IECD, IMF, ESRI, NESC, IPA, CSO, World Bank and United Nations

13   DEPARTMENT OF FINANCE continued

	Publications; substantial EU collection; complete set of Acts.
Subject Specialisation	Economics, Finance and allied subjects.
Bookstock	4,500 volumes.
Periodicals	400 titles.
Catalogue	Author/title.
Other Equipment	1 Microfiche Reader/Printer; 2 PCs.

14   DEPARTMENT OF FOREIGN AFFAIRS
80, St. Stephen's Green,
Dublin 2.
Tel: Dublin (01) 478 0822 ext. 2265/2266/2836
Fax: Dublin (01) 478 5937

Librarian	Mairéad Mullaney (Consultant Librarian)
No. of Staff	4 (1 Professional, 3 Non-professional).
Opening Hours	09.15 - 17.30 (Mon. - Fri.).
Services Offered	Available to staff only; Information service for lending, reference enquiries and on-line searching; Photocopying for other Government libraries.
Special Collections	UN, EU and Legal Collections.
Bookstock	15,000 volumes - available for loan, except reference books; not available for ILL.
Periodicals	100 titles - available for loan, not available for ILL; will photocopy.
A/V Stock	10 compact disks - not available for loan or ILL.
Catalogue	Author; title; subject catalogue (currently being computerised).
Classification	Dewey 20th edition.
Computer Equipment	UNICORN collection management system (SIRSI); ICL Hardware; Database Access to Profile; Business Eye and Lexis-Nexis (Legal).
Other Equipment	Photocopier.

15   DEPARTMENT OF HEALTH AND SOCIAL
SERVICES (N.I.)
Room 530,

Dundonald House,
Upper Newtownards Road,
Belfast BT4 3SF.
Tel: Belfast (01232) 524369
Fax: Belfast (01232) 524778
E-mail: heather.corbett.dhss@nics.gov.uk

Librarian	Heather Corbett, BLib, ACA
No. of Staff	2 (1 Professional, 1 Non-professional).
Opening Hours	09.00 - 17.00.
Services Offered	To Government Departments: loans and enquiries; to other libraries by arrangement.
Special Collections	WHO Publications; Government Publications.
Bookstock	8,000 volumes - 7,500 available for loan to Government libraries and to others at librarian's discretion.
Periodicals	150 titles - not available for loan or ILL; will photocopy.
Catalogue	Heritage Library Management System.
Classification	Dewey.
Computer Equipment	CD-ROM titles: Cochrane Library; Cochrane Pregnancy & Childbirth Database; Cumulative Index to Nursing and Allied Health Literature; Medline (Medfive version); Volnet UK; UKOP and Social Trends.
Other Equipment	Microform Reader; Photocopiers.

DEPARTMENT OF HEALTH - HEALTH PROMOTION UNIT

Public Office, Ground Floor,
Hawkins House,
Poolbeg Street,
Dublin 2.
Tel: Dublin (01) 671 4711
Fax: Dublin (01) 671 1947

No. of Staff	4 (Non-professional).
Opening Hours	09.30 - 13.00, 14.00 - 17.00.
Services Offered	Health Promotion Information - Booklet

16 **DEPARTMENT OF HEALTH - HEALTH PROMOTION UNIT** continued

	Leaflets, Posters.
Subject Specialisation	Health information
A/V Stock	400 video-cassettes - available for loan to health professionals, schools, women's and youth groups.

17 **DEPARTMENT OF HEALTH - LIBRARY AND INFORMATION UNIT**
Hawkins House,
Poolbeg Street,
Dublin 2.
Tel: Dublin (01) 671 4711
Fax: Dublin (01) 671 1947
E-mail: library@doh.ie

Librarian	Aidan Beatty
No. of Staff	5 (2 Professional, 3 Non-professional), 1 part-time.
Opening Hours	09.30 - 17.30.
Services Offered	In-house information updates; Current Awareness services; On-line searching; Information service; ILL - document supply; Internet access.
Special Collections	WHO Publications; Department of Health Reports; Health Policy; Health Management; Health Economics; Public Health; Health Promotion.
Subject Specialisation	Health care.
Bookstock	14,000 volumes (approx.) - all available for loan (to staff only), available for ILL.
Periodicals	250 titles (approx.) - not available for loan or ILL; will photocopy.
Catalogue	Automated - CAIRS.
Classification	Bliss; UDC.
Computer Equipment	Hardware: 8 networked PCs; 3 printers, 2 scanners; 2 CD-ROM towers; Minitel. Software: In-house CAIRS databases; On-line access to DIALOG, Datastar, etc.; Internet access; CD-ROMs: 10 databases; Networked and standalone CD-ROM

access; A range of applications software.
Other Equipment | 2 Photocopiers.

DEPARTMENT OF JUSTICE   18
72-76 St. Stephen's Green,
Dublin 2.
Tel: Dublin (01) 602 8252/602 8254
Fax: Dublin (01) 676 1837

Librarian	Adrienne McGill/Caroline Mooney
No. of Staff	1 (Non-professional) Job Share.
Opening Hours	09.15 - 17.30 (Mon. - Fri.).
Services Offered	The Library is for the use of staff in the Department of Justice and is not open to the public
Special Collections	All-England Law Reports; Irish Law Reports; Halsbury's Laws of England; Archbold Criminal Pleadings; Acts of the Oireachtas; British Acts; Dail and Seanad Debates; English and Irish Statutory Instruments.
Subject Specialisation	Law; Irish and British Legislation.
Bookstock	c.1,600 volumes - not available for ILL.
Periodicals	c.50 titles - occasionally will photocopying.
Catalogue	Card index, by author, subject and title.
Classification	Own subject headings.
Other Equipment	Photocopier.

DEPARTMENT OF SOCIAL WELFARE   19
Áras Mhic Dhiarmada,
Floor 5,
Store Street,
Dublin 1.
Tel: Dublin (01) 874 8444 ext. 2850/3850
Fax: Dublin (01) 704 3686

Librarian	Mary Lynam
No. of Staff	2 (Non-professional).
Opening Hours	09.30 - 17.30 (Mon. - Fri.).
Services Offered	Access restricted to staff of the Department, but people involved in social

19 DEPARTMENT OF SOCIAL WELFARE continued

	administration and research may be given access by arrangement.
Special Collections	Social Administration; Social Policy; Social Security; Employment; Poverty and Welfare.
Bookstock	12,000 volumes - available for loan to Departmental staff and by arrangement with researchers; also available for ILL.
Periodicals	100 titles - not available for loan or ILL; will photocopy.
Catalogue	Computerised system.
Classification	UDC.
Other Equipment	Photocopiers.

20 DEPARTMENT OF THE ENVIRONMENT
Custom House,
Dublin 1.
Tel: Dublin (01) 679 3377
Fax: Dublin (01) 874 2710

Librarian	Noel Hughes
No. of Staff	3 (Non-professional) 2 Full-time, 1 Part-time.
Opening Hours	09.15 - 17.30.
Services Offered	Library service for Department of the Environment staff.
Special Collections	Environmental publications; Infrastructural publications; Housing publications; EU publications; Irish Government publications; Administration publications.
Bookstock	3,000 volumes - all available for loan to DOE staff (1 Month loan period - extendable) and ILL.
Periodicals	200 titles - available for loan, ILL; will photocopy.
Catalogue	Computerised catalogue.
Classification	UDC.
Computer Equipment	Hardware: SYMANTEC. Software: Q & A; Excel.
Other Equipment	1 Microfiche Reader; Photocopier.

DEPARTMENT OF THE ENVIRONMENT FOR NORTHERN IRELAND

The Library,
Room 5-30,
Clarence Court,
10-18, Adelaide Street,
Belfast BT2 8GB.
Tel: Belfast (01232) 541045/6
Fax: Belfast (01232) 541100

Librarian	Anne Loughran
No. of Staff	2 (1 Professional, 1 Non-professional).
Opening Hours	09.00 - 17.00 (Mon. - Fri.).
Services Offered	The library is still in the early stages of development.
Bookstock	Available for loan to members of DOE(NI) staff and for reciprocal ILL.
Periodicals	Available for loan (non-current issues only), not available for ILL; will photocopy.

DEPARTMENT OF THE ENVIRONMENT FOR NORTHERN IRELAND - CONSTRUCTION SERVICE LIBRARY

Room 1408, Churchill House,
Victoria Square,
Belfast BT1 4QW
Tel: Belfast (01232) 250441/250338
Fax: Belfast (01232) 250100

Librarian	Sheila Regan
No. of Staff	2 (Non-professional).
Branches	CIVIL ENGINEERS LIBRARY, Hydebank, 4, Hospital Road, Belfast; Tel: (01232) 647161. DISTRICT ARCHITECTS OFFICE, 21, Hospital Road, Omagh, Co. Tyrone; Tel: (01662) 247727. DISTRICT ARCHITECTS OFFICE, Artillery Road, Coleraine, Co. Derry; Tel: (01265) 42181
Opening Hours	09.00 - 17.00 (Mon. - Fri.).
Services Offered	Photocopying.

22 DEPARTMENT OF THE ENVIRONMENT FOR NORTHERN IRELAND - CONSTRUCTION SERVICE LIBRARY continued

Special Collections	British Standards; Building Legislation; Agreement Certificates; Government Publications; Barbour Microfiles - Technical; Environmental Health; Fire & Safety; Building Engineering; Building Products; Engineering Products; Quantity Surveying; Library Video Service.
Subject Specialisation	Architecture; Building; Engineering.
Bookstock	5,000 volumes.
Periodicals	40 titles.
A/V Stock	Slides; Photographs; Samples of building materials.
Catalogue	Alphabetical (Card).
Classification	CI/SfB.

23 DEPARTMENT OF THE MARINE
Leeson Lane,
Dublin 2.
Tel: Dublin (01) 678 5444 ext. 600/601
Fax: Dublin (01) 661 8214

Librarian	Anne White
No. of Staff	2 (Non-professional).
Opening Hours	09.15 - 13.00, 14.30 - 17.30 (Mon. - Fri.).
Services Offered	Public access allowed; Enquiry; Reference; Photocopying.
Special Collections	Publications of the Food and Agriculture Organisation, Fisheries Division; Publications of the International Maritime Organisation; Publications of the International Oceanographic Commission of UNESCO, OECD, ICES.
Subject Specialisation	Fisheries; Marine Science; Engineering; Maritime Law.
Bookstock	2,000 volumes - not available for loan to individuals, selected titles available for ILL in certain circumstances.
Periodicals	485 titles - not available for loan, available for ILL in special circumstances; will photocopy.

A/V Stock	Microfiche - 6 titles, not available for loan.
Other materials	Oceanographic charts; Official Journal of the EC on microfiche.
Catalogue	Computerised - Inmagic Plus.
Classification	Dewey (20th edition).
Computer Equipment	Tandy 386 with 104 megabyte hard disk, 4 megabytes and Systems of RAM; Software: Inmagic Plus; Windows 3.1.
Other Equipment	Canon Microprinter 50; Photocopier.

DEPARTMENT OF THE TAOISEACH 24
Government Buildings,
Upper Merrion Street,
Dublin 2.
Tel: Dublin (01) 668 9333 ext. 345

Librarian	Desmond Burns
No. of Staff	1 (Non-professional).
Services Offered	Access limited to Department staff.
Subject Specialisation	Public administration; Personnel and Business management; Irish history; Statistics; Energy and transport; Finance and economics; The Arts; Northern Ireland and Anglo-Irish relations; Communications and the media; Security and emergency; Law and the Constitution; EU.
Bookstock	Most available for loan.
Periodicals	Not available for loan.

DEPARTMENT OF TRANSPORT, ENERGY AND 25
COMMUNICATIONS
44, Kildare Street,
Dublin 2.
Tel: Dublin (01) 604 1177/604 1239
Fax: Dublin (01) 670 9633
E-mail: (to be available in late 1996)

Information Officers	Mary Daly/Monica Wallace
No. of Staff	2 (Non-professional).
Opening Hours	09.00 - 17.00 (Mon. - Fri.) by appointment.

25   DEPARTMENT OF TRANSPORT, ENERGY AND COMMUNICATIONS continued

Services Offered	Library services currently being developed.
Subject Specialisation	Energy (International Energy Agency; OECD; EC); Transport.
Bookstock	5,000 volumes - mostly grey literature, available for loan to other Government libraries.
Periodicals	100 titles - not available for loan or ILL, will photocopy.
Catalogue	Under review.
Classification	Under review.
Other Equipment	Microform Readers, Readers/Printers, Photocopiers.

26   ENFO
The Environmental Information Service,
17, St. Andrew Street,
Dublin 2.
Tel: Dublin (01) 679 3144
Fax: Dublin (01) 679 5204
E-mail: 75901234@vax1.dcu.ie

Information Scientist	Noel Hughes
No. of Staff	4 (1 Professional, 3 Non-professional).
Opening Hours	10.00 - 17.00 (Mon. - Sat., including lunch).
Services Offered	Enfo is a public information service, providing easy public access to wide-ranging and authoritative information on the environment. The function of Enfo is to collect and maintain up-to-date information on all aspects of the environment and to make it readily available to anybody who has need of it.
Bookstock	10,000 volumes - not available for loan, available for ILL.
Periodicals	100 titles - not available for loan, available for ILL; will photocopy.
A/V Stock	4 compact disks - not available for loan, available for ILL; 150 video-cassettes - available for loan and ILL; 100 multimedia packs - available for loan (to teachers) and

	ILL.
Other Material	Microfiche: 200,000 reports of the US Environmental Protection Agency 1965 - 1996. Barbour Microfiche Libraries: Health and Safety; Environmental Management; Hazardous Chemicals; Water Quality. Irish Environmental Impact Statements: 500 covering 1988 - 1996. Available in Microfiche and hardcopy.
Catalogue	On-line catalogue.
Classification	UDC.
Computer Equipment	MicroVAX 3100 computer; local area network; database of some 60,000 references used on Enfo and ERU material, available via Eirpac through the public library network; Series of PCs; Access to international databases; 4 track CD-ROM unit.
Other Equipment	2 Microfiche Reader/Printers; 1 Microfiche Reader; 2 Photocopiers.

EUROPEAN COMMISSION 27

European Union House,
18, Dawson Street,
Dublin 2.
Tel: Dublin (01) 662 5113
Fax: Dublin (01) 662 5118
E-mail: Timothy.Kelly@MHSG.CEC.BE

Librarian	Tim Kelly
No. of Staff	4 (1 Professional, 2 Non-professional, 1 Part-time).
Opening Hours	11.00 - 13.00, 14.00 - 16.30 (Mon. - Fri.).
Services Offered	Photocopying; ILL (short loan only).
Special Collections	European Union Publications.
Bookstock	10,000 volumes - available for short-term ILL only.
Periodicals	20 titles - not available for loan or ILL; will photocopy.
A/V Stock	35 compact disks - not available for loan or ILL; 90 video-cassettes - available for loan and ILL.
Catalogue	Q&A on PC.

27   **EUROPEAN COMMISSION continued**

Classification	UDC.
Computer Equipment	UNIX system networked PCs.
Other Equipment	Microfiche reader/printer; Coin-op photocopier.

28   **EUROPEAN COMMISSION OFFICE IN NORTHERN IRELAND**
Windsor House,
9-15, Bedford Street,
Belfast BT2 7EG.
Tel: Belfast (01232) 240708
Fax: Belfast (01232) 248241

Head of Office	Jane Morrice
Librarians	Sinéad Mulligan/Anne Donegan/Paula Woods
No. of Staff	5 (3 Professional, 2 Non-professional) 2 Part-time.
Opening Hours	Phone: 09.00 - 17.30 (Mon. - Fri.); Callers: 14.30 - 17.00 (Mon. - Fri.).
Departmental Libraries	EUROPEAN DOCUMENTATION CENTRES, Queens University, Belfast (Alan McMillan) and University of Ulster, Coleraine (Pamela Compton). All five Education and Library Boards in Northern Ireland are now part of a UK-wide European 'Public Information Network', co-ordinated by the European Union UK Representative.
Services Offered	Access to reference files; European documentation and legislation; Information and sign-posting on European programme funding and policies.
Special Collections	Official Journal of the European Communities: L series (1959 -), C series (1 year), S series (10 issues); COM documents (1983 -).
Bookstock	500 volumes - not available for loan or ILL.
Periodicals	50 titles - not available for loan or ILL; will photocopy.
A/V Stock	10 video-cassettes - available for loan and ILL.

Other Material	Flags available for loan to organisations by prior arrangement.
Other Equipment	Microfiche Reader/Printer; Photocopiers.

FÁS (FORAS ÁISEANNA SAOTHAIR)   29
The Training and Employment Authority
27-33, Upper Baggot Street,
Dublin 4.
Tel: Dublin (01) 668 5777
Fax: Dublin (01) 668 2691
E-mail: careym@iol.ie

Librarian	Margaret Carey
No. of Staff	3 (3 Professional).
Opening Hours	09.00 - 17.00 (Mon. - Fri.).
Services Offered	Full range of services available for staff including lending, reference, photocopying, enquiries, SDI, ILLs, on-line databases, CD-ROMs, multi-media language programmes and Internet. Reference and photocopying facilities available to external users by appointment.
Special Collections	CEDEFOP - European Centre for the Development of Vocational Training - publications.
Subject Specialisation	Vocational education/training; Continuing education; Psychology; Labour Market Studies; Sociology and related EU and Government publications.
Bookstock	18,000 volumes - 17,500 available for loan (to FÁS staff only) and ILL.
Periodicals	100 titles - not available for loan or ILL; will photocopy.
A/V Stock	50 audio-cassettes - available for loan, not available for ILL; 250 video-cassettes, 50 multi-media packs, not available for loan or ILL.
Catalogue	OPAC; library application of BASIS.
Classification	Dewey.
Computer Equipment	Shared Digital 11/780 Mini system; 3 PCs (Dell 486) and multi-media attachments; Windows 95; Microsoft Office; Language programmes; Several CD-ROMs;

29   FÁS (FORAS ÁISEANNA SAOTHAIR) continued

| | Databases include Blaise, Dialog, ESA/IRS, Eurobases, ECHO; Internet. |
| Other Equipment | Microfiche reader/printer Regma LR6; Photocopier. |

30   FISHERIES RESEARCH CENTRE - MARINE INSTITUTE
Abbotstown,
Castleknock,
Dublin 15.
Tel: Dublin (01) 821 0111
Fax: Dublin (01) 820 5078
E-mail: atalbot@frc.ie

Librarian	Alice Talbot
No. of Staff	1 (Non-professional).
Opening Hours	09.30 - 12.45, 14.00 - 17.00 (Mon. - Fri.).
Departmental Libraries	MARINE INSTITUTE (Department of the Marine), see above.
Services Offered	Microfiche machine; Photocopying.
Bookstock	10,800 volumes (approx.) - available for loan to libraries and institutions only.
Periodicals	100 titles (approx.) - not available for loan or ILL; will photocopy.
A/V Stock	25 audio-cassettes; 3 compact disks - not available for loan or ILL.
Catalogue	Computerised - CAIRS Library Management System.
Classification	Dewey (20th edition).
Computer Equipment	Connected to Novell local area network; IBM compatible; Windows package; Word; Excel; Current Contents on diskette; CD-ROM with Aquatic Sciences and Fisheries abstracts; CELEX and waves databases.
Other Equipment	3M Microfiche Reader/Printer; Photocopier; Video; Tape-Slide machine.

31   FORBAIRT
Glasnevin,
Dublin 9.
Tel: Dublin (01) 808 2335/808 2379/808 2325
Fax: Dublin (01) 837 8854

E-mail: infodesk@forbairt.ie

Librarian	Joan McCluskey
No. of Staff	15 (12 Professional, 3 Non-professional).
Opening Hours	09.15 - 13.00, 14.00 - 17.15 (Mon. - Fri.).
Services Offered	Loans; Photocopies (by post, fax); Information Enquiry Desk.
Special Collections	International and National Standards: ISO, IEC, ENs, B.S., Irish Standards; French; German; Japanese.
Bookstock	35,000 volumes - 15,000 available for loan to companies and ILL.
Periodicals	350 titles - not available for loan; will photocopy.
A/V Stock	18 compact disks - not available for loan or ILL.
Catalogue	OPAC - OLIB (Oracle); Catalogue available on IRIS.
Classification	UDC.
Computer Equipment	Local Area Network; CD-ROM Network; Internet; Microsoft Word; E-mail; Excel; Z39.50 Server.
Other Equipment	1 Bell & Howell ABR1300; 2 Rank Xerox Photocopiers.

GEOLOGICAL SURVEY IRELAND   **32**
Beggar's Bush,
Dublin 4.
Tel: Dublin (01) 670 7444
Fax: Dublin (01) 668 1782

Librarian	David Ivers
No. of Staff	1 (Non-professional)
Opening Hours	09.30 - 12.30; 14.00 - 16.30 (Mon. - Fri.).
Services Offered	Reference; BLLD; Photocopying; Professional advice relating to Geological and Environmental matters.
Special Collections	US Geological Survey and US Air Force publications; Irish Author pamphlet series, 2,500 reprints; Archival Collection; David Burdon Hydrogeological Collection.
Bookstock	8,000 volumes - not available for loan; ILL

32   GEOLOGICAL SURVEY IRELAND continued

	on BLLD.
Periodicals	165 titles - not available for loan; ILL on
	BLLD; will photocopy.
Computer Systems	In-magic.
Classification	Part UDC; Part Geosaurus.
Other Equipment	Microfiche reader; Photocopier.

33   GOVERNMENT SUPPLIES AGENCY
Publications Division,
4-5, Harcourt Road,
Dublin 2.
Tel: Dublin (01) 661 3111
Fax: Dublin (01) 475 2760

Information Officer	Anne Healy
No. of Staff	40 approx.
Department	RETAIL DIVISION, Molesworth Street, Dublin 2.
Opening Hours	09.15 - 17.30.
Services Offered	Marketing and distribution of Government Publications and also marketing and distribution of publications for the following agencies: OECD, EBRD, World Bank, Customs Co-operation Council, Council of Europe, European Union, FAO, GATT, ILO, OIE, UN and HMSO.
A/V Stock	2 compact disks - Finance Act 1995, Finance Bill 1996.

34   JUDGES' LIBRARY
Department of Justice (Courts Division),
Four Courts,
Inns Quay,
Dublin 7.
Tel: Dublin (01) 872 5555 ext. 589/242
Fax: Dublin (01) 872 1620

Librarian	Joseph Donnelly
No. of Staff	2 (1 Professional, 1 Non-professional).
Opening Hours	09.30 - 17.00 (Mon. - Fri.), often available

	later.
Special Offered	Reference and loans (Courts only); Photocopying; ILLs; Site for judicial research assistants.
Special Collections	In addition to UK, EU and Irish Law (reports, journals and text books); US Supreme Court Reports; Dominion Law Reports; Commonwealth Law Reports; New Zealand Law Reports; Hong Kong Law Reports.
Bookstock	16,000 volumes - all available for loan to Courts only, Occasionally available to ILL.
Periodicals	45 titles (and c.65 series of Law Reports) - available for loan and ILL (rarely); will photocopy.
A/V Stock	2 audio-cassettes, 4 video-cassettes - available for loan and ILL.
Catalogue	Card catalogue - hoping to move to electronic library system in 1996.
Classification	Subject headings - will probably change to Moys.
Computer Equipment	7 microcomputers; Novell Netware Local Area Network; Laser printer; CD-ROM reader (to be delivered); DOS & Windows; OS/2; Lotus notes; WordPerfect, (access to Lexis soon).
Other Equipment	Photocopier.

MET ÉIREANN 35
(Irish Meteorological Service),
Glasnevin Hill,
Dublin 9.
Tel: Dublin (01) 806 4235
Fax: Dublin (01) 806 4247

Librarian	Lisa Shields
No. of Staff	2 (1 Professional, 1 Non-professional) 1 Part-time.
Departmental Libraries	LOCAL (HISTORIC) COLLECTION held at The Observatory, Cahirciveen, Co. Kerry.
Opening Hours	By appointment with Librarian.

Services Offered	Services to Meteorological service staff; others given access by arrangement and allowed use of photocopier in library; ILL (with exception of some items).
Special Collections	World Meteorological Organisation publications; publications of foreign meteorological services.
Bookstock	27,000 volumes (books, reports and data) - available for ILL with restrictions.
Periodicals	220 titles (80 current) - not available for ILL; will photocopy.
A/V Stock	8 compact disks - not available for loan or ILL; 25 video-cassettes - certain ones available for loan and ILL.
Catalogue	In-house computerised catalogue on network (PC and UNIX), linked to automated loans system.
Classification	UDC.
Computer Equipment	486 PC linked to PC and UNIX networks; CD-ROM database: American Meteorological Society's Meteorological and Geoastrophysical Abstracts (1974 -); Toshiba CD-ROM drive; Modem for Internet connection.
Other Equipment	Microfiche Reader; Microform Reader/Printer; Zeiss microform reader; Photocopier.

36   NATIONAL ARCHIVES
**Bishop Street,
Dublin 8.
Tel: (01) 478 3711
Fax: (01) 478 3650
Web site: Http://147.252.133.152/nat-arch/**

Director	David Craig
No. of Staff	35 (13 Professional, 22 Non-professional).
Opening Hours	10.00 - 17.00 (Mon. - Fri.), excluding Public Holidays.
Services Offered	Public Reading Room (opening hours as above); Provision of copies of Archives

	(mainly photocopies, also microfilm print-outs and photographs); Group visits by arrangements only.
Major Collections	c. 190,000 boxes of archives. Archives of Government Departments relating mainly to the period 1922 - 63; Archives of the Chief Secretary's Office and its associated offices for the period 1790 - 1922; Archives of other state agencies operating mainly in the 19th and 20th centuries, but including some archives from the 17th and 18th centuries; Archives of the court and probate registers dating mainly from the late 19th and 20th centuries, but including a few items dating back to the 14th century; Archives acquired from other sources, including Church of Ireland parish, harbour boards, health boards, hospitals, schools, charities, trade unions, business, solicitor's offices, estate offices and private individuals, relating especially to the 19th and 20th centuries, but including material for the 17th and 18th centuries; Transcripts, calendars, abstracts and indexes of archives dating from the 13th to the 19th century which were destroyed in 1922.
Computer Equipment	PC network (staff use only); Stand-alone PC (public use, dedicated to database concerning transportation to Australia, 1788-1868).
Other Equipment	Public use: 15 Microform Readers, 5 Microform Reader/Printers. Staff use: 1 Microform Reader/Printer, 3 Photocopiers.

NATIONAL BOTANIC GARDENS LIBRARY 37
(Branch of Office of Public Works Library)
Glasnevin,
Dublin 9.
Tel: Dublin (01) 837 4388/837 7596/837 1636/837 1637
Fax: Dublin (01) 836 0080

37   NATIONAL BOTANIC GARDENS LIBRARY continued

Librarian	Valerie Ingram (present Thursday only)
Assistant Librarian	Sarah Ball
No. of Staff	2 (2 Professional).
Opening Hours	09.15 - 13.00, 14.15 - 17.30 (Mon. - Fri.)
Services Offered	Full library service to National Botanic Gardens staff and students; others may visit by appointment for research; ILLs; BLDSC.
Subject Specialisation	Botany; Horticulture.
Bookstock	20,000 volumes - Certain books, excluding reference works and older material, available for loan to staff and ILL.
Periodicals	500 titles - not available for lending or ILL; will photocopy.
A/V Stock	10 video-cassettes - available for loan, but not ILL.
Other Materials	1,500 water-colours (botanical art); Manuscripts.
Catalogue	Card catalogues; computerised catalogue AACR2.
Classification	DDC 20 modified.
Computer Equipment	AST SVGA-LR; Cardbox Plus; Microsoft Windows for Workgroups.
Other Equipment	Microfiche reader; Photocopier.

38   NATIONAL COUNCIL FOR EDUCATIONAL AWARDS
26, Mountjoy Square,
Dublin 1.
Tel: Dublin (01) 855 6526
Fax: Dublin (01) 855 4250

Librarian	Margaret Purcell
No. of Staff	1 (Professional) Part-time.
Opening Hours	09.15 - 17.00 (Mon. - Fri.). Library open to public by appointment only.
Special Collections	Stock devoted to assessment, validation, prior learning and many other topics in higher and further education; Significant stock of current and past reports on education published in Ireland, UK, US and Europe; Reference section; Irish

	Government Acts in Education.
Bookstock	7,000 volumes - available for loan to staff
	only, available for ILL with reservations.
Periodicals	240 titles - not available for loan or ILL;
	will photocopy.
A/V Stock	5 language packs.
Catalogue	In process of computerisation.
Classification	Dewey 20.
Computer Equipment	IBM; In-magic db/textworks (Windows).

NATIONAL GALLERY OF IRELAND   39
Art Library,
Merrion Square,
Dublin 2 .
Tel: Dublin (01) 661 5133
Fax: Dublin (01) 661 5372

Librarian	Ann Stewart
No. of Staff	2 (1 Professional, 1 Non-professional).
Services offered	The Library is currently under
	reconstruction, and is expected to be
	reopened to the public in 1998.

NATIONAL LIBRARY OF IRELAND   40
(Leabharlann Náisiúnta na hÉireann)
Kildare Street,
Dublin 2.
Tel: Dublin (01) 661 8811
Fax: Dublin (01) 676 6690

Director	Dr. Patricia Donlon
No. of Staff	62 (13 Professional, 46 Non-professional, 3
	Part-time).
Departments	GENEALOGICAL OFFICE, 2-3, Kildare
	Street, Dublin 2; Tel: (01) 661 8811, Fax:
	(01) 662 1062; (Feargus MacGiolla
	Easpaig, Keeper; Dr. Patricia Donlon,
	Chief Herald of Ireland).
	PHOTOGRAPHIC DEPARTMENT,
	National Library, Kildare Street, Dublin 2;
	Tel: (01) 661 8811, Fax: (01) 676 6690;

(Grainne MacLochlainn, Librarian). PRINTS AND DRAWINGS, National Library, Kildare Street, Dublin 2; Tel: (01) 661 8811, Fax: (01) 676 6690; (Colette O'Daly, Librarian). THE DEPARTMENT OF MANUSCRIPTS, 2 Kildare Street, Dublin 2; Tel: (01) 661 8811, Fax: (01) 676 6690; (Dr. Noel Kissane, Colete O'Flaherty, E.M. Kirwan, Assistant Keepers).

Opening Hours	10.00 - 21.00 (Mon.), 14.00 - 21.00 (Tues. - Wed.), 10.00 - 17.00 (Thurs. - Fri.), 10.00 - 13.00 (Sat.).
Services Offered	Irish Studies; c.800,000 books, periodicals, newspapers, official publications (public access to reference only); Photocopying; Photography; Microfilming.
Special Collections	Manuscripts; Prints and Drawings; Microfilms; Photographs.
Subject Specialisation	Irish bibliography; Irish studies; Irish history.
Bookstock	c.800,000 volumes - not available for loan.
Periodicals	1,500 titles - not available for loan or ILL; will photocopy where copyright and conservation restrictions permit.
Catalogue	Sheaf (to 1969); Card (from 1969); On-line (from 1992).
Classification	Dewey.
Computer Equipment	DYNIX library system (Cataloguing, Acquisitions, OPAC) running on an IBM RS/6000 computer over an Ethernet local area network; CD-ROMs.
Other Equipment	Microform readers, reader/printers; Photocopiers.

41   NATIONAL MUSEUM OF IRELAND
Kildare Street,
Dublin 2.
Tel: Dublin (01) 677 7444
Fax: Dublin (01) 676 6116

Librarian	Felicity Devlin (Acting)
No. of Staff	1
Opening Hours	Not open to general public, researchers welcome; Apply to Acting Librarian.
Services	Photocopying.
Special Collections	St. Joseph Collection of Aerial Photographs.
Bookstock	12,500 - will lend to other libraries.
Periodicals	140 titles - not available for loan; will photocopy.
Catalogue	Partially catalogued.
Classification	Dewey.
Other Equipment	Microform Reader/Printer; Photocopier (shared facility).

NATIONAL SOCIAL SERVICE BOARD 42
71, Lower Leeson Street,
Dublin 2.
Tel: Dublin (01) 661 6422
Fax: Dublin (01) 676 4908
E-mail: nssb@nssb.ie

Librarian	Hilary Frazer
No. of Staff	1 (Professional, Part-time).
Opening Hours	09.30 - 12.45, 14.00 - 17.30 (Mon. - Fri.)
Services	Staff library for NSSB. Open to the public 09.30 - 12.45 (Wed. ,Fri.), by arrangement with the Librarian.
Bookstock	2,500 volumes - will lend to other libraries.
Periodicals	150 titles - not available for loan or ILL; will photocopy.
A/V Stock	40 video-cassettes - only 2 titles available for loan.
Catalogue	Card catalogue, being computerised.
Classification	Own.
Computer Equipment	Apple Macintosh; Catalogue will be on Lotus Notes database; MS Word.
Other Equipment	Photocopier.

43   NORTHERN IRELAND ASSEMBLY
Gate Lodge, Massey Avenue,
Stormont Estate,
Belfast BT4 2JT.
Tel: Belfast (01232) 521250
Fax: Belfast (01232) 521715

Librarian	George D. Woodman
No. of Staff	6 (2 Professional, 4 Non-professional).
Opening Hours	09.05 - 17.15 (Mon. - Fri.).
Services Offered	Lending service only to Government Departments; photocopying for others.
Special Collections	Northern Ireland & GB Parliamentary publications; Dail & Seanad Eireann debates; 200,000 copies of Westminster Papers and N.I. Parliamentary papers; Statutes and Statutory Instruments; Journals of pre-1800 Irish Parliament and Irish Statutes; material of Irish interest.
Subject Specialisation	Legislation; Political science and related subjects.
Bookstock	14,500 volumes - 13,000 available for loan to Government Departments only.
Periodicals	50 titles - not available for loan or ILL (normally); will photocopy.
Catalogue	Card: Author/title/subject; (being replaced by computer catalogue using Heritage system).
Classification	Dewey 19.
Computer Equipment	2 PCs (Zenith data systems), 1 with CD-ROM drive.
Other Equipment	Microform reader/printer; Microfiche reader/printer; Photocopier.

44   NORTHERN IRELAND COUNCIL FOR THE CURRICULUM EXAMINATIONS AND ASSESSMENT
Beechill House,
42, Beechill Road,
Belfast BT8 4RS.
Tel: Belfast (01232) 704666
Fax: Belfast (01232) 799913

Librarian	Claire Graham
No of Staff	2 (1 Professional, 1 Non-professional).
Opening Hours	09.00 - 17.00.
Services Offered	Current awareness service; Weekly digest.
Bookstock	4,000 volumes (approx.) - available for ILL.
Periodicals	80 titles - will photocopy.
A/V Stock	Video-cassettes; available for ILL.

NORTHERN IRELAND HOUSING EXECUTIVE 45
Library Information Services,
The Housing Centre,
2, Adelaide Street,
Belfast BT2 8PB
Tel: Belfast (01232) 318021/2/3
Fax: Belfast (01232) 318024
E-mail: vhalton@nihexec.eunet.co.uk

Librarian	Vivienne Halton
No. of Staff	3 (2 Professional, 1 Non-professional).
Opening Hours	10.00 - 17.00 (Mon. - Thurs.), 10.00 - 16.00 (Fri.).
Services Offered	To Housing Executive Staff; Photocopying; ILL; Available to general public by appointment.
Special Collections	TI Construction Information Service on CD-ROM; Housing Executive publications; Housing Executive board meeting slides.
Subject Specialisation	Housing (policy, law, sociology, planning, design, management and maintenance); Building science; Regional and urban planning; Landscape design.
Bookstock	12,000 volumes - available for loan to staff only; available for ILL only if not required by staff.
Periodicals	200 titles - not available for loan or ILL; will photocopy.
Catalogue	Multi access points to automated database.
Classification	DC20.
Computer Equipment	Bookshelf Automated Library Management System, connected to internal networked office automation; Digital and Samsung

45   NORTHERN IRELAND HOUSING EXECUTIVE continued

	PCs (486); CD-ROM file server; Technical, health and safety, management information on CD-ROM; Access to the Internet.
Other Equipment	Photocopier.

46   NORTHERN IRELAND TOURIST INFORMATION BOARD
St. Anne's Court,
59, North Street,
Belfast BT1 1NB.
Tel: Belfast (01232) 231221
Fax: Belfast (01232) 240960
E-mail: general.enquiries.nitb@nics.gov.uk

Librarian	Kristine Gillespie
No of Staff	1 (Professional).
Opening Hours	By appointment.
Services Offered	Reference only; photocopy service available.
Bookstock	3,500 volumes - available for ILL at the discretion of the Librarian.
Periodicals	60 titles - will photocopy.
A/V Stock	Promotional videos available for loan to the general public.
Other Materials	Photographs available for reproduction in newspapers, periodicals, etc.
Catalogue	Tinlib.
Classification	In-house.
Computer Equipment	Tinlib software; Fujitsu ICL FergoPro14IV.
Other Equipment	Microform readers/printers; Photocopiers.

47   OFFICE OF PUBLIC WORKS LIBRARY
51, St. Stephen's Green,
Dublin 2.
Tel: Dublin (01) 661 3111 ext. 2159
Fax: Dublin (01) 661 0747

Librarian	Valerie M. Ingram
No. of Staff	2 (1 Professional, 1 Non-professional).
Branch Libraries	NATIONAL BOTANIC GARDENS

	LIBRARY, Glasnevin, Dublin 9; Tel: (01) 837 4388/837 7596/837 1636/837 1637, Fax: (01) 836 0080; (Sarah Ball, Assistant Librarian). (See separate entry).
Opening Hours	09.30 - 12.30, 14.00 - 17.00 (Mon. - Fri.).
Services Offered	Full library service to Office of Public Works staff; others may visit by appointment; ILLs; BLDSC.
Subject Specialisation	Official reports; Architecture; Engineering; Building; Historic Monuments; Parks; Natural History; Waterways.
Bookstock	13,500 volumes - all except reference books and older material available for loan (to OPW staff) and ILL.
Periodicals	1,100 titles - not available for loan or ILL; will photocopy.
A/V Stock	290 audio-cassettes, 160 video-cassettes available for loan.
Catalogue	Computerised AACR2.
Classification	DDC 20.
Computer Systems	2 AST SVGA; 1 AST Bravo MS P/75 on network; Cardbox Plus; Microsoft Works for Windows; APId CD-ROM.
Other Equipment	Microform reader/printer; Microfiche reader; Photocopier; Video-cassette recorder; Radio-cassette recorder.

OFFICE OF THE ATTORNEY GENERAL   48

**Government Buildings,
Upper Merrion Street,
Dublin 2.
Tel: Dublin (01) 661 6944 ext. 306
Fax: Dublin (01) 676 1806
E-mail: denisonm@iol.ie**

Librarian	Madelaine Dennison
No. of Staff	2 (1 Professional, 1 Non-professional).
Opening Hours	09.00 - 17.30 (Mon. - Fri.).
Services Offered	Services offered within the Office include research services (including on-line, CD-ROM and Internet searching), current awareness services, access to subscription

OFFICE OF THE ATTORNEY GENERAL continued

	information services and ILLs.
Special Collections	Judgements (reported and unreported) of the High, Supreme and Central Criminal Courts since 1975.
Bookstock	10,000 volumes - all available for loan and ILL (lending criteria varies).
Periodicals	55 titles - not available for loan; available for ILL; will photocopy.
Catalogue	Cardbox Plus.
Computer Equipment	3 Pentium PCs running Windows 3.1 over Novell Netware 3.12; On-line databases include Lexis/Nexis and FT Profile; CD-ROM databases include Justis Celex and Justis Statutory Instruments; The Legal Information Resources databases are accessed via Lotus Notes; Lotus Notes is used for a number of internal databases.
Other Equipment	Photocopier.

49 **OIREACHTAS LIBRARY**
Houses of the Oireachtas),
Leinster House,
Kildare Street,
Dublin 2.
Tel: Dublin (01) 678 9911 ext. 264/310
Fax: Dublin (01) 661 5583

Librarian	Maura Corcoran
No. of Staff	10 (5 Professional, 5 Non-professional).
Opening Hours	During sittings of the Houses; or when neither House is sitting 10.00 - 17.30.
Services Offered	Use of library restricted to members and officials of both Houses of the Oireachtas.
Special Collections	Debates, Statutes and Journals of Pre-Union Irish Parliament; British Parliamentary papers from early 1800's to date; Oireachtas Acts and Debates; UN, OECD and EC publications.
Subject Specialisation	Politics; public administration.

Bookstock	51,500 volumes.
Periodicals	110 current titles.
Catalogue	Computerised - UNICORN.
Classification	Dewey.
Computer Equipment	UNICORN Collection Management System; AST PCs; CD-ROMs; Access to Internet.
Other Equipment	Microform reader/printer; Photocopier.

PUBLIC RECORD OFFICE OF NORTHERN IRELAND   50
66, Balmoral Avenue,
Belfast BT9 6NY
Tel: Belfast (01232) 251318
Fax: Belfast (01232) 255999
E-mail: proni@nics.gov.uk
Web site: Http://www.nics.gov.uk/proni/pro-home.ptm

Information Officer	Ursula Harrison
No. of Staff	c. 90 (17 Professional, 73 Non-professional, 3 Part-time).
Opening Hours	09.15 - 16.45 (Mon. - Wed., Fri.), 09.15 - 20.45 (Thurs.).
Services Offered	Reference only; open to the public; sale of books to the public.
Special Collections	Various landed estates' papers including the Abercorn, Downshire and Londonderry estate papers; Various business archives including the Harland and Wolff papers; Church records; School records; Poor Law Union and hospital records; N.I. Government records.
Catalogue	Card catalogues (personal names) and Indexes etc. are available to access the records and a computerised geographical (N.I.) and subject index are available; Bound calendars provide descriptions of documents.
Other Equipment	15 Microfilm readers, self-service facility; Photocopying can be undertaken by the staff for the public (A4 = 30p).

51   RADIOLOGICAL PROTECTION INSTITUTE OF IRELAND
3, Clonskeagh Square,
Clonskeagh Road,
Dublin 14.
Tel: Dublin (01) 269 7766
Fax: Dublin (01) 269 7437
E-mail: marie@rpii.ie

Librarian	Marie Kelly
No. of Staff	2 (1 Professional, 1 Non-professional).
Opening Hours	09.00 - 17.00 (Mon. - Fri.).
Services Offered	RPII library open to all readers - particularly suited to those engaged in research in nuclear science.
Special Collections	International Atomic Energy Agency publications, OECD/NEA reports.
Subject Specialisation	Radiological protection; Nuclear energy.
Bookstock	7,500 volumes - not available for loan or ILL.
Periodicals	100 titles - not available for loan or ILL; will photocopy.
A/V Stock	1 compact disk, 70 video-cassettes - not available for loan or ILL.
Catalogue	STATUS - PC version.
Computer Equipment	Dell Optiplex 4100/LE; 2 Apple Power Macs 6100; Scanner (HP Scanjet 11c); 3 CD-ROMs.
Other Equipment	1 Microform reader/printer; Photocopier.

52   STATE LABORATORY
Abbotstown,
Dublin 15.
Tel: Dublin (01) 821 7700
Fax: Dublin (01) 821 7320
E-mail: statelab@iol.ie

Librarian	Michael O'Gorman
No. of Staff	1.
Opening Hours	10.00 - 12.30, 14.00 - 16.00.
Services Offered	On-line searching; CAS; SDI; ILL; Visits by appointment only.
Special Collections	Analytical chemistry; Microbiology;

	Toxicology; Environmental science; Art conservation; Instrumental analysis.
Bookstock	6,000 volumes - 4,700 available for ILL only.
Periodicals	104 titles - not available for loan or ILL; will photocopy.
A/V Stock	10 compact disks, 70 video-cassettes - not available for loan or ILL.
Other Materials	Maps; Slides.
Catalogue	Inmagic DB/Textworks.
Classification	Dewey 19.
Computer Equipment	CD-ROMs; 2 PCs on Laboratory Network; Access to Dialog, ESA and STN data hosts; Internet; Scanner; Presentation Graphics Software; DTP; Chemical Structure Drawing Software.
Other Equipment	Microform reader; Photocopier; Printers.

TEAGASC 53
Agriculture and Food Development Authority
19 Sandymount Avenue,
Dublin 4.
Tel: Dublin (01) 668 8188
Fax: Dublin (01) 668 8023

Librarian	Deirdre Brennan
No. of Staff	8 (1 Professional, 7 Non-professional).
Branches	Library at each major TEAGASC centre. BELCLARE RESEARCH CENTRE, Belclare, Tuam, Co. Galway; Tel: (093) 55455, Fax: (093) 55430; (Marion Moloney, Librarian). GRANGE RESEARCH CENTRE, Grange, Dunsany, Co. Meath. Tel: (046) 25214, Fax: (046) 26154; (Ann Gilsenan, Librarian). HORTICULTURAL RESEARCH CENTRE, Kinsealy, Malahide Road, Dublin 17; Tel: (01) 846 0644, Fax: (01) 846 0524; (Diana Hickey, Librarian). JOHNSTOWN CASTLE RESEARCH CENTRE, Co. Wexford; Tel: (053) 42888, Fax: (053) 42004; (Sarah Lacey,

	Librarian). MOOREPARK RESEARCH CENTRE, Fermoy, Co. Cork; Tel: (025) 31422, Fax: (025) 32563; (Siobhán Keating, Librarian). NATIONAL FOOD CENTRE, Castleknock, Dublin 15; Tel: (01) 838 3222, Fax: (01) 838 3684; (Ann McLoughlin, Librarian). OAKPARK RESEARCH CENTRE, Oakpark, Carlow; Tel: (0503) 70200, Fax: (0503) 42423, (Margaret Collins, Librarian).
Opening Hours	HQ: 08.00 - 16.00 (Mon. - Fri.).
Services Offered	Book (loan service); Periodicals (photocopy).
Bookstock	37,000 volumes (approx.) - 36,000 available for loan and ILL.
Periodicals	300 titles (approx.) - not available for loan or ILL; will photocopy
A/V Stock	160 video-cassettes - not available for loan or ILL.
Catalogue	Card catalogue (1958 - 1987), Computerised (1988 -).
Classification	UDC, Dewey.
Computer Systems	Internal computerised system for cataloguing books.
Other Equipment	Microfiche reader; Photocopier for general use in organisation, none specifically in the library.

54   VALUATION OFFICE
6, Ely Place,
Dublin 2.
Tel: Dublin (01) 676 3211
Fax: Dublin (01) 678 9646
E-mail: gilbert@valoff.ie

Librarian	Mary Rose Doris
No. of Staff	1 (Part-time).
Opening Hours	Internal only; 09.15 - 17.30.
Services Offered	Books on Property Valuation.
Bookstock	600 volumes - available for loan; not available for ILL.

Periodicals	10 titles - not available for loan or ILL; will photocopy.
Catalogue	Computer Index
Classification	Title; Author.
Computer Equipment	Available to staff on PC; database index.

VETERINARY RESEARCH LABORATORY 55
Department of Agriculture, Food & Forestry
Abbotstown,
Castleknock,
Dublin 15.
Tel: Dublin (01) 607 2869 ext. 1002
Fax: Dublin (01) 821 3010
E-mail: abbot@us7.iva.ie

Librarian	Eileen Gavin
No. of Staff	1.
Opening Hours	09.30 - 17.30.
Services Offered	ILL; BLDSC; Current awareness; Literature searches; Translations; Internet (newsgroups and e-mail).
Bookstock	1,200 volumes - all available for loan and ILL (if not in constant use).
Periodicals	180 titles - available for loan; not available for ILL; will photocopy.
A/V Stock	2 video-cassettes - available for loan and ILL.
Catalogue	Textbook catalogue (on computer); Periodicals catalogue (list form).
Classification	In house (DAFF).
Computer Equipment	PC and printer; Cardbox; CCOD (ISI).
Other Equipment	Microfiche reader; Photocopier.

PUBLIC LIBRARIES

56 **AN CHOMHAIRLE LEABHARLANNA**
The Library Council,
53-54, Upper Mount Street,
Dublin 2.
Tel: Dublin (01) 676 1167/676 1963
Fax: Dublin (01) 676 6721
E-mail: libcounc@iol.ie
Web site: Http://dallas.ucd.ie/ ~ library

Librarian	Alun Bevan
No. of Staff	2 (1 Professional, 1 Non-professional).
Opening Hours	09.30 - 13.00, 14.15 - 17.00, (Mon. - Fri.), strictly by appointment only.
Services Offered	Research Library collections include: books, serials and audio-visual training aids on librarianship and other related disciplines; Database of suppliers of library equipment and services; Newspaper cutting files on Irish libraries; Statistical databases on Irish public libraries; Trade literature collection covering library equipment and service providers.

Services provided by the Research Library include: Brief bibliographic searches; Current awareness service; Photocopying service; Quick reference answers to enquiries by post or telephone.
The Research and Information Department, which maintains the Research Library also maintains a permanent exhibition of library shelving and other furniture in the Library Equipment Display Centre. This Centre is open to visitors by appointment with the Research & Information Officer.
The services of the Research and Information Department are geared primarily to meet the informational needs of the staff of An Chomhairle

	Leabharlanna and to provide information on library matters to public library authorities. Requests from non-public librarians are dealt with at the discretion of the Research and Information Officer, dependent on staff resources being available.
Bookstock	3,000 volumes - available for loan and ILL.
Periodicals	200 titles - not available for loan or ILL; will photocopy.
A/V Stock	4 audio-cassettes, 27 video-cassettes - available for loan and ILL; Catalogue of A/V Stock available on request.
Other Materials	18 16mm films, 28 tape/slides.
Catalogue	Card.
Classification	Dewey
Computer Equipment	PCs; CD-ROM drives; Modems; Access to CD-ROM drive; Web page at http://dallas.ucd.ie/ ~ library; In-house databases - Library service and equipment suppliers; Catalogue of library (1985 -); Bibliographic databases.
Other Equipment	Microform readers; Photocopiers.

BELFAST EDUCATION AND LIBRARY BOARD   57
Belfast Public Libraries,
Central Library,
Royal Avenue,
Belfast BT1 1EA.
Tel: Belfast (01232) 243233
Fax: Belfast (01232) 332819
Telex: BT Gold 9312132609

Chief Librarian	J.N. Montgomery, A.L.A.
No. of Staff	178 (49 Professional, 129 Non-professional).
Reference Departments	Humanities & General; Business; Science & Technology; Fine Arts; Music; Irish & Local Studies.
Opening Hours	09.30-20.00 (Mon., Thur.), 09.30-17.30 (Tues., Wed., Fri.), 09.30-13.00 (Sat.).

57   BELFAST EDUCATION AND LIBRARY BOARD continued

Branch Libraries &

Opening Hours

CENTRAL LENDING, Royal Avenue, Belfast BT1 1EA; Tel: (01232) 243233; Opening Hours: 13.30 - 20.00 (Mon. and Thur.), 09.30 - 17.30 (Tue., Wed., Fri.), 09.30 - 13.00 (Sat.). ANDERSONSTOWN, Slievegallion Drive, Belfast BT11 7GH; Tel: (01232) 301786; Opening Hours: 13.30 - 20.00 (Mon., Thur.), 09.30 - 12.30, 13.30 - 17.30 (Tues., Wed., Fri.). ARDOYNE, 446-450, Crumlin Road, Belfast BT14 7GH; Tel: (01232) 391579.; Opening Hours: 09.30 - 13.00, 14.00 - 17.30 (Mon., Tue., Wed., Fri.), 13.30 - 20.00 (Thur.), 09.30 - 13.00 (Sat.). BALLYHACKAMORE, 1-3, Eastleigh Drive, Belfast BT4 3DX, Tel: (01232) 471387, Opening Hours: 13.30 - 20.00 (Mon., Thur.), 09.30 - 17.30 (Tue., Wed., Fri.), 09.30 -13.00 (Sat.). BALLYMACARRETT, 19-35, Templemore Avenue, Belfast BT5 4FP; Tel: (01232) 451533; Opening Hours: 13.30 - 20.00 (Mon., Thur.), 09.30 - 17.30 (Tue., Wed., Fri.), 09.30 - 13.00 (Sat.). CAIRNMARTIN, Cairnmartin Secondary School, Ballygomartin Road, Belfast BT13 3NL; Tel: (01232) 712601; Opening Hours: 13.30 - 17.30, (Mon., Wed., Fri.), 13.30 - 20.00, (Tue., Thur.). CHICHESTER, Salisbury Avenue, Belfast BT15 5EB; Tel: (01232) 370896; Opening Hours: 13.30 - 20.00 (Mon., Thur.), 09.30 - 17.30 (Tue., Wed., Fri.), 09.30 - 13.00 (Sat.). FALLS ROAD, 49, Falls Road, Belfast BT12 4PD; Tel: (01232) 326052; Opening Hours: 13.30 - 20.00 (Mon., Thur.), 09.30 - 17.30 (Tue., Wed., Fri.), 09.30 - 13.00 (Sat.). FINAGHY, 13, Finaghy Road South, Belfast BT10 0BW; Tel: (01232) 301226. Opening Hours: 10.00 - 20.00 - (Mon.), 10.00 - 17.30 (Tues., Wed., Fri.), 13.00 - 20.00 (Thur.).

HOLYWOOD ROAD, 85-89, Holywood Road, Belfast BT4 3BD; Tel: (01232) 471309; Opening Hours: 13.30 - 20.00 (Mon., Thur.), 09.30 - 17.30 (Tue., Wed., Fri.), 09.30 - 13.00 (Sat.). LIGONIEL, 53-55, Ligoniel Road, Belfast BT14 8BW; Tel: (01232) 391615; Opening Hours: 13.30 - 20.00 (Mon., Thur.), 09.30 - 17.30 (Tue., Wed., Fri.), 09.30 - 13.00 (Sat.). LISBURN ROAD, 440, Lisburn Road, Belfast BT9 6GR; Tel: (01232) 381170; Opening Hours: 13.30 - 20.00 (Mon., Thur.), 09.30 - 17.30 (Tue., Wed., Fri.), 09.30 - 13.00 (Sat.). OLDPARK ROAD, 46, Oldpark Road, Belfast BT14 6FS; Tel: (01232) 351591; Opening Hours: 13.30 - 19.00 (Mon.), 09.30 - 12.30, 13.30 - 17.30 (Wed., Fri.). ORMEAU ROAD, Ormeau Road Embankment, Belfast BT7 3GG; Tel: (01232) 491591; Opening Hours: 13.30 - 20.00 (Mon., Thur.), 09.30 - 17.30 (Tue., Wed., Fri.), 09.30 - 13.00 (Sat.). SANDY ROW, 127, Sandy Row, BT12 5ET; Tel: (01232) 326089; Opening Hours: 13.30 - 19.00 (Mon., Thur.), 09.30 - 17.30 (Tue., Wed., Fri.), 09.30 - 13.00 (Sat.). SHANKILL, 298-300, Shankill Road, Belfast BT13 1FT; Tel: (01232) 326330; Opening Hours: 13.30 - 20.00 (Mon., Thur.), 09.30 - 17.30 (Tue., Wed., Fri.), 09.30 - 13.00 (Sat.). SKEGONEILL, Skegoneill Avenue, Belfast BT15 3JN; Tel: (01232) 370455; Opening Hours: 13.30 - 20.00 (Mon., Thur.), 09.30 - 17.30 (Tue., Wed., Fri.), 09.30 - 13.00 (Sat.). SUFFOLK, Stewartstown Road, Belfast BT11 9JP; Tel: (01232) 301183; Opening Hours: 13.30 - 20.00 (Mon., Thur.), 09.30 - 17.30 (Tue., Wed., Fri.), 09.30 - 13.00 (Sat.). WHITEROCK, Whiterock Road, Belfast BT12 7PG; Tel: (01232) 249846; Opening Hours: 13.30 - 20.00 (Mon., Thur.), 09.30

- 17.30 (Tue., Wed., Fri.).
WHITEWELL, 17, Navarra Place,
Newtownabbey, BT36 7JX; Tel: (01232)
772677; Opening Hours: 14.00 - 20.00
(Mon.), 14.00 - 17.00 (Wed.), 10.00 -
13.00, 14.00 - 17.00 (Fri.).
WOODSTOCK, 358, Woodstock Road,
Belfast BT6 9DQ; Tel: (01232) 732917;
Opening Hours: 13.30 - 20.00 (Mon.,
Thur.), 09.30 - 17.30 (Tue., Wed., Fri.),
09.30 - 13.00 (Sat.).

Mobile Libraries	2.
Services Offered	On-line services (Dialog, Program, Infoline, etc.); 3 Talking Newspapers (copy and distribute only); Music listening facilities; Teletext; Fax; ILL; Photocopying.
Other Services	SCHOOLS LIBRARY SERVICE (Primary, Secondary, Audio Visual and Educational Film Library), The Ulida Centre, Somerset Street, Ormeau Road, Belfast BT7 2GS; Tel: (01232) 491058, Fax: (01232) 491972. COLLEGES: (The colleges operate independently of Belfast Public Library but still within the Belfast Education and Library Board) COLLEGE OF TECHNOLOGY, College Square East, Belfast BT1 6DS; Tel: (01232) 327244; (Millfield Building), Millfield, Belfast BT1 6DJ; Tel: (01232) 327244. COLLEGE OF BUSINESS STUDIES, Brunswick Street, Belfast BT2 7EX; Tel: (01232) 245891. RUPERT STANLEY COLLEGE, Tower Street, Belfast BT5 4FH; Tel: (01232) 452111. SCHOOL OF MUSIC, 99, Donegall Pass, Belfast BT7 1DR; Tel: (01232) 322435.
Special Services	Hospitals; Housebound; Visually Impaired; Prisons; Mobile Libraries; CENTRAL LIBRARY, Royal Avenue, Belfast BT1 1EA; Tel: (01232) 243233.
Special Collections	Patents; UN and Agency publications;

	British and Irish Government publications; Northern Ireland Newspapers; Colour Plate Books; IJFR "B", "C".
Bookstock	1,650,000 volumes - all stock available for loan to any accredited customer or organisation (with exception of rare or fine books).
Periodicals	1,170 current titles plus substantial back files - not available for loan; will photocopy.
A/V Stock	7,000 audio-cassettes (plus 750 spoken word for visually impaired), 8,230 compact discs - available for loan to BPL members only; not available for ILL; 1,400 video-cassettes (mainly educational) - available for loan to BPL members, schools and organised groups; not available for ILL; 1,020 multimedia packs (educational) - available for loan to schools within BELB area; not available for ILL.
Other Materials	57,000 slides (mainly art); 1,400 filmstrips; 4,500 prints; 660 photographs (local history); 5,700 postcards; 1,400 portfolios; 4,000 wallcharts - available for loan to schools within BELB area.
Manuscripts	350 approx. (mainly literary - includes typescripts annotated by author) - not available for loan; applications for ILL considered.
Catalogue	Reference: Author/Classified/Subject index (card, also on-line OPACs). Lending: Author/title On-line.
Classification	Reference: Dewey. Lending: Dewey (abbreviated).
Computer Equipment	DS Module 3 Plus Library Circulation System using a WAN comprising of a central processor, circulation terminals, VDUs, printers and ancillary equipment; CD-ROM network using a Novell LAN and 10 Compaq PCs as workstations and file servers; 4 standalone CD-ROM stations using Compaq Prolineau PCs; 4 workstations (Compaq Prolineau and

BELFAST EDUCATION AND LIBRARY BOARD continued

	Compaq 286) for use with database; spread-sheet and word-processing software.
Other Equipment	Microform readers/printers; Microcard readers; Photocopiers; Slide Projectors; VCRs.

58   CARLOW COUNTY LIBRARY
Dublin Street,
Carlow.
Tel: Carlow (0503) 31126
Fax: Carlow (0503) 41503

(0503) 70094 Tillowstown Library,

County Librarian	Thomas King
No. of Staff	11 (3 Professional, 5 Non-professional, 3 Part-time).
Branch Libraries	CARLOW, Dublin Street, Carlow; Tel: (0503) 31126; (Carmel Flahavan, Assistant Librarian); MUINEBHEAG, Main Street, Muinebheag, Co Carlow; Tel: (0503) 22208. TULLOW, The Courthouse, Barrack Street, Tullow, Co. Carlow; Tel: (0503) 51497.
Opening Hours	Carlow Branch: 10.00 - 13.00, 14.00 - 17.30 (Mon. - Fri.), late opening 18.30 - 20.30 (Tue., Thurs.).
Mobile Libraries	1 Schools/Branches delivery vehicle.
Services Offered	Lending; Special request service and ILL; Reference and Information service; Photocopying service; Local Studies Service.
Special Collections	Careers and Education Section; Publications Collection of the European Union; Local Studies Collection; Jackson Collection; Bruen Collection; Tyndall Collection; Burton Papers; Vigors Papers.
Bookstock	100,000 volumes - 90,000 available for lending (4 books per adult; 2 books per child) and ILL.
Periodicals	120 titles - back issues of selected titles available for loan and ILL; will photocopy.
A/V Stock	1,500 audio-cassettes - available for loan

	and ILL; 50 video-cassettes - available for loan not ILL.
Other Materials	1,000 Microform Sets ; Art for Loan: Prints.
Catalogue	In preparation for computerisation.
Classification	DDC 20th Edition.
Computer Equipment	Tulip Vision Line DT 486; 4 WYSE terminals; Gateway 2000 Pentium; Canon LBP 460 printer; Panasonic laser printer KX-P6100; New Books Database; Local Studies Database; BNB on CD-ROM; MS Word/Works/Office.
Other Equipment	2 Microform reader/printers; 1 Microform reader only; 2 Photocopiers (HQ/Muinebheag Library); Video Receiver; Overhead projector with screen.

CAVAN COUNTY LIBRARY   59
Farnham Street,
Cavan.
Tel: Cavan (049) 31799
Fax: Cavan (049) 31384

County Librarian	Josephine Brady
No. of Staff	9 Full-time (3 Professional, 6 Non-professional) 11 Part-time.
Branch Libraries	CAVAN TOWN, Farnham Street, Cavan; Tel: (049) 31799; (T. Sullivan, Assistant Librarian). ARVA, Health Centre, Arva, Co. Cavan; (M. Sheridan, Branch Librarian). BAILIEBOROUGH, Market House, Bailieborough, Co. Cavan; Tel: (049) 65779; (B. Kettle, Branch Librarian). BALLINAGH, Community Centre Ballinagh, Co. Cavan; (B. Swords, Branch Librarian). BALLYCONNELL, Church Street, Ballyconnell, Co. Cavan; (B. O'Neill, Branch Librarian). BALLYJAMESDUFF, Health Centre, Percy French Park, Ballyjamesduff, Co. Cavan; (M. Lynch, Branch Librarian). BELTURBET, Town Hall, Belturbet, Co.

	Cavan; (E. Bannon, Branch Librarian). COOTEHILL, Courthouse, Cootehill, Co. Cavan; (B. Kettle, Branch Librarian). KILLESHANDRA, Community Centre, Killeshandra, Co. Cavan; (M. Tiernan, Branch Librarian). KILNALECK, Community Centre, Kilnaleck, Co. Cavan; (M. Boylan, Branch Librarian). KINGSCOURT, St. Mary's Hall, Kingscourt, Co. Cavan; (B. Kelly, Branch Librarian). VIRGINIA, Health Centre, Virginia, Co. Cavan; (R. Elliot, Branch Librarian). LOUGHAN HOUSE PRISON LIBRARY SERVICE, Blacklion, Co. Cavan; Tel: (072) 53020; (M. Gaughan, Prison Officer).
Opening Hours	For opening hours contact HQ, Tel. (049) 31799
Mobile Libraries	Library van used for mobile library stop at Shercock (monthly), branch exchanges and schools service.
Services Offered	Branch library services; Reference and Local History service; Primary schools' library service; Service to Loughan House Prison.
Special Collections	Extensive local history collection: includes local newspapers; photographs; topographic prints; microform material; archival material.
Bookstock	126,943 volumes - available for loan (with exception of reference material) on a three week loan period; available for ILL.
Periodicals	100 titles - only popular "light" material available for loan. Not available for ILL; will photocopy.
A/V Stock	2,121 audio-cassettes - available for loan and ILL; 20 compact discs, 72 video-cassettes - not available for loan or ILL.
Other Materials	277 Microform sets.
Catalogue	Author/Title and Classified.
Classification	Dewey 20th edition.
Computer Equipment	3 PCs: one has Smart software, one has

	software developed by LGCSB for local history.
Other Equipment	3 Microform readers; 2 Photocopiers; Exhibition stands.

CLARE COUNTY LIBRARY 60
Library HQ,
Mill Road,
Ennis,
Co. Clare.
Tel: Ennis (065) 21616
Fax: Ennis (065) 42461

County Librarian	Noel Crowley
No. of Staff	35 (8 Professional, 12 Non-professional, 15 Part-time).
Branch Libraries	FULL-TIME: DE VALERA LIBRARY, Harmony Row, Ennis, Co. Clare; Tel: (065) 21616, Fax: (065) 42462; (Carolyn Stafford, Librarian). ENNISTYMON, Ennistymon, Co. Clare; Tel: (065) 71245, Fax: (065) 71017; (Brian Doyle, Librarian). KILRUSH, Kilrush, Co. Clare; Tel: (065) 51504; (Frances Pender, Librarian). KILLALOE, The Lock House, Killaloe, Co. Clare; Tel: (061) 376062, Fax: (061) 376062 (Gráinne Ryan, Librarian). NEWMARKET-ON-FERGUS, Newmarket-on-Fergus, Co. Clare; Tel: (061) 368411; (Vacant at Present). SEAN LEMASS LIBRARY, Shannon, Co. Clare; Tel: (061) 364266; (Peter Beirne, Librarian). SWEENEY MEMORIAL LIBRARY, Kilkee, Co. Clare; Tel: (065) 56034 (Anne Finucane, Librarian). PART-TIME: COROFIN, Corofin, Co. Clare; Tel: (065) 37219; (Mary Greene, Librarian). KILDYSART, Kildysart, Co. Clare; (Debbie Carroll, Librarian). KILMIHILL, Vocational School, Kilmihill, Co. Clare; (Mary Kilkenny, Librarian). LISDOONVARNA, Lisdoonvarna, Co.

Clare. (Maureen Connolly, Librarian).
MILTOWN MALBAY, Ballard Road,
Milltown Malbay, Co. Clare; Tel: (065)
84822; (Vera McKenna, Librarian).
SCARRIFF, Scariff, Co. Clare; (Maureen
Devanney, Librarian). SIXMILEBRIDGE,
The Courthouse, Sixmilebridge, Co. Clare;
(Dolores O'Loughlin, Librarian). TULLA,
Tulla, Co. Clare; (Catheryn Moloney,
Librarian).

Opening Hours | HQ: 09.30 - 13.00, 14.00 - 17.00 (Mon. - Fri.). For branch library opening hours check with HQ

Services Offered | Irish Joint Fiction Reserve "PL - PZ".

Special Collections | LOCAL STUDIES CENTRE, The Manse, Harmony Row, Ennis, Co. Clare; Tel: (065) 21616, Fax: (065) 42462; (Maureen Comber, Librarian).

Bookstock | 328,778 volumes - available for loan and ILL except reference material.

Periodicals | 65 titles - not available for loan or ILL; will photocopy.

A/V Stock | 2,321 audio-cassettes (including books on tape) - available for loan but not ILL.

Other Materials | Slides; Paintings; Photographs.

Catalogue | Non-fiction: Author/title/class. Fiction Catalogue in full-time branches.

Classification | Dewey.

Computer Equipment | PC with ENFO database in DeValera Library, Ennis; ACER 1120 2X in Sean Lemass Library, Shannon; PCs in Library HQ Library service will be computerised in late '96/early '97 - all service points.

Other Equipment | Microform reader/printers; 7 Photocopiers.

021-4277110

61   **CORK CITY LIBRARY**
Grand Parade,
Cork.
Tel: Cork (021) 277110
Fax: Cork (021) 275684
Telnet: 192.0.0.1

City Librarian	Hanna O'Sullivan
No. of Staff	50 (12 Professional, 38 Non-professional).
Branches	DOUGLAS, Douglas Shopping Centre, Douglas, Cork; Tel: (021) 277110, Fax: (021) 275684; (Peggy Barrett, Librarian). HOLLYHILL Branch Library, Community College, Hollyhill, Cork; Tel: (021) 392998, Fax: (021) 275684; (David O'Brien, Librarian). MAYFIELD Branch Library, Old Youghal Road, Cork; Tel: (021) 277110, Fax: (021) 275684; (Sinead Feely, Librarian). ST. MARY'S ROAD BRANCH, St. Mary's Road, Gurranabraher, Cork; Tel: (021) 277110, Fax: (021) 275684; (Noreen O'Sullivan, Librarian). TORY TOP ROAD BRANCH, Ballyphehane, Cork; Tel: (021) 277110, Fax: (021) 275684; (Breda Hassett, Librarian).
Opening Hours	Please contact Central Library, Tel: (021) 277110.
Mobile Libraries	One trailer type unit at Bishopstown and Blackrock - one day each week; (Sinead Feely, Librarian).
Services Offered	Photocopying; ILL.
Special Services	LOCAL HISTORY COLLECTION, Grand Parade, Cork; (Kieran Burke, Librarian). MUSIC LIBRARY, Grand Parade, Cork; (Kitty Buckley, Librarian). REFERENCE LIBRARY, Grand Parade, Cork; (Tina Healy, Librarian).
Special Collections	Local History Collection; Newspaper Archives; IJFR - "S".
Bookstock	228,000 volumes - 194,000 available for loan (2 weeks) and ILL (excluding reference and local history material).
Periodicals	195 titles - not available for loan or ILL; will photocopy.
A/V Stock	5,800 audio-cassettes, 11,200 compact disks - available for loan but not ILL; 130 video-cassettes, 15 multimedia packs - not available for loan or ILL.
Catalogue	On-line Catalogue (DYNIX).

61 **CORK CITY LIBRARY continued**

Classification	Dewey 20th ed..
Computer Equipment	Host machine IBM RS6000; 25 PCs; 15 dumb terminals; Software: DYNIX; Databases: books, patrons, voters' register; External databases: ENFO, ECHO, IRIS Minitel, BNB, Bookbank, OCLC (Music), LCSH.
Other Equipment	1 Microfilm reader with printer; 1 Microfiche reader with printer; 1 Microfilm reader; 1 Microfiche reader; 10 Photocopiers; Television and video viewing facilities.

62 **CORK COUNTY LIBRARY**
Farranlea Road,
Cork.
Tel: Cork (021) 546499/546591/546539
Fax: Cork (021) 343254

County Librarian	Ruth Flanagan
No. of Staff	79 (9 Professional, 41 Non-professional, 29 Part-time).
Branches	BALLINCOLLIG, Community Centre, Ballincollig, Co. Cork; Tel: (021) 873024; (Coral O'Sullivan, Assistant Librarian). BALLYVOURNEY, Vocational School, Ballyvourney, Co. Cork; (Eibhlin Ní Laoghaire, Branch Librarian). BANDON, South Main Street, Bandon, Co. Cork; Tel: (023) 44830; (Emer O'Connell, Senior Library Assistant). BANTRY, Bridge Street, Bantry, Co. Cork; Tel: (027) 50460, Fax: (027) 51389; (Noel O'Mahony, Assistant Librarian). BLARNEY, The Green, Blarney, Co. Cork; (opening Summer 1996). CARRIGALINE, Former Oakwood Cinema, Main Street, Carrigaline, Co. Cork; Tel: (021) 371888; (David Treacy, Assistant Librarian). CASTLETOWNBERE, The Square,

Castletownbere, Co. Cork; (Dorothy Creedon, Branch Librarian). CHARLEVILLE, Main Street, Charleville, Co. Cork; Tel: (063) 89769; (Nora O'Driscoll, Senior Library Assistant). CLONAKILTY, The Old Mill, Kent Street, Clonakilty, Co. Cork; Tel: (023) 34275, Fax: (023) 33147 (shared with local area officer); (Kate Coveney, Librarian). COBH, Arch Building, Casement Square, Cobh, Co. Cork; Tel: (021) 811130; (Anne-Marie Hayes, Acting Senior Library Assistant). CORK, Lending Department, Farranlea Road, Cork; Tel: (021) 546499, Fax: (021) 343254; (Sinead Collins, Library Assistant). DUNMANWAY, The Square, Dunmanway, Co. Cork; (J. McCarthy, Branch Librarian). FERMOY, Connolly Street, Fermoy, Co. Cork; Tel: (025) 31318; (Mary Neville, Assistant Librarian). KANTURK, Main Street, Kanturk, Co. Cork; (B. Cunningham, Branch Librarian). KINSALE, The Methodist Hall, Market Quay, Kinsale, Co. Cork; (E. O'Connell, Branch Librarian). MACROOM, Castle Lodge, The Square, Macroom, Co. Cork; Tel: (026) 42483; (Diarmuid Hurley, Library Assistant). MALLOW, Town Hall, Mallow, Co. Cork; Tel: (022) 21821; (Bernie Wallace, Senior Library Assistant). MIDLETON, 66, Main Street, Midleton, Co. Cork; Tel: (021) 613929; (Nora Linehan, Acting Senior Library Assistant). MILLSTREET, Carnegie Hall, Killarney Road, Millstreet, Co. Cork; (Breda O'Leary, Library Assistant). MITCHELSTOWN, Courthouse, Mitchelstown, Co. Cork; (Sheila Casey, Branch Librarian). NEWMARKET, Church Street, Newmarket, Co. Cork; (J. Tobin, Branch Librarian). OILEANN CLEIRE, Parochial Hall, South Harbour,

Cape Clear, off Baltimore, Co. Cork; (J. O'Loideoin, Branch Librarian). PASSAGE WEST, Main Street, Passage West, Co. Cork; (M. O'Connell, Branch Librarian). SCHULL, Main Street, Schull, Co. Cork; Tel: (028) 28290; (K. Brooke, Branch Librarian). SHERKIN ISLAND, National School, Sherkin Island, Baltimore, Co. Cork; (B. Collins , Branch Librarian). SKIBBEREEN, North Main Street, Skibbereen, Co. Cork; Tel: (028) 22400; (Bernie O'Connor, Senior Library Assistant). YOUGHAL, Church Street, Youghal, Co. Cork; Tel: (024) 93459;(Marion O'Halloran, Library Assistant).

Opening Hours	HQ: 09.00 - 17.30 (Mon. - Fri.). Branch libraries vary from 48 hours per week to 14 hours per week, please contact HQ for opening hours.
Mobile Libraries	5 mobile libraries
Services Offered	Lending service to adults and juvenile; Reference; Local Studies.
Special Collections	SHEET MUSIC COLLECTION, (Choral Music only), HQ (see above); (Christine Daly, Librarian). DRAMA COLLECTION, (large collection of plays, full length and 1 act. Also supporting material, i.e., lighting, direction etc.), HQ (see above); (Ruth Flanagan, Librarian). LOCAL STUDIES, (including newspapers, microfilms etc. Works about Cork and by Cork authors), HQ (see above); (Tim Cadogan, Librarian).
Bookstock	1,000,000 volumes - 900,000 available for loan to registered readers and ILL.
Periodicals	120 titles - not available for loan or ILL; will photocopy.
A/V Stock	2,670 audio-cassettes - available for loan and ILL; 70 video-cassettes - not available for loan or ILL.
Catalogue	Dictionary Card Catalogue currently being

	updated to computer.
Classification	Dewey 20.
Computer Equipment	Hardware: IBM RS6000; Software - DYNIX; CD-ROMs: BNB; Library of Congress Subject Headings; Bookfind; "IRIS/Uncover" & Minitel in Bantry and Clonakilty Libraries.
Other Equipment	2 Microform readers; 3 Microform reader/printers; 10 photocopiers.

DONEGAL COUNTY LIBRARY 63
County Library Administrative Centre,
Rosemount,
Letterkenny
Co. Donegal.
Tel: Letterkenny (074) 21968 (2 lines)
Fax: Letterkenny (074) 26402
Telex: 42124 DGCC
E-mail (X400 address): C=IE, A=EIRMAIL400,
P=DONEGAL.CO.CO, O=DONEGAL, OU=LIFFORD,
S=ADMIN

County Librarian	Liam Ó Rónáin
No. of Staff	28 Full-time (3 Professional, 25 Non-professional) 16 Part-time.
Branch Libraries.	CENTRAL LIBRARY AND ARTS CENTRE, Oliver Plunkett Road, Letterkenny, Co. Donegal; Tel: (074) 24950, Fax: (074) 24950; Opening Hours: 10.30 - 17.30 (Mon., Wed., Fri.), 10.30 - 20.00 (Tues., Thurs.), 10.30 - 13.00 (Sat.); (Noreen O'Neill, Assistant Librarian). FANAD/LAGAN: BALLYBOFEY, Butt Hall, Co. Donegal; Tel: (074) 31822; Opening Hours: 16.00 - 18.00 (Wed., Sat.), 11.00 - 13.00 (Sun); (Eileen Harkin, Branch Librarian). LIFFORD, Lifford Community Courthouse, Co. Donegal; Tel: (074) 41066; Opening Hours: 15.00 - 19.00 (Mon.),15.00 - 20.30 (Tue., Thurs.), 10.00 - 13.00, 15.00 - 18.00 (Fri.); (Jane

Friel, Branch Librarian). MILFORD, Main
Street, Co. Donegal; Opening Hours:
16.00 - 18.00 (Mon., Sat.), 15.00 - 17.30
(Thurs.); (Helen McNutt, Branch
Librarian). RAMELTON, Ramelton
Community, Old Meeting House; Tel:
(074) 51414; Opening Hours: 15.00 -
20.30 (Mon., Wed.), 10.00 - 13.00, 15.00
- 19.00 (Fri.), 15.00 - 19.00 (Sat.);
(Phyllis Loughrey, Temporary Branch
Librarian). RAPHOE, The Diamond, Co.
Donegal; Opening Hours: 15.00 - 16.30
(Wed.), 15.30 - 17.30 (Sat.), 11.30 - 13.00
(Sun.); (Rita Gallagher, Branch Librarian).
INIS EOGHAIN: BUNCRANA,
Courthouse, Co. Donegal; Opening Hours:
16.00 - 18.00 (Mon., Fri.), 18.30 - 20.30
(Wed.), 11.30 - 13.30 (Sun.); (Nina
Quigley, Branch Librarian).
CARNDONAGH, Courthouse, Co.
Donegal; Opening Hours: 15.30 - 17.00
(Wed.), 19.00 - 21.00 (Sat.), 12.00 - 13.30
(Sun.); (Anna Hegarty, Branch Librarian).
CLONMANY, Parochial Hall, Co.
Donegal; Opening Hours: 15.00 - 17.00
(Tues., Thurs.), 12.00 - 13.00(Sun.); (Nell
Lavelle, Branch Librarian). MOVILLE,
St. Eugene's Hall, Co. Donegal; Opening
Hours: 15.00 - 17.00 (Tues., Thurs., Sat.),
16.00 - 20.30 (Wed.); (Carmel Barron,
Branch Librarian).
SOUTH DONEGAL: BALLYSHANNON,
Credit Union, East Port, Co. Donegal;
Opening Hours: 19.00 - 21.00 (Mon.),
17.00 - 19.00 (Wed.), 11.00 - 13.00 (Sat.);
(Mary Walsh, Branch Librarian).
BUNDORAN, UDC Offices, Main Street,
Bundoran, Co. Donegal; Opening Hours:
14.00 - 17.00 (Mon., Wed., Fri.); (Jill
O'Doherty, Branch Librarian).
DONEGAL, Mountcharles Road, Co.
Donegal; Opening Hours: 15.00 - 18.00

(Mon., Wed., Fri.), 11.00 - 13.00, 14.00 - 18.00 (Sat.); (Rita Kerrigan, Branch Librarian). GLENTIES, Courthouse, Co. Donegal; Opening Hours: 18.30 - 20.30 (Tues., Thurs.), 14.00 - 16.30 (Sat.); (Mary McIntyre, Branch Librarian). KILLYBEGS, Bruach na Mara, Co. Donegal; Opening Hours: 17.30 - 19.30 (Mon.), 19.00 - 21.00 (Wed., Fri.); (Sylvia Murrin, Branch Librarian). GAELTACHT: GAOTH DOBHAIR, Sean tSeipeal, Co. Donegal; Opening Hours: 15.00 - 18.00 (De Luain, De Sathairn), 15.00 - 18.00, 18.30 - 20.00 (De Ceadaoin), 10.00 - 13.00, 15.00 - 18.00 (De hAoine); (Máire Bean Uí Bhaoill, Branch Librarian).

Opening Hours	Admin. Centre: 09.00 - 16.30 (Mon. - Fri.).
Mobile Libraries	1 Mobile on fortnightly schedule.
Services Offered	Administration of County Library Service; Support services for Central Library and branches; Processing and distribution of stock; Lending services to Adults and Children; Children's activities; Donegal Studies; Research and Information; Open learning; Audio-visual lending and listening.
Other Services	Service to Arainn Mhóir and Tóraigh Islands; Oileain Arainn Mhóir - Cultúrlann, Oileain Thoraigh. Service to Letterkenny Hospital and Old People's Homes in Ramelton and Fahan. For details contact Admin. Centre.
Special Collections	Staff Collection: books and journals on library & information studies; local studies methodology; public administration, etc. Donegal Studies Collection; Patrick McGill Collection; Seamus MacManus Collection; John Kells Ingram Collection; Older printed books (pre - 1851).
Bookstock	296,290 volumes - 232,000 (approx.) available for loan on a three week lending

DONEGAL COUNTY LIBRARY continued

	period; available for ILL.
Periodicals	203 titles - not available for loan or ILL; will photocopy.
A/V Stock	2,742 audio-cassettes and 1,015 TBs - 2,231 and 1,015 available for loan; 1,109 compact disks - 959 available for loan; 904 video-cassettes - 864 available for loan; 124 multimedia packs - not available for loan. No A/V stock available for ILL.
Other Materials	157 Artworks.
Catalogue	OPAC, searchable through author, title, subject, keyword. In non-automated branches searchable through author, subject.
Classification	Dewey; Categorisation for popular fiction and non-fiction.
Computer Equipment	Genesis automated system with Bull DPX 150S and Zenith 486 PCs (x11); 5 Bull Zenith 286 PCs for open learning; 1 Tulip 486 PC for Admin.; 2 printers.
Other Equipment	Minolta RP 6072; Agfa Gevaert LF303; Gestetner 2620 (2 No) & Toshiba 1210 photocopiers; PA and Sound System; projectors, VCRs, TVs.

64 **DUBLIN CITY LIBRARIES**
Central Department,
Cumberland House,
Fenian Street,
Dublin 2.
Tel: Dublin (01) 661 9000
Fax: Dublin (01) 676 1628
E-mail: dublin.city.libs@iol.ie

City Librarian	Deirdre Ellis-King
No. of Staff	388 (95 Professional, 293 Non-professional).
Branch Libraries	BALLYFERMOT, Ballyfermot Road, Dublin 10; Tel: (01) 626 9324/626 9325. BALLYMUN, Ballymun Road, Dublin 11; Tel: (01) 842 1890. CENTRAL

LIBRARY, ILAC Centre, Henry Street, Dublin 1; Tel: (01) 873 4333, Fax: (01) 872 1451, E-mail: dubcelib@iol.ie. CHARLEVILLE MALL, North Strand, Dublin 1; Tel: (01) 874 9619. COOLOCK, Barryscourt Road, Dublin 5; Tel: (01) 847 7781. DOLPHIN'S BARN, Parnell Road, Dublin 8; Tel: (01) 4540681. DONAGHMEDE, Donaghmede Shopping Centre, Dublin 13; Tel: (01) 848 2833. DRUMCONDRA, Millmount Avenue, Dublin 9; Tel: (01) 8377206. FINGLAS, Finglas Shopping Centre, Jamestown Road, Dublin 11; Tel: (01) 834 4906. INCHICORE, 34, Emmet Road, Dublin 8; Tel: (01) 453 3793. KEVIN STREET, 18, Lower Kevin Street, Dublin 8; Tel: (01) 475 3794. MARINO, Marino Mart, Dublin 3; Tel: (01) 833 6297. PEARSE STREET, 138-142, Pearse Street, Dublin 2; Tel: (01) 677 2764. PEMBROKE, Anglesea Road, Ballsbridge, Dublin 4; Tel: (01) 668 9575. PHIBSBORO, Blackquire Bridge, Dublin 7; Tel: (01) 830 4341. RAHENY, Howth Road, Raheny, Dublin 5; Tel: (01) 831 5521. RATHMINES, 157, Rathmines Road, Dublin 6; Tel: (01) 497 3539. RINGSEND, Fitzwilliam Street, Dublin 4; Tel: (01) 668 0063. TERENURE, Templeogue Road, Dublin 6; Tel: (01) 490 7035. WALKINSTOWN, Percy French Road, Walkinstown, Dublin 12; Tel: (01) 455 8159.

Special Services ARTS SECTION, 19-20, Parnell Square, Dublin 1; Tel: (01) 872 2816, Fax: (01) 872 2933. BUSINESS INFORMATION CENTRE, Central Library, ILAC Centre, Henry Street, Dublin 2; Tel: (01) 873 3996, Fax: (01) 872 1451, E-mail: dubcelib@iol.ie. CHILDREN'S & SCHOOLS' LIBRARIES SECTION, Kevin Street Library, Lower Kevin Street, Dublin 8; Tel: (01) 475 8791. CITY

ARCHIVES, 58, South William Street, Dublin 2; Tel: (01) 677 5877, Fax: (01) 677 5954. CIVIC MUSEUM, 58, South William Street, Dublin 2; Tel: (01) 679 4260. COMMUNITY & YOUTH INFORMATION CENTRE, Sackville Place, Dublin 1; Tel: (01) 878 6844, Fax: (01) 878 6610. DUBLIN & IRISH COLLECTIONS (GILBERT LIBRARY), 138-142, Pearse Street, Dublin 2; Tel: (01) 677 7662. DUBLIN HERITAGE GROUP, Dublin City Libraries (see above); Tel: (01) 661 9000, Fax: (01) 676 1628, E-mail: dublin.city.libs@iol.ie. HUGH LANE MUNICIPAL GALLERY OF MODERN ART, Charlemont House, Parnell Square, Dublin 1; Tel: (01) 874 1903, Fax: (01) 872 2182. INTERNATIONAL IMPAC DUBLIN LITERARY AWARD, Dublin City Libraries (see above); Tel: (01) 661 9000, Fax: (01) 676 1628, E-mail: dublin.city.libs@iol.ie. MOBILE LIBRARY HQ, Copper Alley, Dublin 8; Tel: (01) 677 9747. MUSIC LIBRARY, Central Library, ILAC Centre, Henry Street, Dublin 1; Tel: (01) 873 4333, Fax: (01) 872 1451, E-mail: dubcelib@iol.ie. PRISON LIBRARY SERVICE, Library Office, Wheatfield Place of Detention, Clondalkin, Co. Dublin, Tel: (01) 626 0011.

Opening Hours   HQ: 09.30 - 13.00, 14.15 - 17.15 (Mon. - Sat.). For branch or service point hours please contact HQ or particular service point.

Mobile Libraries   4 Mobile Library Units; 2 Delivery Vehicles (General); 1 Delivery Vehicle (Schools).

Services Offered   Certification of Adult Learning Experience; Computer literacy; Language learning; Database development; Public

	access to the Internet; Participation in EU projects; International Literary Award; Publications; Agency services for Departments of Justice, Education, and City of Dublin Vocational Education Committee; Research and Database developments in Heritage areas: Genealogy, Architecture, Local newspapers, Civic history.
Special Collections	Dublin and Irish Collections, including the Gilbert Library, Dix Collection, Yeats Collection and selected Dublin and Irish Newspaper files; IJFR "L", "M".
Subject Specialisation	Dublin and Irish local studies; Business Information; Youth and Community Information; Children's Literature; Contemporary World Fiction.
Bookstock	2,057,963 volumes - 75% available for loan and ILL.
Periodicals	1,754 current titles - not available for loan; will photocopy.
A/V Stock	30,517 audio-cassettes, 2,203 multimedia packs, 14,295 gramophone records and compact disks - available for loan and ILL; 2,395 educational video-cassettes, and some self-instructional software packages, not available for loan or ILL.
Manuscripts	400 (approx.) (mainly Gilbert Library stock) - not available for loan; will photocopy in certain circumstances.
Catalogue	Card; Microfiche; OPAC: Author/Title/Classified /Subject index.
Classification	Dewey 20th edition.
Computer Equipment	DS Galaxy 2000 system; PCs; CD-ROMs; International Databases; In-house databases; DPLNET (available on Minitel); Community & Youth Information; 3 ENFO PCs.
Other Equipment	Microform readers; TV; Audio and video recorders; Audio and video listening and viewing facilities; Cameras; Kurzweil reading machine for the Blind; PCs (including multimedia) for public use.

DÚN LAOGHAIRE/RATHDOWN PUBLIC LIBRARY SERVICE
Headquarters,
1st Floor, Duncairn House,
14, Carysfort Avenue,
Blackrock,
Co. Dublin.
Tel: Dublin (01) 278 1789/278 1790/278 1791
Fax: Dublin (01) 278 1792

County Librarian	Muiris O Raghaill
No. of Staff	69 (20 Professional, 44 Non-professional, 5 Part-time).
Branch Libraries	BLACKROCK Library, Newtown Avenue, Blackrock, Co. Dublin; Tel: (01) 288 8117; (Maureen Heuston, Librarian). CABINTEELY Library, Old Bray Road, Cabinteely, Dublin 18; Tel: (01) 285 5363; (Pat Walsh, Librarian). DALKEY Library, Castle Street, Dalkey, Co. Dublin; Tel: (01) 285 5277; (Pauline Moore, Librarian). DEANSGRANGE Library, Clonkeen Drive, Deansgrange, Co. Dublin; Tel: (01) 285 0860; (Joan Ann Lloyd, Librarian). DUNDRUM Library, Lr. Churchtown Road, Dundrum, Dublin 14; Tel: (01) 298 5000; (Kathleen Guinan, Librarian). DÚN LAOGHAIRE Library, Lr. Georges Street, Dún Laoghaire, Co. Dublin; Tel: (01) 280 1147; (Geraldine McHugh, Librarian). GLENCULLEN Library, Glencullen, Co. Dublin; (Jennie Conlon, Librarian). SALLYNOGGIN Library, Sallynoggin Community School, Dún Laoghaire, Co. Dublin; Tel: (01) 285 0127; (Anne Duffy and Mary Mitchell, Librarians). SHANKILL Library, Library Road, Shankill, Co. Dublin; Tel: (01) 282 3081; (Denise Duffy, Librarian). STILLORGAN Library, St. Laurence's Park, Stillorgan, Co. Dublin; Tel: (01) 288 9655; (Don Griffin, Librarian).
Opening Hours	HQ: 09.30 - 17.15 (Mon., Fri., Sat.), 09.30 - 20.15 (Tues., Wed., Thurs.). For

	opening hours please contact any library.
Services Offered	SCHOOL LIBRARY SERVICE, HQ (see above), (Sandra Trappe, Librarian). HOUSEBOUND, Public Library, Newtown Road, Blackrock, Co. Dublin; Tel: (01) 288 8117; (Mary O'Driscoll, Librarian). MOBILE LIBRARY SERVICE, c/o Fingal County Library Service, Copper Alley, Dublin 8; Tel: (01) 677 9747; (Marian Coakley, Librarian). Computer literacy; Language learning facilities; Music books (Harp and Piano); ILL; CD-ROM; Video viewing; Music practise rooms; Educational toys; Listening facilities; Language exchange sessions; Activities for young and old; Comórtas Filíochta/Féile Filíochta - Seven Languages - Annual Festival of Poetry, Music and Dance.
Special Services	Irish Collection; Adult Literacy; ENFO Files; LOCAL HISTORY COLLECTION, Public Library, Lr. George's Street, Dún Laoghaire, Co. Dublin; Tel: (01) 280 1147; (Carmel Kelly, Librarian).
Bookstock	886,815 items - all available for loan (except reference) and ILL.
Periodicals	100 titles - backnumbers available for loan and ILL; will photocopy.
A/V Stock	34,104 items (including cassettes, compact disks and videos) - available for loan.
Other Materials	Print loan scheme: 200 pictures.
Catalogue	OPAC.
Classification	Dewey.
Computer Equipment	Galaxy 2000: Acquisitions, Cataloguing and Circulation; OPACs; CD-ROMs; Self Learning Computers; Educational software; ENFO access; Listed Buildings.
Other Equipment	Microform reader/printer; Photocopiers; Video viewing; Self learning Language booths; Computers; Listening facilities; Spéirscéalaí storytelling (on tape) via loudspeaker/lamp; Educational toys; Piano, harp, music practice rooms.

FINGAL COUNTY LIBRARIES
Headquarters,
11, Parnell Square,
Dublin 1.
Tel: Dublin (01) 872 7777
Fax: Dublin (01) 873 2021

County Librarian	Paul Harris
No. of Staff	54 (15 Professional, 36 Non-professional, 3 Part-time).
Branch Libraries	BALBRIGGAN Library, George's Square, Balbriggan, Co. Dublin; Tel: (01) 841 1128. BALDOYLE Library, 7, Strand Road, Baldoyle, Dublin 13; Tel: (01) 832 2549. BLANCHARDSTOWN Library, Roselawn Shopping Centre, Blanchardstown, Dublin 15; Tel: (01) 821 2701. GARRISTOWN Library, Garristown, Co. Dublin. HOWTH Library, Main Street, Howth, Co. Dublin; Tel: (01) 832 2130. MALAHIDE Library, Main Street, Malahide, Co. Dublin; Tel: (01) 845 2026. RATHBEALE Library, Swords Shopping Centre, Rathbeale Road, Swords, Co. Dublin; Tel: (01) 840 4179. SKERRIES Library, Strand Street, Skerries, Co. Dublin; Tel: (01) 849 1900.
Opening Hours	HQ: 09.30 - 13.00, 14.00 - 17.00 (Mon. - Sat.). For opening hours of Branch Libraries please contact HQ.
Services Offered	Computer literacy; Language learning; Certification of Adult Learning; Photocopying; ILLs; Optical Scanner for the visually impaired; Database development; Publications; Housebound service.
Special Services	Reference collection; Music Loan collection (CD/Cassette, contemporary and classical collection); Print Loan Collection; FINGAL PRIMARY SCHOOLS LIBRARY SERVICE, HQ (see above); FINGAL LOCAL STUDIES COLLECTION, HQ (see above);

	COUNTY ARCHIVES DIVISION, HQ (see above).
Mobile Libraries	4 plus 1 delivery van.
Bookstock	173,483 volumes - 167,944 items available for loan and ILL.
Periodicals	57 titles - backnumbers available for loan and ILL; will photocopy.
A/V Stock	5,887 audio-cassettes, 789 compact disks, 569 multimedia packs - available for loan and ILL; 213 video-cassettes.
Other Materials	514 prints available for lending.
Catalogue	OPAC: Author, Title, Classified/subject index.
Classification	Dewey 20th Edition.
Computer Equipment	Galaxy 2000 integrated system in HQ and Branch Libraries; CD-ROM bibliographic titles include: BNB (1950 -), Global Bookbank Premium service, Ulrich's Periodicals, ENFO PC.
Other Equipment	OPACs; Photocopiers; Microfiche readers; Televisions; Video recorders; Audio-cassette players; O.H. Projectors; CD Players; PA System; Language learning booths; PCs for public use.

GALWAY COUNTY LIBRARIES 67
Island House,
Cathedral Square,
Galway.
Tel: Galway (091) 562471/65039
Fax: Galway (091) 65039

County Librarian	Pat McMahon
No. of Staff	43 (11 Professional, 10 Non-professional, 22 Part-time).
Branch Libraries	AHASCRAGH, Ahascragh, Co. Galway; (M. Concannon, Branch Librarian). ATHENRY, Athenry, Co. Galway; (M. Kennedy, Branch Librarian). BALLINASLOE, Fair Green, Ballinasloe, Co. Galway; Tel: (0905) 43464; (Mary Dillon, Assistant Librarian). BALLYGAR,

Ballygar, Co. Galway; (N. Kenny, Branch Librarian). CLIFDEN, Clifden, Co. Galway; Tel: (0905) 21092; (Paul Keogh, Senior Library Assistant). CRAUGHWELL, Craughwell, Co. Galway; (U. Kerse, Branch Librarian). DUNMORE, Dunmore, Co. Galway; (Linda Morris, Branch Librarian). GALWAY CITY, St. Augustine Street, Galway; Tel: (091) 61666. (Bernie Kelly, Assistant Librarian). GLENAMADDY, Glenamaddy, Co. Galway; (K. Geraghty, Branch Librarian). GORT, Gort, Co. Galway; (J. Hickey, Branch Librarian). KILLIMOR, Killimor, Co. Galway; (C. Shiel, Branch Librarian). KILRONAN, Kilronan, Aran, Co. Galway; (Una Bean Uí Droighneain, Branch Librarian). LOUGHREA, Loughrea, Co. Galway; (M. Jennings, Branch Librarian). MOYLOUGH, Moylough, Co. Galway; (E. Curran, Branch Librarian). OUGHTERARD, Oughterard, Co. Galway; (M. O'Connor, Branch Librarian). PORTUMNA, Portumna, Co. Galway; Tel: (0509) 41261; (Teresa Tierney, Library Assistant). ROUNDSTONE, Roundstone, Co. Galway; (K. McGlynn, Branch Librarian). SPIDDAL, Spiddal, Co. Galway; (M. Gavin, Branch Librarian). TIERNEA, Tiernea, Lettermore, Co. Galway; (Margaret Vaughan, Branch Librarian). TUAM, Tuam, Co. Galway; Tel: (093) 24287; (Petrina Mee, Senior Library Assistant). WOODFORD, Woodford, Co. Galway; (Yvette O'Malley, Branch Librarian).

Opening Hours

HQ: 09.30 - 13.00, 14.00 - 17.00 (Mon. - Fri.).

Mobile Libraries

A mobile library service operates on eleven routes, visiting sixty-five rural stops on a

	bi-monthly basis.
Services Offered	Schools Libraries' Service; Branch Libraries' Service; VISUALLY IMPAIRED SERVICE of Audio Books, HQ (see above), (Maureen Moran, Librarian).
Special Collections	LOCAL HISTORY Collection, HQ (see above), (Catherine Farragher, Librarian).
Bookstock	363,542 volumes - 320,000 available for loan and ILL.
Periodicals	50 titles - not available for loan or ILL; will photocopy.
A/V Stock	9,614 audio-cassettes and compact disks; 14 video-cassettes - not available for loan or ILL.
Other Materials	Microfilms of newspapers; Microfiche; 3,000 Photographs and Postcards; Slides; Maps; Manuscripts; Archives, including Minute Books of the Boards of Guardians of Ballinasloe, Clifden, Galway, Gort, Mountbellew (not available for loan or photocopying).
Catalogue	Author; Classified (non-fiction).
Classification	Dewey.
Computer Equipment	3 PCs.
Other Equipment	3 Microfilm reader/printers (at HQ, Tuam and Ballinasloe); 2 Microfilm readers (at HQ); 4 Photocopiers (at HQ, Galway City, Tuam and Ballinasloe); Cassette players; CD players; 2 Libraries cabled for music (Galway City and Tuam); Slide projector; Light box; Film projector.

KERRY COUNTY LIBRARY   **68**
Moyderwell,
Tralee,
Co. Kerry.
Tel: Tralee (066) 21200
Fax: Tralee (066) 29202

County Librarian	Kathleen Browne
No. of Staff	24 (8 Professional, 16 Non-professional).

Branch Libraries	BALLYBUNION, Ballybunion, Co. Kerry; Tel: (068) 27615; (Madeline Fitzmorris, Library Assistant). CAHIRCIVEEN, Cahirciveen, Co. Kerry; Tel: (066) 72287; (Noreen O'Sullivan and Margaret Murphy, Library Assistants). CASTLEISLAND, Castleisland, Co. Kerry; Tel: (066) 41485; (Lucy Kerins, Library Assistant). DINGLE, Dingle, Co. Kerry; Tel: (066) 51499; (Kathleen Murphy, Senior Library Assistant). KENMARE, Kenmare, Co. Kerry; Tel: (064) 41416; (Mary Murray, Senior Library Assistant). KILLARNEY, Killarney, Co. Kerry; Tel: (064) 32972/32655; (Tommy O'Connor, Assistant Librarian). KILLORGLIN, Killorglin, Co. Kerry; Tel: (066) 61272; (Kathleen Rice, Library Assistant). LISTOWEL, Listowel, Co. Kerry; Tel: (068) 23044; (Eileen O'Sullivan, Senior Library Assistant).
Opening Hours	Tralee: 10.30 - 17.00 (Mon. - Sat.); Killarney: 10.30 - 17.00 (Tues. - Sat.); All other branches 10.30 - 1.30, 2.30 - 17.00 (Tues. - Sat.).
Mobile Libraries	2 (1 Branches, Hospitals; 1 Schools service).
Services Offered	Reference and Local History; Photocopying; ILL.
Special Collections	LOCAL HISTORY, Kerry County Library (see above); (Michael Costello, Assistant Librarian); Microfilm collection of Kerry newspapers and Irish Times; IJFR "U".
Special Services	SCHOOLS AND HOSPITALS, Kerry County Library (see above); (Seamus Dowling, Assistant Librarian).
Bookstock	306,000 volumes - 289,000 available for loan and ILL, except Reference and Local History.
Periodicals	150 titles - not available for loan or ILL; will photocopy.
A/V Stock	3,100 audio-cassettes - available for loan

and ILL; 640 video-cassettes - not available for loan, but available for ILL; 800 records - available for loan; 200 multimedia packs.

Other Materials	2,500 Microfilms; Slides; Filmstrips.
Catalogue	Author; Classified; Subject.
Classification	Dewey.
Computer Equipment	ENFO PC in Tralee; 2 PCs in Listowel - 1 with CD-ROM Drive.
Other Equipment	Microform readers, reader/printers (at Tralee, Killarney and Dingle); Photocopiers in all branches; Video Camera; Video Recorder and TVs (at Tralee, Killarney, Listowel and Dingle); Projector and Screen; Slide and filmstrip viewers; Camera; Radio/Cassette recorders; Stereo systems.

KILDARE COUNTY LIBRARIES 69
**Athgarvan Road,
Newbridge,
Co. Kildare.
Tel: Newbridge (045) 431486/431109
Fax: Newbridge (045) 432490**

County Librarian	Breda Gleeson
No. of Staff	43 (10 Professional, 33 Non-professional).
Branch Libraries	ATHY COMMUNITY LIBRARY, Town Hall, Athy, Co. Kildare; Tel: (0507) 431144; (Brendan Martin, Senior Library Assistant). CELBRIDGE, St. Patrick's Park, Celbridge, Co. Kildare; Tel: (01) 6272207; (Mary Condron-Dunne, Senior Library Assistant). LEIXLIP, Newtown House, Captain's Hill, Leixlip, Co. Kildare; Tel: (01) 6244240; (Fiona White, Senior Library Assistant). MAYNOOTH, Main Street, Maynooth, Co. Kildare; Tel: (01) 6285530; (Margaret Gannon and Lorraine Daly, Library Assistants). NAAS, Canal Harbour, Naas, Co. Kildare; Tel: (045) 479111; (Mike McInerney, Library Assistant). NEWBRIDGE, Athgarvan

Road, Newbridge, Co. Kildare; Tel: (045) 431486/431109; (Margaret Howard, Library Assistant). BALLITORE, Ballitore, Athy, Co. Kildare; (Pat O'Connor, Branch Librarian). BALLYMORE-EUSTACE, Ardenode, Brannockstown, Co. Kildare; (Sally Redmond, Branch Librarian). CASTLEDERMOT, Main Street, Castledermot, Co. Kildare; (Una Kane, Branch Librarian). CLANE, Capdoo, Clane, Co. Kildare; (Eithne Moffat, Branch Librarian). COILL DUBH, Coill Dubh, Naas, Co. Kildare; (Mary Byrne, Branch Librarian). CURRAGH, Curragh Camp, Curragh, Co. Kildare; (Elizabeth Burke, Branch Librarian). KILCOCK, Cill Iochtar, Kilcock, Co. Kildare; (Bernadette Gilligan, Branch Librarian). KILCULLEN, Kilcullen, Co. Kildare; (Julie O'Donoghue, Branch Librarian). KILDARE, Round Tower House, Kildare; (Carmel Hester, Branch Librarian). MONASTEREVIN, The Square, Monasterevin, Co. Kildare; (Rose Clancy, Branch Librarian). RATHANGAN, Rathangan, Co. Kildare; (Kathleen Dunne, Branch Librarian).

Opening Hours   Please contact Kildare County Library for details.

Mobile Libraries   1 mobile library, 1 school library delivery van.

Special Services   MOBILE LIBRARY SERVICE, Kildare County Library (see above); (Caroline McGrath, Librarian). SCHOOL LIBRARY SERVICE, Kildare County Library (see above); (Anne McNeill, Librarian). KILDARE GENEALOGICAL SERVICE, Old Vocational School, Main Street, Newbridge, Co. Kildare; Tel: (045) 431486/431109 ext. 22; (Karel Kiely, Librarian). LEINSTER LEADER NEWSPAPER INDEXATION PROJECT,

	Basin Street, Naas, Co. Kildare; Tel: (045) 479275, Fax: (045) 432490; (Mary Carroll, Librarian).
Special Collections	KILDARE LOCAL COLLECTION, Kildare County Library (see above); (Michael Kavanagh, Librarian). Ballitore Quaker Collection; Teresa Brayton Collection.
Bookstock	406,100 volumes - available for loan and ILL, except reference works and local history items.
Periodicals	43 titles - available for loan and ILL; will photocopy.
A/V Stock	3,200 audio-cassettes, 320 video-cassettes, 50 multimedia packs - available for loan and ILL.
Catalogue	Author, Classified - on cards.
Classification	Dewey.
Computer Equipment	Genesis Library Management System; 9 IBM Compatible 386 PCs; MSDOS; WordPerfect; Corel Draw; Lotus at Work; Pagemaker; Typequick; ENFO Database.
Other Equipment	2 Microform reader/printers; 8 Photocopiers; 2 Laser printers; 2 Dot Matrix printers.

KILKENNY COUNTY LIBRARY   70
6, John's Quay,
Kilkenny.
Tel: Kilkenny (056) 22021/22606   056 - 7794174
Fax: Kilkenny (056) 63384

County Librarian	James Fogarty, Dip. Lib., ALAI
No. of Staff	20 (4 Professional, 16 Non-professional).
Branch Libraries	KILKENNY, John's Quay, Kilkenny; Tel: (056) 22021, ext. 293; (Declan MacAuley, Dip. Lib., ALAI, Assistant Librarian). GRAIGUENAMANAGH, Convent Road, Graiguenamanagh, Co. Kilkenny; Tel: (0503) 24224; (Brenda Ward, Dip. Lib., ALAI, Assistant Librarian). LOUGHBOY, Shopping Centre, Waterford Road,

Kilkenny; Tel: (056) 22021 ext. 296; (Dorothy O'Reilly, Dip. Lib., ALAI, Assistant Librarian). CALLAN, Clonmel Road, Callan, Co. Kilkenny; (Bridie Bergin, Branch Librarian). THOMASTOWN, Marsh's Street, Thomastown, Co. Kilkenny; (William Barron, Branch Librarian). URLINGFORD, The Courthouse, Urlingford, Co. Kilkenny; Tel: (056) 31656; (Annette Purcell, Branch Librarian).

Opening Hours	HQ: 09.00 - 13.00, 14.00 - 17.00 (Mon. - Fri.). For branch opening hours contact County Library HQ.
Services Offered	HQ: Local History; Schools Service; Service Points; Lending and Reference Service (including Business Information); ILLs.
Special Collections	LOCAL STUDIES/ARCHIVES, County Library HQ, (Declan Macauley, Dip. Lib., Assistant Librarian); IJFR "PA-PK"; Adult Literary; NSSB files.
Mobile Libraries	1 plus 1 schools service/delivery van.
Bookstock	219,000 volumes - 175,000 available for loan and ILL.
Periodicals	120 titles - available for loan but not ILL; will photocopy.
A/V Stock	5,000 audio-cassettes, 350 compact disks, 173 video-cassettes, 50 multimedia packs - all available for loan but not ILL.
Other Materials	Paintings; Prints; Photographs; Microfilm/fiche.
Catalogue	Author; classified Subject; (card). Also starting to catalogue on Genesis Library & Information Management System (Cataloguing Module) and hope to have an automated catalogue for branches in 1996.
Classification	Dewey.
Computer Equipment	Genesis Library & Information Management System and associated software (cataloguing, circulation and

community information modules) and hardware (Bull DPX20, PCs 486 and 386s; VDUs, bar-code scanners; flathead scanner; printers; data capture units; etc.). Also Genesis Indexed BNB on CD-ROM; PCs for office use; Windows 95 and Windows 3.1; Minitel; ENFO; EUROPA. Multimedia PC with selection of reference work type CD-ROMs. Currently negotiating with Ireland On-Line for Internet access.

Other Equipment — 2 Microform reader/printers; 4 Photocopiers.

LAOIS COUNTY LIBRARY 71
County Hall,
James Fintan Lalor Avenue,
Portlaoise,
Co. Laois.
Tel: Portlaoise (0502) 22044

County Librarian	Edwin Phelan
No. of Staff	22 (6 Professional, 1 Non-professional, 15 Part-time).
Branch Libraries	ABBEYLEIX; MOUNTMELLICK; MOUNTRATH; PORTLAOISE; PORTARLINGTON; RATHDOWNEY and STRADBALLY.
Opening Hours	HQ: 09.00 - 13.00, 14.00 - 17.00 (Mon. - Fri.). For opening hours of branch libraries please contact HQ (see above).
Services Offered	Public library; PRIMARY SCHOOL SERVICE, HQ (see above).
Special Collections	Local History.
Bookstock	165,000 volumes - 95% available for loan and ILL.
Periodicals	20 titles - available for loan and ILL; will photocopy.
A/V Stock	2,734 audio-cassettes, 163 video-cassettes - available for loan, but not ILL.
Catalogue	Author, Classified (part automated).
Classification	Dewey

71   LAOIS COUNTY LIBRARY continued

Computer Equipment	Automated system: Cataloguing, Circulation, OPAC and Computer learning.
Other Equipment	1 Microform reader; 2 Microfiche readers; 1 Photocopier.

72   LEITRIM COUNTY LIBRARY
Ballinamore,
Co. Leitrim.
Tel: Ballinamore (078) 44012/44424
Fax: Ballinamore (078) 44425

County Librarian	Sean O Suilleabhain
No. of Staff	12 (2 Professional, 3 Non-professional, 7 Part-time).
Branch Libraries	BALLINAMORE, Co. Leitrim; Tel: (078) 44012. CARRICK-ON-SHANNON, Priest's Lane, Carrick-on-Shannon, Co. Leitrim; Tel: (078) 20789. DROMAHAIR, Co. Leitrim. DRUMSHANBO, Main Street, Drumshanbo, Co. Leitrim; Tel: (078) 41258. KINLOUGH, Co. Leitrim. MANORHAMILTON, Comprehensive School, Manorhamilton, Co. Leitrim; Tel: (078) 55087. MOHILL, Castle St., Mohill, Co. Leitrim; Tel: (078) 31360.
Opening Hours	HQ: 09.30 - 17.30 (Mon. - Fri.). Branches vary, for opening hours please contact Leitrim County Library (see above).
Services Offered	Photocopying; Genealogical; Archives; Museum; ILLs; ENFO; Minitel.
Special Collections	Local Studies; Photographs; Ballads, etc.
Bookstock	60,000 volumes - 58,000 available for loan (charge per book) and ILL.
Periodicals	50 titles - not available for loan; will photocopy.
A/V Stock	400 audio-cassettes, 100 video-cassettes - available for loan and ILL.
Manuscripts	400 - not available for loan.
Catalogue	Card.
Classification	Dewey.
Computer Equipment	Genealogical; ENFO; Minitel.

Other Equipment	3 Microfilm readers; Reader/printer; 4 photocopiers.

LIMERICK CITY LIBRARY 73
The Granary,
Michael Street,
Limerick.
Tel: Limerick (061) 314668/415799
Fax: Limerick: (061) 415266 (Limerick Corporation Number)

City Librarian	Dolores Doyle
No. of Staff	17 (5 Professional, 12 Non-professional).
Branch Libraries	ROXBORO Branch Library, Roxboro Shopping Centre, Limerick; Tel: (061) 417906.
Opening Hours	10.30 - 17.30 (Mon., Tues.), 10.30 - 20.00 (Wed. - Fri.), 10.00 - 13.00 (Sat.).
Services Offered	Adult Lending; Reference and Local History; Junior Lending and Reference; Music Library; Adult Literacy Scheme; Pre-schools; Primary Schools; Youth Service; Community Group.
Special Collections	IJFR "O".
Bookstock	223,507 volumes - 110,000 available for loan (2 week period) and ILL.
Periodicals	26 titles - available for loan and ILL; will photocopy .
A/V Stock	2,100 audio-cassettes (1,450 music, 650 talking books), 501 compact disks, 60 multimedia packs - all available for loan and ILL.
Other Materials	456 music records; Microfilm reels of local newspapers.
Catalogue	OPAC (Author, Title, Subject).
Classification	Dewey 20th edition.
Computer Equipment	DYNIX Automated Library System; UNIX Server (Pentium 1.5 GB disk); DYNIX Software; P.K. Harmony; UNIX Software; 4 Scanners; 6 Light pens and Bar-code readers; 5 CD-ROM drives; Parallel printer; Inkjet printer; 14 Monochrome comm. terminals; 1 Diagnostic modem;

73   LIMERICK CITY LIBRARY continued

                          Access to ENFO Database provided by 1
                          120 MB PC; Modem; Printer; Smarterm
                          Software.
Other Equipment   Bell and Howell Microfilm reader/printer;
                          Microfiche reader; 2 Canon Photocopiers;
                          Stereo hi-fi Equipment; 4 Listening Posts
                          (Music Library).

74   LIMERICK COUNTY LIBRARY
58, O'Connell Street,
Limerick.
Tel: Limerick (061) 318477
Fax: Limerick (061) 318478

County Librarian   Damien Brady
No. of Staff   42 (5 Professional, 37 Non-professional).
Branch Libraries   ABBEYFEALE, Abbeyfeale, Co.
                          Limerick; (Mary Pharahan, Branch
                          Librarian). ADARE, Adare, Co. Limerick;
                          Tel: (061) 396822; (Margaret O'Reilly,
                          Branch Librarian). ASKEATON,
                          Askeaton, Co. Limerick; (S. Gallagher,
                          Branch Librarian). ATHEA, Athea, Co.
                          Limerick; (Marian Missorici, Branch
                          Librarian). BALLINGARRY, Ballingarry,
                          Co. Limerick; (A. Treacy, Branch
                          Librarian). BRUFF, Bruff, Co. Limerick;
                          (M. Leo, Branch Librarian).
                          CAHERCONLISH, Caherconlish, Co.
                          Limerick; (K. O'Sullivan, Branch
                          Librarian). CAHERDAVIN, The
                          Community Centre, Caherdavin, Co.
                          Limerick; (Brenda McCormack, Branch
                          Librarian). CAPPAMORE, Cappamore,
                          Co. Limerick; (Justine O'Malley, Branch
                          Librarian). CROOM, Croom, Co.
                          Limerick; (C. Fahy, Branch Librarian).
                          DOON, Doon, Co. Limerick; (Willie
                          Ryan, Branch Librarian).
                          DOORADOYLE, The Crescent Shopping
                          Centre, Dooradoyle, Co. Limerick; Tel:

(061) 301101; (Anne Bennett, Assistant Librarian). DRUMCOLLOGHER, Dromcollogher, Co. Limerick; (Mary O'Gorman, Branch Librarian). FOYNES, Foynes, Co. Limerick; Tel: (069) 65365; (Irene Kelly, Assistant Librarian). GALBALLY, Galbally, Co. Limerick; (G. Fitzgerald, Branch Librarian). GLIN, Glin, Co. Limerick; (Mary Fitzgerald, Branch Librarian). HOSPITAL, Hospital, Co. Limerick; (B. Herr, Branch Librarian). KILFINANE, Kilfinane, Co. Limerick; (Carmel Cleary, Branch Librarian). KILMALLOCK, Kilmallock, Co. Limerick; (C. Kenny, Branch Librarian). NEWCASTLEWEST, Gorboy, Newcastlewest; Tel: (069) 62273; (Aileen Dillane, Assistant Librarian). PALLASKENRY, Pallaskenry, Co. Limerick; (D. Neville, Branch Librarian). RATHKEALE, Rathkeale, Co. Limerick; (J. O'Toole, Branch Librarian). SHANAGOLDEN, Shanagolden, Co. Limerick; (Irene Kelly, Branch Librarian).

Opening Hours	HQ: 09.30 - 13.00, 14.00 - 17.00 (Mon. - Fri.).
Mobile Libraries	2
Services Offered	Reference; Information Service; Schools Service; Local History Department.
Special Collections	IJFR "N"; County Limerick Local Studies Collection.
Bookstock	440,000 volumes - 300,000 (all non-reference material) available for loan and ILL.
Periodicals	54 titles - not available for loan or ILL; will photocopy.
A/V Stock	1,563 audio-cassettes and multimedia packs - all available for loan and ILL; 1,857 video-cassettes - all non-reference material available for loan and ILL.
Catalogue	Author; Classified catalogue. In process of automation to DYNIX - Horizon.
Classification	Dewey 20th edition.

LIMERICK COUNTY LIBRARY continued

Computer Equipment	DYNIX - Horizon; PC for accessing ENFO database.
Other Equipment	Microform readers; 3 Photocopiers.

75   LONGFORD COUNTY LIBRARY
Town Centre,
Longford.
Tel: Longford (043) 41124/41125
Fax: Longford (043) 41124/41125
E-mail: Longlib@iol.ie

County Librarian	Mary Carleton Reynolds
No. of Staff	13 (3 Professional, 10 Non-professional).
Branch Libraries	LONGFORD, Town Centre, Longford; Tel: (043) 41124/5. BALLYMAHON, The Court House, Ballymahon, Co. Longford; Tel: (0902) 32546; (C. Farrell, Branch Librarian). DRUMLISH, Mary St., Drumlish, Co. Longford; Tel: (043) 24760; (Isabella Mallon, Branch Librarian). EDGEWORTHSTOWN, Pound Street, Edgeworthstown, Co. Longford; (Stella O'Sullivan, Branch Librarian). GRANARD, Market House, Granard, Co. Longford; Tel: (043) 86164; (R. McGivney, Branch Librarian). LANESBORO, The Green, Lanesboro, Co. Longford; (T. Murphy, Branch Librarian).
Opening Hours	HQ: 09.30 - 17.30 (Mon. - Thurs.), 09.30 - 17.15 (Fri.). For opening hours of Branch Libraries please contact Library HQ (see above).
Mobile Libraries	1 Schools/Exchange Van.
Services Offered	ILL (with restrictions on rare and o/p items); Photocopying; Reference and Local Studies information service.
Special Collections	Local Studies and works of Oliver Goldsmith, Maria Edgeworth and Padraic Colum. Irish Studies Collection.
Bookstock	90,000 volumes - all available for loan and

	ILL, with restrictions on reference material, rare Irish studies material, o/p material and some Local Studies material.
Periodicals	35 titles - not available for loan or ILL; will photocopy.
A/V Stock	500 audio-cassettes, 10 video-cassettes - available for loan but not ILL; 5 CD-ROMs (reference only).
Other Materials	Schools Folklore Collection; Lawrence Collection of photographs; Longford Journal 1837 - 1888 on microfilm; Longford Leader 1907 - 1942. Not available for loan or ILL.
Catalogue	Author/title; classified (card).
Classification	DDC 20th edition.
Computer Equipment	5 PCs, 3 with CD-ROM drives; Access to the Internet and the IRIS database.
Other Equipment	2 Microfilm reader/printers; 2 Microfiche readers; 2 Photocopiers; 3 Printers (2 b/w, 1 colour); TV and video.

LOUTH COUNTY LIBRARY 76
Roden Place,
Dundalk,
Co. Louth.
Tel: Dundalk (042) 35457 ext. 138/139
Fax: Dundalk (042) 34549

County Librarian	Ann Ward
No. of Staff	21 (4 Professional, 12 Non-professional, 2 Part-time).
Branch Libraries	ARDEE, Market Square, Ardee, Co. Louth; Tel: (041) 56080; (Betty Coyle, Part-time Librarian). DROGHEDA, Stockwell Lane, Drogheda, Co. Louth; Tel:(041) 36649; (Anne Keavney, Librarian). DUNDALK, Roden Place, Dundalk, Co. Louth; Tel: (042) 35457 ext. 138/139, Fax: (042) 34549; (Ann Ward, Librarian).
Opening Hours	HQ: 09.00 - 17.00 (Mon. - Fri.);

	DUNDALK & DROGHEDA: 10.00 - 17.00 (Tue. - Sat.), 18.00 - 20.00 (Tue., Thur.); ARDEE: 14.00 - 17.00, 18.00 - 20.00 (Tue.), 10.00 - 13.00 (Wed.), 18.00 - 20.00 (Thur.), 10.00 - 13.00, 14.00 - 17.00 (Fri.), 10.00 - 13.00 (Sat.).
Mobile Libraries	1 Schools van.
Services Offered	Adult and Children's Lending; Reference; Local History; Photocopying.
Special Collections	Irish and Local History.
Bookstock	193,288 volumes - all available for loan and ILL, except Reference and Local History.
Periodicals	28 titles - available for loan (except Local History); not available for ILL; will photocopy.
A/V Stock	4.194 audio-cassettes - available for loan, not available for ILL; 286 compact disks, 352 video-cassettes - not available for loan or ILL; 22 multimedia packs - available for loan and ILL.
Other Materials	Microfiche; Microfilm; Photographs.
Catalogue	DYNIX Computerised Catalogue.
Classification	Dewey.
Computer Equipment	Hardware: Bull DPX/20 Model 140 (IGB) with peripherals (Terminals, Printers, Scanners, Modems, etc.); 3 Zenith 23865X PCs; 2 Zenith Z4865X PCs; 2 Toshiba CD-ROM drives; Software: DYNIX Automated Library System; BNB on CD-ROM; Whitakers Bookbank on CD-ROM; Kompass Ireland on Disk; A People's Europe EC database on disk; Local History database on Smartware; Dial up access to ENFO Database; Type Quick and Teach Yourself Microsoft Word for Windows available to public via PC in Dundalk branch.
Other Equipment	2 Microfilm readers; 2 reader/printers; 2 Microfiche readers; 3 Photocopiers; TV/Video recorder.

Mountain View,
Castlebar,
Co. Mayo.
Tel: Castlebar (094) 24444
Fax: Castlebar (094) 24774

County Librarian	Austin Vaughan
No. of Staff	34 (4 Professional, 17 Non-professional, 13 Part-time).
Branch Libraries	CASTLEBAR, Pavilion Road, Castlebar, Co. Mayo; Tel: (094) 24444, Fax: (094) 24774; (Ann Coyne and Mary Conway, Branch Librarians). BALLINA, Killala Road, Ballina, Co. Mayo; Tel: (096) 22180, Fax: (096) 22180; (Breege Gordon, Branch Librarian). BALLINROBE, Glebe Street, Ballinrobe, Co. Mayo; Tel: (092) 41896; (Mary Farragher, Branch Librarian). BALLYHAUNIS, Clare Street, Ballyhaunis, Co. Mayo; Tel: (0907) 30161; (Eleanor Freyne, Branch Librarian). BELMULLET, American Street, Belmullet, Co. Mayo; Tel: (097) 82374; (Breege Lavelle, Branch Librarian). CLAREMORRIS, Dalton Street, Claremorris, Co. Mayo; Tel: (094) 71666; (Chris White, Branch Librarian). CROSSMOLINA, Mullenmore Street, Crossmolina, Co. Mayo; Tel: (096) 31939; (Maureen Gallagher, Branch Librarian). KILTIMAGH, Church Street, Kiltimagh, Co. Mayo; Tel: (094) 81786; (Bridie Wimsey, Branch Librarian). LOUISBURGH, Main Street, Louisburgh, Co. Mayo; (Mary Keane, Branch Librarian). SWINFORD, Main Street, Swinford, Co. Mayo; Tel: (094) 52065 (Mary Murphy, Branch Librarian). WESTPORT, The Crescent, Westport, Co. Mayo; Tel:(098) 25747, Fax: (098) 25747; (Eleanor O'Toole, Branch Librarian).
Opening Hours	CASTLEBAR: 11.30 - 13.00, 14.00 -

	20.00 (Tue., Wed.), 11.30 - 13.00, 14.00 - 17.00 (Thur., Fri., Sat.). For opening hours of other branches contact (094) 24444.
Mobile Libraries	2 plus 1 Schools van.
Services Offered	Photocopying; ILL; Exhibition facilities; Children's' facilities; Writer/Artist/Dancer-in-Residence.
Special Collections	Local history; Local newspapers; Periodicals; Official publications; Tapes, Audio & Video; Adult Literacy; Business Library.
Bookstock	200,000 volumes - 170,000 available for loan and ILL.
Periodicals	50 titles - available for loan and ILL; will photocopy.
A/V Stock	175 audio-cassettes, 12 multimedia packs - available for loan but not ILL; 90 video-cassettes - not available for loan or ILL.
Catalogue	URICA.
Classification	Dewey 19.
Computer Equipment	14 PCs; URICA system; Various Microsoft Products; Bookbank on CD-ROM and a number of Educational CD-ROMs.
Other Equipment	3 Microform readers, 2 reader/printers; 8 Photocopiers; TV and video recorders

78   MEATH COUNTY LIBRARY
Railway Street,
Navan,
Co. Meath.
Tel: Navan (046) 21134/21451
Fax: Navan (046) 21463

County Librarian	W.P. Smith
No. of Staff	12 (6 Professional, 6 Non-professional) 11 Part-time.
Branch Libraries	NAVAN, Railway Street, Navan, Co. Meath; Tel: (046) 21134/ 21451, Fax: (046) 21463; (G, Donnelly, Assistant Librarian). ASHBOURNE, Killegland,

Ashbourne, Co. Meath; (P. Synnott, Branch Librarian). ATHBOY, Main Street, Athboy, Co. Meath; Tel: (046) 32539; (T. Doherty, Branch Librarian). DULEEK, The Courthouse, Duleek, Co. Meath; Tel: (041) 23789; (O. McGuinness, Branch Librarian). DUNBOYNE, Castle View, Dunboyne, Co. Meath; Tel: (01) 825 1248; (C. Cunningham, Branch Librarian). DUNSHAUGHLIN, Main St., Dunshaughlin, Co. Meath; (M. Foley, Branch Librarian). KELLS, Maudlin Street, Kells, Co. Meath; Tel: (046) 41592; (R. Grimes, Branch Librarian). LAYTOWN, Laytown, Co. Meath; (I. Cunningham, Branch Librarian). NOBBER, Nobber, Co. Meath; (I Griffin, Branch Librarian). OLDCASTLE, Millbrook Road, Oldcastle, Co. Meath; (K. Husband, Branch Librarian). SLANE, Castle Hill, Slane, Co. Meath; (M. Morgan, Branch Librarian). TRIM, High Street, Trim, Co. Meath. Tel: (046) 36014; (Peter Crinion, Branch Librarian).

Opening Hours	HQ: 09.30 - 17.00 (Mon. - Fri.).
Services Offered	Lending; Reference; ILLs; Special Requests.
Special Collections	LOCAL STUDIES, County HQ (see above), (A. Bennett, Assistant Librarian); Meath Authors; Mss. relating to County Meath; Music Scores; Audio books; IJFR "T".
Bookstock	294,868 volumes - 288,018 available for loan and ILL.
Periodicals	70 titles - all available for loan and ILL; will photocopy.
A/V Stock	1,681 audio-cassettes, 73 compact disks, 165 video-cassettes - all available for loan and ILL.
Catalogue	Author/Title Classified.
Classification	Dewey
Computer Equipment	12 PCs including 20 Pacs (66Mhz AMD 486d x 2 - 12 MB ROM); 1 Dec Alpha

| | Server 400 4/160 with 32 MB memory; 1 Kva 30 minutes UPS; 1 Maintenance modem; 2 Dot matrix printers; Horizon cataloguing and circulation modules. |
| Other Equipment | Microform reader; Photocopiers. |

79   MONAGHAN COUNTY LIBRARY
The Diamond,
Clones,
Co. Monaghan.
Tel: Clones (047) 51143
Fax: Clones (047) 51863

County Librarian	Joe McElvaney (Acting)
No. of Staff	11 (1 Professional, 7 Non-professional, 3 Part-time).
Branch Libraries	CLONES, The Diamond, Clones, Co. Monaghan; Tel: (047) 51143, Fax: (047) 51863; (Joan Ryan, Senior Library Assistant). BALLYBAY, Ballybay, Co. Monaghan; Tel: (042) 41256; (Anastasia Leonard, Branch Librarian). CARRICKMACROSS, Market Square, Carrickmacross, Co. Monaghan; Tel: (042) 61148; (Breda Moore, Library Assistant). CASTLEBLAYNEY, Market Square, Castleblayney, Co. Monaghan; Tel: (042) 40281; (Barney McDonald, Branch Librarian); MONAGHAN, North Road, Monaghan, Co. Monaghan; Tel: (047) 81830; (John Patton, Library Assistant).
Opening Hours	09.15 - 17.15 (Mon. - Fri.).
Mobile Libraries	2 (1 Adult, 1 Schools); (Niall Geenan, Driver/Assistant).
Services Offered	Schools; Old Peoples Homes; Photocopying; ILLs; Genealogy; Service to Local Business.
Special Collections	Monaghan collection includes material relevant to the literary and local history of County Monaghan; Records of local sports organisations.

Bookstock	157,171 volumes - 154,276 available for loan.
Periodicals	90 titles - not available for loan, available for ILL; will photocopy.
A/V Stock	2,699 audio-cassettes - available for loan and ILL; 201 multimedia packs - not available for loan, available for ILL.
Other Materials	Maps; Charts.
Catalogue	Author/Class.
Classification	Dewey.
Computer Equipment	1 PC 386; 1 PC 486; 1 Dot Matrix printer; 1 EPL 5200 printer; Modem; DOS 5; Windows 3.1; dBase IV.
Other Equipment	Microform reader; reader/printer; 2 Photocopiers; 4 Minitel; ENFO.

NORTH EASTERN EDUCATION AND LIBRARY BOARD 80
Library Headquarters,
25-31, Demesne Avenue,
Ballymena,
Co. Antrim BT43 7BG
Tel: Ballymena (01266) 664100
Fax: Ballymena (01266) 632038

Chief Librarian	P. Valentine, B.A.(Hons.), FLA.
No. of Staff	154 (20 Professional, 129 Non-professional).
Divisional Libraries	CENTRAL DIVISIONAL HEADQUARTERS, Area Library HQ, 25-31, Demesne Avenue, Ballymena, BT43 7BG; Tel: (01266) 664100, Fax: (01266) 46680; (Vacant). NORTH DIVISIONAL HEADQUARTERS, County Hall, Castlerock Road, Coleraine, BT51 3HP; Tel: (01265) 51026, Fax: (01265) 51247; (E. E. Cooper, M.A.(Hons.), B.A.(Hons.), ALA, Dip. Lib. Studies, Librarian). SOUTH DIVISIONAL HEADQUARTERS, 2, Joymount Court, Carrickfergus, BT38 7DQ; Tel: (01960) 362261, Fax: (01960) 360589; (M. McFaul, M.B.A., D.M.S., ALA, Dip.

Branch Libraries

Lib. Studies, Librarian).
AHOGHILL, Brooke Street, Ahoghill,
BT42 1LD; Tel: (01266) 871768; (L.
McFadden, AIC). ANTRIM, 41, Church
Street, Antrim, BT41 4B; Tel: (01849)
461942; (C. Carey, AIC). BALLEE, 2,
Neighbourhood Centre, Ballee, BT42 2SX;
Tel: (01266) 45761; (R. Dickey, AIC).
BALLYCASTLE, 5, Leyland Road,
Ballycastle, BT54 6DT; Tel: (012657)
62566; (J. Coyles, AIC). BALLYCLARE,
The Market House, School Street,
Ballyclare, BT39 9BE; Tel: (019603)
52269; (C. Kane, AIC). BALLYMENA,
25-31, Demesne Avenue, Ballymena, BT43
7BG; Tel: (01266) 664110; (M. Bryson,
B.A., ALA, Dip. Lib. Studies, District
Librarian). BALLYMONEY, Rodden
Foot, Queen Street, Ballymoney, BT53
6JB; Tel: (012656) 63589; (A.
Maconaghie, AIC). BELLAGHY, 79,
William Street, Bellaghy, BT45 8HZ; Tel:
(01648) 386627; (M.A. Jones, AIC).
BROUGHSHANE, Main Street,
Broughshane, BT42 4JW; (F. Watson,
AIC). BUSHMILLS, 44, Main Street,
Bushmills, BT57 8QA; Tel: (012657)
31424; (Y. Hill, B.A., Dip. Ed., AIC).
CARNLOUGH, Town Hall, Carnlough,
BT44 0EU; Tel: (01574) 885552; (M.
Fyfe, AIC). CARRICKFERGUS, 2,
Joymount Court, Carrickfergus, BT38
7DQ; Tel: (01960) 362261; (A.
Armstrong, B.A.(Hons.), D.M.S., ALA,
Dip. Lib. Studies, District Librarian).
CASTLEROCK, 57, Main Street,
Castlerock, BT51 4RA; Tel: (01265)
848463; (G. Hanns, B.A., Dip. in Social
Studies, AIC). CLOUGHFERN, 2a,
King's Crescent, Newtownabbey, BT37
0DH; Tel: (01232) 854789; (I. McCrea,

AIC). CLOUGHMILLS, Cloughmills Primary School, Main Street, Cloughmills, BT44 9LG; Tel: (012656) 38537; (A. M. Dickson, AIC). COLERAINE, Queen Street, Coleraine, BT52 1BE; Tel: (01265) 42561; (B. Porter, B.Sc., ALA, Dip. Lib. Studies, District Librarian). CRUMLIN, Orchard Road, Crumlin, BT29 4SD; Tel: (018489) 423066; (S. Sullivan, AIC). CULLYBACKEY, 153, Tobar Park, Cullybackey, BT42 1NW; Tel: (01266) 881878; (M. Donaghy, B.A., AIC). CUSHENDALL, Mill Street, Cushendall, BT44 0RR; Tel: (012667) 71297; (A. Blaney, AIC). DRAPERSTOWN, High Street, Draperstown, BT45 7AD;Tel: (01648) 28249; (E. Sewell, B.A., Dip. Lib. Studies, AIC). GARVAGH, Bridge Street, Garvagh, BT51 5AF; Tel: (012665) 58500; (E. Murphy, AIC). GLENGORMLEY, 40, Carnmoney Road, Newtownabbey, BT36 6HP;Tel: (01232) 833797; (P. Magee, ALA, District Librarian). GREENISLAND, 17, Glassillan Grove, Greenisland, BT38 8PE; Tel: (01232) 865419; (M. Waite, AIC). GREYSTONE, Greystone Road, Antrim, BT41 1JW; Tel: (01849) 463891; (A. Crawford, AIC). KILREA, Town Hall, 27, The Diamond, Kilrea, BT51 5QN; Tel: (012665) 40630; (R. Kirkpatrick, AIC). LARNE, 36, Pound Street, Larne, BT40 1SQ; Tel: (01574) 277047; (P. McAuley, AIC). MAGHERA, 1, Main Street, Maghera, BT46 5EA; Tel: (01648) 42578; (L. O'Neill, AIC). MAGHERAFELT, 43, Queen's Avenue, Magherafelt, BT45 6BX; Tel: (01648) 32278; (A. Wilson, AIC). MONKSTOWN, Monkstown Secondary School, Bridge Road, Monkstown, BT37 OEG; Tel: (01232) 853138; (C. Bradley, AIC). PORTGLENONE, 19, Townhill Road, Portglenone, BT44 8AD; Tel:

(01266) 822228; (C. Mulholland, AIC). PORTRUSH, Technical College, Dunluce Street, Portrush, BT56 8DN; Tel: (01265) 823752; (F. McCallum, AIC). PORTSTEWART, Town Hall, The Crescent, Portstewart, BT55 7AB; Tel: (0126583) 2712; (J. A. Davies, AIC). RANDALSTOWN, 34, New Street, Randalstown, BT41 3AF; Tel: (01849) 472725; (F.C. McGonigal ,AIC). RATHCOOLE, 2, Rosslea Way,Rathcoole, BT37 9BJ; Tel: (01232) 851157; (J. Stafford, Dip. Lib. Studies, AIC). RATHLIN, Temporarily Closed; (K. McFaul, AIC). TEMPLEPATRICK, 23, The Village, Templepatrick, BT39 0AA; Tel: (01849) 432953; (G. Doyle, AIC). WHITEHEAD, 17b, Edward Road, Whitehead, BT38 9QB; Tel: (019603) 53249; (H. Lynagh, AIC). [AIC = Assistant in Charge]

Opening Hours	Vary.
Mobile Libraries	9 Public; 3 Schools; 1 Schools Exhibition only; 2 Health & Welfare.
Special Services	LOCAL STUDIES LIBRARY, Area Library HQ (see above), (L. Buick, B.L.S., ALA, Reference Librarian). IRISH LIBRARY, North Divisional HQ, (see above), (E. E. Cooper, M.A.(Hons.), B.A.(Hons.), ALA, Dip. Lib. Studies, Divisional Librarian).
Other Services	Public Library - including Local Government; Local Studies; Schools Library Service; Health & Welfare.
Special Collections	Local Authors.
Bookstock	1,000,795 volumes, plus 955,123 Education and 44,737 Health & Welfare - most available for loan and ILL.
Periodicals	416 titles - some available for loan and ILL; will photocopy.
A/V Stock	25,028 audio-cassettes (plus 3,713 -

	Education), 2,121 video-cassettes (plus 1,864 - Education); 5 multimedia packs (plus 2,711 - Education).
Other Materials	Public: 3,013 Postcards, etc., 1,571 Wallcharts, 1,046 Games, Jigsaws, 4 Slide sets. Education: 2,530 Filmstrips/loops, 590 Portfolios, 1,958 Slide sets.
Manuscripts	Few.
Catalogue	AACR2 Format on BLCMP (1991 -). Card Catalogue earlier.
Classification	DC20.
Computer Equipment	BLCMP system operating on a Data General machine at QUB. Landline links between Ballymena and QUB and between Divisional HQ in Carrickfergus, Coleraine and Ballymena. CD-ROMs: BBIP - Bookbank, American Books in Print. Also Macintosh and IBM compatible machines.
Other Equipment	Microfilm readers in all branches - Bell and Howell and Micron 780 machines. Canon reader/printer, Regima reader/printer, Allen Down Projector microfilm reader; Photocopiers - UBM, UBIX, KONICA.

OFFALY COUNTY LIBRARY   81
O'Connor Square,
Tullamore,
Co. Offaly.
Tel: Tullamore (0506) 21419
Fax: Tullamore (0506) 52769

County Librarian	A.M. Coughlan.
No. of Staff	19
Branch Libraries	BANAGHER, Moore's Corner, Banagher, Co. Offaly; Tel: (0509) 51471. BIRR, John's Mall, Birr, Co. Offaly; Tel: (0509) 20961. CLARA, Clara, Co. Offaly; Tel: (0506) 31389. DAINGEAN, Main Street, Daingean, Co. Offaly; Tel: (0506) 53005. EDENDERRY, J.K.L. Street, Edenderry, Co. Offaly; Tel: (0405) 31028.

FERBANE, Ferbane, Co. Offaly; Tel: (0902) 54259. KILCORMAC, Main Street, Kilcormac, Co. Offaly; Tel: (0509) 35086. SHINRONE, Brosna Road, Shinrone, Co. Offaly. TULLAMORE, O'Connor Square, Tullamore, Co. Offaly; Tel: (0506) 21419.

Opening Hours	Contact Library HQ (0506) 21419.
Mobile Libraries	Delivery Van.
Services Offered	Photocopying service; ILL; Service to Primary Schools; Service to Welfare Homes; Adult Literacy Service.
Special Collections	Local Studies, Irish History, Irish Authors.
Bookstock	176,000 volumes - 150,000 available for loan and ILL
Periodicals	150 titles - not available for loan or ILL; will photocopy
A/V Stock	Audio-cassettes - available for loan.
Computer Equipment	6 Personal Computers.
Catalogue	Author/Classified.
Classification	Dewey.
Other Equipment	Microform Reader/Printers; 5 Photocopiers; Tape/Slide Presentation Unit; TV and Video.

82   ROSCOMMON COUNTY LIBRARY
Abbey Street,
Roscommon.
Tel: Roscommon (0903) 26100
Fax: Roscommon (0903) 25474

County Librarian	Helen Kilcline
No. of Staff	18 (4 Professional, 8 Non-professional, 6 Part-time).
Branch Libraries	ROSCOMMON County Library, Abbey Street, Roscommon; Tel: (0903) 26100, Fax: (0903) 25474; (Helen Kilcline, Librarian). BALLAGHADERREEN, Dublin Road, Ballaghaderreen, Co. Roscommon; Tel: (0907) 60940; (Olive Feely, Branch Librarian). BALLYFORAN, Courthouse, Ballyforan,

Co. Roscommon; (M. Doheny, Branch Librarian). BOYLE, c/o Teagasc Offices, Boyle, Co. Roscommon; Tel:(079) 62101; (C. Morgan, Library Assistant). CASTLEREA, Main Street, Castlerea, Co. Roscommon; Tel: (0907) 20745; (M. Carroll, Branch Librarian). ELPHIN, Main Street, Elphin, Co. Roscommon; Tel: (078) 35091; (M. Walsh, Branch Librarian). STOKESTOWN, The Square, Strokestown, Co. Roscommon; (M. Lane, Branch Librarian).

Opening Hours	For opening hours contact HQ (see above).
Mobile Libraries	1 library delivery van.
Services Offered	OPAC; Photocopying; ILLs; Schools Library Service; Service to WHB Geriatric Homes; ENFO Data Base; Microfilm Newspaper Collection; European Union Information Point; Postal Service for Registered Blind.
Special Collections	Local Studies Collection; Lloyd-Kenny Loan Collection; Crofton Papers; Local Authority Archives.
Bookstock	226,319 volumes - 221,508 available for loan and ILL.
Periodicals	60 titles - not available for loan or ILL; will photocopy.
A/V Stock	7,842 audio-cassettes, 100 multimedia packs - available for loan and ILL; 80 video-cassettes - not for loan, but available for ILL.
Catalogue	DYNIX OPAC; Automated Union Catalogue of all circulating stock; AACR2.
Classification	DDC 20.
Computer Equipment	Zenith 90 Mhz Pentium; 32 MB memory; 2 GB disk; 525 MB Tape drive; 3M DAT tape drive; 16 port specialix card; UPS 900 VA; Multiplex Modem. UNIX software base; UNIVERSE on UNIX; DYNIX Release 142E.
Other Equipment	4 Microform readers; 1 Microform reader/printer; 4 Photocopiers; Microfiche reader.

83   SLIGO COUNTY LIBRARY
The Courthouse,
Teeling Street,
Sligo.
Tel: Sligo (071) 42212
Fax: Sligo (071) 46798

County Librarian	Donal Tinney, B.A., D.L.I.S., ALAI.
No. of Staff	3 Professional, 6 Non-professional, 3 Branch Librarians.
Branch Libraries	ADMINISTRATIVE & CENTRAL REFERENCE, Courthouse, Sligo. SLIGO Branch Library, Stephen Street, Sligo; BALLYMOTE Branch Library, Courthouse, Ballymote, Co. Sligo; ENNISCRONE Branch Library, Enniscrone, Co. Sligo; TUBBERCURRY Branch Library, St. Brigid's Hall, Tubbercurry, Co. Sligo.
Opening Hours	Administrative & Central Reference: 10.00 - 13.00, 14.00 - 17.00 (Mon. - Fri.). Contact HQ for opening hours of branch libraries.
Mobile Libraries	Schools/delivery van.
Services Offered	Photocopying; ILL; Enterprise Information.
Special Collections	Yeatsiana; Anglo-Irish literature; Local History.
Bookstock	112,000 volumes.
Periodicals	35 titles.
A/V Stock	Tapes; Microfilms; Slides; CD-ROM.
Catalogue	Author; Classified (card).
Classification	Dewey 20.
Other Equipment	Microfilm reader/printer.

84   SOUTH DUBLIN COUNTY LIBRARIES
Unit 1,
Belgard Square,
Tallaght,
Dublin 24.
Tel: Dublin (01) 462 0000

County Librarian	Richard Lennon
No. of Staff	58 (16 Professional, 42 Non-professional).
Branch Libraries	BALLYROAN, Orchardstown Avenue, Rathfarnham, Dublin 14; Tel: (01) 494 1900; (Maria Hodgins, Senior Librarian). CASTLETYMON, Castletymon Shopping Centre, Castletymon, Tallaght, Dublin 24; Tel: (01) 452 4888; (Bridget Cribben, Senior Librarian). CLONDALKIN, Monastery Road, Clondalkin, Dublin 22; Tel: (01) 459 3315, Fax: (01) 459 5509; (Margaret Bentley, Senior Librarian). COUNTY LIBRARY, Town Centre, Tallaght, Dublin 22; Tel: (01) 462 0073, Fax: (01) 462 0207; (Georgina Byrne, Senior Librarian).
Departments	ACQUISITIONS & CIRCULATIONS SECTION, HQ (see above); (Ann Wrigley, Senior Librarian). FINANCE & PERSONNEL SECTION, HQ (see above); (Una Phelan, Senior Librarian).
Opening Hours	HQ: 09.30 - 13.00, 14.00 - 17.00 (Mon. - Fri.). For hours of branch libraries please contact HQ, Tel: (01) 661 9000.
Mobile Libraries	4 Mobile Libraries; MOBILE LIBRARY SERVICE, Copper Alley, Dublin 2; Tel: (01) 6779747; (Teresa Walsh, Librarian).
Services Offered	Computer literacy certification; Language learning certification.
Special Services	PRIMARY SCHOOLS LIBRARY SERVICE, HQ (see above); (Ann Wrigley, Senior Librarian.
Special Collections	Local Government Collection; Local Studies Collection.
Bookstock	181,042 volumes - 177,141 available for loan and ILL.
Periodicals	146 titles - back issues available for loan, not available for ILL; will photocopy.
A/V Stock	5,125 audio-cassettes, 1,224 multimedia packs - available for loan and ILL; 18 compact disks, 811 video-cassettes - not available for loan or ILL.
Other Materials	899 paintings; 64 Computek software; 14

SOUTH DUBLIN COUNTY LIBRARIES continued

	CD-ROMs.
Catalogue	OPAC.
Classification	Dewey 20th edition.
Computer Equipment	Galaxy 2000 Integrated Library System (includes Circulation, Acquisitions, Cataloguing); Public access PCs; CD-ROMs: Adult and Junior reference and Bibliographical Tools; 2 ENFO PCs.
Other Equipment	Microfiche readers; PCs; PC Printers; Photocopiers (in every branch); TVs; Video Recorders; Language Labs; Electronic Keyboard.

85 **SOUTH EASTERN EDUCATION AND LIBRARY BOARD**
Library Headquarters,
Windmill Hill,
Ballynahinch, BT24 8DH.
Tel: Ballynahinch (01238) 562639
Fax: Ballynahinch (01238) 565072

Chief Librarian	Mr. D.H. Welch, FLA
No. of Staff	201 (51 Professional, 150 Non-professional).
Branch Libraries	BALLYNAHINCH, Main Street, Ballynahinch, BT24 8DN; Tel: (01238) 562639; (Pamela Cooper, Librarian). BANGOR, Hamilton Road, Bangor, BT20 4LH; Tel: (01247) 270591, Fax: (01247) 462744; (Mary Bradley, Librarian). BELVOIR PARK, Drumart Square, Belfast, BT8 4EY, Tel: (01232) 644331; (Joan Smith, Librarian). BRANIEL, Glen Road, Belfast, BT5 7JH; Tel: (01232) 797420; (Maisie Reid, Librarian). CARRYDUFF, Church Road, Carryduff, Belfast, BT8 3DT; Tel: (01232) 813568; (Patricia Ramsay, Librarian). CASTLEWELLAN, Main Street, Castlewellan, BT31 9DA; Tel: (013967) 78433; (Ann Crilly, Librarian). COMBER, Newtownards Road, Comber,

Newtownards, BT23 5AU; Tel: (01247) 872610; (Margaret Martin, Librarian). CREGAGH, 409-413, Cregagh Road, Belfast, BT6 0LF; Tel: (01232) 401365; (Martha Anne Loan, Librarian). DAIRY FARM, Dairy Farm Centre, Unit 17, Stewartstown Road, Dunmurry, Belfast, BT17 OAW; Tel: (01232) 431266, Fax: (01232) 431278; (Helen O'Hare, Librarian). DONAGHADEE, 5, Killaughey Road, Donaghadee, BT21 0BL; Tel: (01247) 882507; (Norma Millar, Librarian). DOWNPATRICK, Market Street, Downpatrick, BT30 6LZ; Tel: (01396) 612895; (Kathleen Smyth, Librarian). DUNDONALD, 16, Church Road, Dundonald, Belfast, BT16 0LN; Tel: (01232) 483994; (Rosemary Wright, Librarian). DUNMURRY, Upper Dunmurry Lane, Dunmurry, BT17 0AA; Tel: (01232) 623007; (Josephine Quinn, Librarian). GILNAHIRK, Gilnahirk Rise, Belfast, BT5 7DT; Tel: (01232) 796573; (Lynn Rice, Librarian). HOLYWOOD, Sullivan Buildings, 86-88, High Street, Holywood, BT18 9AE; Tel: (01232) 424232, Fax: (01232) 424194; (Sharon Gregg, Librarian). KILLYLEAGH, High Street, Killyleagh, Downpatrick, BT30 9QF; Tel: (01396) 828407; (Bridget Napier, Librarian). LAURELHILL Community Branch, Laurelhill Road, Lisburn, BT28 2UH; Tel: (01846) 664596; (Michael Bell, Librarian). LISBURN, 29, Railway Street, Lisburn, BT28 1XP; Tel: (01846) 601749; (Margaret Bell, Librarian). MOIRA, Backwood Road, Moira, Craigavon, BT67 OLJ; Tel: (01846) 619330; (Ann Bell, Librarian). NEWTOWNBREDA, Saintfield Road, Belfast, BT8 4HL; Tel: (01232) 701620; (Eileen Parker, Librarian). NEWCASTLE, 141-143, Main Street, Newcastle, BT33

OAE, Tel: (013967) 22710; (Helen Mills, Librarian). NEWTOWNARDS, Queen's Hall, Regent Street, Newtownards, BT23 4AB; Tel: (01247) 814732, Fax: (01247) 810265; (Joan Thompson, Librarian). POLEGLASS, Good Shepherd Road, Poleglass, Belfast, BT19 0LD; Tel: (01232) 629740; (Elizabeth McMullan, Librarian). PORTAFERRY, 47, High Street, Portaferry, BT22 1QU; Tel: (012477) 28194; (Geraldine McGrattan, Librarian). SAINTFIELD, Ballynahinch Road, Saintfield, Ballynahinch, BT24 7AD; Tel: (01238) 510550; (Pamela Macrory, Librarian). TULLYCARNET, Kinross Avenue, Belfast, BT5 7GF; Tel: (01232) 485079, Fax: (01232) 482342; (Vivien Marshall, Librarian).

Opening Hours	For opening hours please contact Library HQ: Tel: (01238) 562639.
Mobile Libraries	5.
Services Offered	General range of public library services, together with services to schools, penal institutions, hospitals and homes.
Special Services	Reference and Information Section; Special Services Unit; Irish and Local Studies Section; Music Section.
Bookstock	c. 1,201,415 volumes - available for loan and ILL.
Periodicals	c. 561 titles - not available for loan or ILL; will photocopy.
A/V Stock	Audio-cassettes and compact disks - available for loan and ILL; video-cassettes - available for loan, but not for ILL; multimedia packs - not available for loan or ILL.
Other Materials	CD-ROM.
Catalogue	On-line (Acclaim); AACR2.
Classification	DC.
Computer Equipment	On-line Acclaim system on VAX; SWETS serials; In-house ILL on ART TEL; CD-

| Other Equipment | ROM Bookbank and various newspapers, etc.; CD-ROM Cat. of 3 Education and Library Boards available in branches. Microform readers in major branches and HQ; 3 Readers/printers; Photocopiers in all branches and HQ; 6 Faxes. |

SOUTHERN EDUCATION AND LIBRARY BOARD
Library Headquarters,
1 Markethill Road,
Armagh, BT60 1NR.
Tel: Armagh (01861) 525353
Fax: Armagh (01861) 526879

Chief Librarian	Andrew Morrow
No. of Staff	207 (39 Professional, 168 Non-professional), 76 Part-time.
Divisional Libraries	CRAIGAVON Divisional Library HQ, 113, Church Street, Portadown, Co. Armagh, BT62 3DB; Tel: (01762) 335247/335296; (Gerry Burns, Librarian). DUNGANNON Divisional Library HQ, Market Square, Dungannon, Co. Tyrone, BT70 1JD; Tel: (01868) 722885, Fax: (01868) 753620; (Brendan McGeown, Librarian). NEWRY Divisional Library HQ, 79, Hill Street, Newry, Co. Down, BT34 1DG; Tel: (01693) 64077/61652, Fax: (01693) 251739; (Janet Blair, Librarian).
Branch Libraries	ARMAGH, Market Street, Armagh, BT61 7BU; Tel: (01861) 524072; (Cathy Pomeroy, Librarian). BANBRIDGE, Scarva Street, Banbridge, Co. Down, BT32 3AD; Tel: (018206) 23973; (Sheila Scarlett, Librarian). BESSBROOK, Church Road, Bessbrook, Co. Down, BT35 7AQ; Tel: (01693) 830424; (Ann Morgan, Librarian). BROWNLOW, Brownlow Road, Legahory, Craigavon, Co. Armagh, BT65 5DP; Tel: (01762) 341946; (Maurice McDonagh, Librarian). COALISLAND,

The Square, Coalisland, Co. Tyrone, BT71 4LN; Tel: (01868) 740569; (Grace Hamilton, Librarian). COOKSTOWN, Burn Road, Cookstown, Co. Tyrone, BT80 8DJ; Tel: (016487) 63702; (Yvonne Baxter, Librarian). CROSSMAGLEN, The Square, Crossmaglen, Co. Armagh, BT35 9AA; Tel: (01693) 861951; (Rosemarie McDonnell, Librarian). DROMORE, Town Hall, Dromore, Co. Down, BT25 1AW.; Tel: (01846) 692280; (Ilena Given, Librarian). DUNGANNON, Market Square, Dungannon, Co. Tyrone, BT70 1JD; Tel: (01868) 722952, Fax: (01868) 753620; (Monica Montgomery, Librarian). FIVEMILETOWN, Main Street, Fivemiletown, Co. Tyrone, BT75 0PG; Tel: (013655) 21409; (Mairead McKenna, Librarian). GILFORD, Main Street, Gilford BT63 6HY; Tel: (01762) 831770; (Lorraine Wilson, Librarian). KEADY, Market Street, Keady, Co. Armagh, BT60 3RP; Tel: (01861) 531365; (Frances Toner, Librarian). KILKEEL, Greencastle Street, Kilkeel, Co. Down, BT34 4BH; Tel: (016937) 62278; (Eileen Colgan, Librarian). LURGAN, Carnegie Street, Lurgan, Co. Armagh, BT66 6AS; Tel: (01762) 323912; (Maryan McNeill, Librarian). MONEYMORE, 8, Main Street, Moneymore, Co. Derry, BT45 7PD; Tel: (016487) 48380; (Lil Chambers, Librarian). MOY, The Square, Moy, Co. Tyrone, BT71 7SG; Tel: (01868) 784661; (Elizabeth Liggett, Librarian). NEWRY, 79, Hill Street, Newry, Co. Down, BT34 1BS; Tel: (01693) 64683, Fax: (01693) 251739; (Christina Sloan, Librarian). PORTADOWN, Edward Street, Portadown, Co. Armagh, BT62 3LX; Tel: (01762) 332499; (Aideen D'Arcy, Librarian). RATHFRILAND, John Street,

Rathfriland, Co. Down, BT34 5QH; Tel: (018206) 3066; (Mary Loy, Librarian). RICHHILL, 1, Maynooth Road, Richhill, Co. Armagh, BT61 9PE; Tel: (01762) 870639; (Janet Brown, Librarian). TANDRAGEE, Market Street, Tandragee, Co Armagh, BT62 2BW; Tel: (01762) 840694; (Shirley Anderson, Librarian). WARINGSTOWN, Main Street, Waringstown, Co. Armagh; Tel: (01762) 881077; (Cara Leigh Hamill, Librarian). WARRENPOINT, Summerhill, Warrenpoint, Co. Down, BT34 3JB; Tel: (016937) 5335; (Anne Marie Quinn, Librarian).

Opening Hours	For opening hours contact HQ (see above).
Mobile Libraries	Public 5; Housebound 2; Schools 4.
Services Offered	General range of public library services together with services to schools, hospitals, homes and house-bound.
Special Services	INFORMATION SERVICES FOR LOCAL GOVERNMENT, 113 Church Street, Portadown, Co. Armagh, BT62 3DB; Tel: (01762) 335247/335296, Fax: (01762) 391759. IRISH STUDIES LIBRARY, 1, Markethill Road, Armagh, BT60 1NR. Tel: (01861) 525353, Fax: (01861) 526879.
Special Collections	Local and Irish History; Crosslé Collection (Newry Family History).
Bookstock	1,354,457 volumes - all available for loan and ILL.
Periodicals	525 titles - available for ILL; will photocopy.
A/V Stock	33,685 audio-cassettes, 5,653 compact disks, 23,107 video-cassettes, multimedia packs - available for loan and ILL.
Other Materials	Charts; Prints.
Catalogue	Author, Title, Classified - fiche; On-line with Author, Title, Keyword and Subject Searching
Classification	Dewey (20th edition).
Computer Equipment	PCs and VT terminals connected on-line to

SOUTHERN EDUCATION AND LIBRARY BOARD continued

Other Equipment	cluster of VAX mini computers located in Belfast City Council Computer Services; Variety of Microcomputers; CD-ROM. Microfiche readers in HQ and branch libraries; 2 Microfilm reader/printers in Irish Studies Library; Photocopiers in most branch libraries; Fax available for public use in Dungannon and Newry Branch Libraries and Information Services.

87   TIPPERARY JOINT LIBRARIES COMMITTEE
Castle Avenue,
Thurles,
Co. Tipperary.
Tel: Thurles (0504) 21555
Fax: Thurles (0504) 23442
E-Mail: tipplibs@iol.ie,
Website: Http://www.iol.ie/ ~ tipplibs/library.html

County Librarian	Martin Maher
No. of Staff	33 (7 Professional, 13 Non-professional, 13 Part-time).
Branch Libraries	BORRISOKANE, Main Street, Borrisokane, Co. Tipperary; (Frankie O'Carroll, Branch Librarian). CAHIR, The Square, Cahir, Co. Tipperary; (Ann Tuohy, Branch Librarian). CARRICK-ON-SUIR, Fair Green, Carrick-on-Suir, Co. Tipperary; Tel: (051) 540591; (Oliver Corbett, Senior Library Assistant). CASHEL, The Green, Cashel, Co. Tipperary; (Margaret Corbett, Branch Librarian). CLONMEL, Emmet Street, Clonmel, Co. Tipperary; Tel: (052) 24545; (Marie Boland, Assistant Librarian). CLOUGHJORDAN, Main Street, Cloughjordan, Co. Tipperary; (Maire Brady, Branch Librarian). FETHARD, Main Street, Fethard, Co. Tipperary; (Alice Curtin, Branch Librarian). KILLENAULE, Bailey Street, Killenaule,

Thurles, Co. Tipperary; (Rena Lahart, Branch Librarian). NENAGH, O'Rahilly Street, Nenagh, Co. Tipperary; Tel: (067) 34404, Fax: (067) 34405, E-mail: nenalib@iol.ie; (Catherine Kennedy, Assistant Librarian). ROSCREA, Birr Road, Roscrea, Co. Tipperary; Tel: (0505) 22032; (Gerard Flannery, Assistant Librarian). TEMPLEMORE, Town Hall, Templemore, Co. Tipperary; (Bridget Kennedy, Branch Librarian). THURLES, Castle Avenue, Thurles, Co. Tipperary; Tel: (0504) 21555; (Anne Marie Gallagher, Assistant Librarian). TIPPERARY, Dan Breen House, Tipperary, Co. Tipperary; Tel: (062) 51761; (Nollaig Butler, Branch Librarian).

Opening Hours	HQ: 09.25 - 13.00, 14.00 - 17.30 (Mon. - Fri.). For opening hours of branch libraries please contact HQ (see above) or individual library.
Mobile Libraries	1 Delivery van; 1 Schools van.
Services Offered	Schools service to 150+ Primary Schools; 20+ Rural centres; Photocopying; ILL; County Tipperary Historical Society based here.
Special Collections	Local Studies Department; Archives; IJFR "Y".
Bookstock	500,000 volumes - 450,000 available for loan and ILL.
Periodicals	120 titles - available for loan, ILL; will photocopy.
A/V Stock	2,500 audio-cassettes; 1,600 video-cassettes; 20 multimedia packs - all available for loan and ILL.
Catalogue	Card; Non-Fiction: Author/Title/Class; Fiction: Author.
Classification	Dewey 20.
Computer Equipment	Hardware: Various Pentium, 486 and 386 PCs; Laser Inkjet and Colour InkjetPrinters; CD drives and Modems. Software: Windows '95; MsOffice Professional; MsWorks; GSP Pressworks;

	GSP Designworks; Illuminatus; Bookfind CD.
Other Equipment	Readers/printers at Local Studies; Microfiche Readers; TVs; Video recorders; Slide Projector; Overhead projector; Colour Video Magnification System; Photocopiers: HQ, Thurles, Clonmel, Nenagh.

88   WATERFORD COUNTY LIBRARY
Library Headquarters,
Lismore,
Co. Waterford.
Tel: Waterford (058) 54128
Fax: Waterford (058) 54877

County Librarian	Donald Brady.
No. of Staff	14 (4 Professional, 8 Non-professional, 2 Part-time).
Branch Libraries	CAPPOQUIN, Cappoquin, Co. Waterford; (Mary Tobin, Branch Librarian). DUNGARVAN, Old Market House, Lower Main Street, Dungarvan, Co. Waterford; Tel: (058) 54128; (Margaret O'Brien, Assistant Librarian). DUNMORE EAST, Fisherman's Hall, Dunmore East, Co. Waterford; Tel: (051) 383211; (Marie Coffey, Library Assistant). LISMORE, West Street, Lismore, Co. Waterford; Tel: (058) 54128, Fax: (058) 54877; (Richard Walsh, Senior Library Assistant). PORTLAW, The Square, Portlaw, Co. Waterford; Tel: (051) 387402; (Ger Croughan, Senior Library Assistant). STRADBALLY, Stradbally, Co. Waterford; (Kitty Gough, Branch Librarian).
Opening Hours	HQ: 09.00 - 13.00, 14.00 - 17.00 (Mon. - Fri.).
Special Collections	LOCAL HISTORY: Villiers Stuart Papers; Lismore Papers; Chearnley Papers;

	Christmas Papers; Board of Guardian Minute Books; Local Authority Archives. LOCAL STUDIES COLLECTION, HQ (see above); (Evelyn Coady, Library Assistant).
Bookstock	82,778 volumes - 76,276 available for loan and ILL.
Periodicals	12 titles - not available for loan or ILL; will photocopy.
A/V Stock	1,211 audio-cassettes - 1,207 available for loan and ILL; 391 compact discs - available for loan and ILL; 228 video-cassettes - 213 available for loan and ILL; 131 records - available for loan and ILL.
Catalogue	AACR2
Classification	Dewey 20
Computer Equipment	DYNIX Release 135 running on an Ultimate 1435; BNB (1950 -); Groliers and Compton's Encyclopaedia; MS Office Pro 4.3; MS Publisher 2.
Other Equipment	Microform reader/printer in HQ; Microfiche reader in Dungarvan; Photocopiers in HQ, Dungarvan, Tramore, Lismore; System printer and laser printer in HQ; Dot-matrix printer in Dungarvan Branch.

WATERFORD MUNICIPAL LIBRARY <span></span> 89
Lady Lane,
Waterford.
Tel: Waterford (051) 73501
Fax: Waterford (051) 50031

Librarian	Richard Fennessy
No. of Staff	6 (3 Professional, 3 Non-professional).
Branch Libraries	LISDUGGAN, Paddy Brown's Road, Waterford; Tel: (051) 73501 ext. 490; (Bill Murphy, Branch Librarian).
Opening Hours	Central Library, Lady Lane: 11.00 - 13.00, 14.30 - 17.30 (Tues., Thurs., Sat.), 14.00 - 20.00 (Wed., Fri.). For Lisduggan Branch opening hours call (051) 73501.

Services Offered	Book lending; A/V Lending; Reference; Adult Literacy; ILL; Minitel; ENFO Access; Photocopying; Educational CD-ROM.
Special Collections	Large local history collection and local newspaper collections (indexed); Archives of the City and County Infirmary; Irish Regional History Collection.
Bookstock	73,000 volumes - 60,000 available for loan (Adults: 3 books for 3 weeks; Junior: 1 book for 3 weeks) and ILL.
Periodicals	42 titles - not available for loan, available for ILL; will photocopy.
A/V Stock	1,800 audio-cassettes (1,250 music, 65 language, 485 audio); 800 compact disks - available for loan and ILL; 300 video-cassettes - not for loan, available for ILL.
Other Materials	1,400 LP records; 520 Microform sets; 255 Slides; Photographs; 300 Maps.
Catalogue	DYNIX Automated.
Classification	Dewey 20th edition.
Computer Equipment	DYNIX Integrated Library System - Cataloguing, Circulation and OPAC modules; CD-ROM Drive with subscription to BNB and OCLC (Music) on CD ROM; Complete novels of Jane Austen on CD-ROM; 4 PCs; 2 Dot Matrix Printers; 2 Modems; Databases: On-line links to DYNIX Public and Academic Libraries; BLAISE; ARTEL; ENFO.
Other Equipment	2 Microform reader/printers; 3 Microfilm readers; 1 Microfiche reader; 1 Photocopier.

90 **WESTERN EDUCATION AND LIBRARY BOARD**
Library Headquarters,
1, Spillars Place,
Omagh,
Co. Tyrone BT78 1HL.
Tel: Omagh (01662) 244821/244826
Fax: Omagh (01662) 246716

Chief Librarian	Russell T.A. Farrow
No. of Staff	126 (29 Professional, 97 Non-professional).
Divisional Libraries	LIBRARY HEADQUARTERS, 1, Spillars Place, Omagh, BT78 1HL; Tel: (01662) 244821; (R. Farrow). NORTH WEST DIVISIONAL LIBRARY, 35, Foyle Street, Londonderry, BT48 6AL; Tel: (01504) 266888; (A, Peoples). SOUTH WEST DIVISIONAL LIBRARY, Halls Lane, Enniskillen, BT74 7DR; Tel: (01365) 322886; (D. Preston).
Branch Libraries	CASTLEDERG, Main Street, Castlederg, BT81 7AY; Tel: (016626) 71419; (T. Lecky). CENTRAL, 35, Foyle Street, Londonderry, BT48 6AL; Tel: (01504) 266888; (P. Ward). CREGGAN, Central Drive, Creggan Estate, Londonderry, BT48 9QH; Tel: (01504) 266168; (J. Campbell). DUNGIVEN, 25, Main Street, Dungiven, Co. Londonderry, BT47 4LD; Tel: (015047) 41475; (M. McReynolds). ENNISKILLEN, Halls Lane, Enniskillen, BT74 7DR; Tel: (01365) 322886; (R. Elliot). FINTONA, Ecclesville Park, Fintona, BT78 2BY; Tel: (01662) 841774; (A. McCusker). IRVINESTOWN, Main Street, Irvinestown, Co. Fermanagh, BT94 1GT; Tel: (013656) 321383; (I. Hetherington). LIMAVADY, 5, Connell Street, Limavady, Co. Londonderry, BT49 0EA; Tel: (01504) 762540; (Liam Kennedy). LISNASKEA, Drumhaw, Lisnaskea, Co. Fermanagh, BT92 0FC; Tel: (013657) 321222; (P. Kerr). NEWTOWNSTEWART, Main Street, Newtownstewart, BT78 4AA; Tel: (016626) 61245; (A. Kerrigan). OMAGH, 1, Spillars Place, Omagh, BT78 1HL; Tel: (01662) 244821; (S. Graham). SHANTALLOW, 92, Racecourse Road, Shantallow, Londonderry, BT48 8DA; Tel: (01504) 354185; (J Campbell). SION

	MILLS, The Square, Sion Mills, BT78 9HA; Tel: (016626) 58513; (R. Thompson). STRABANE, Butcher Street, Strabane, BT82 8BJ; Tel: (01504) 883686; (A. Harron). STRATHFOYLE, Claragh Crescent, Strathfoyle, Co. Londonderry, BT47 7HQ; Tel: (01504) 860385; (P. McLaughlin). WATERSIDE, 137, Spencer Road, Waterside, Londonderry, BT47 1AQ; Tel: (01504) 42963; (J. Austen).
Opening Hours	Library HQ and Divisional HQs: 09.00 - 17.15. For opening hours of branch libraries please contact Library HQ (see above).
Mobile Libraries	9 - Public; 3 - Housebound; 4 - Schools.
Services Offered	Lending; Children's; A/V; Reference; Business; Local studies; Housebound; Hospital & homes; Schools library service; Prison library service; ILL; Photocopying; Teletext; On-line services.
Special Collections	Local and Irish History; The Nawn Collection (Local & Irish History); William Carleton Collection; IJFR "A", "F", "I".
Bookstock	673,532 volumes - all available for loan and ILL.
Periodicals	460 titles (Irish titles) - not available for loan; will photocopy.
A/V Stock	35,523 sound recordings - 2,054 available for loan but not ILL.
Other Materials	4,471 Maps; 3834 Microforms.
Catalogue	On-line and CD-ROM at main libraries.
Classification	Dewey 19th edition with selective updates to 20th edition.
Computer Equipment	Belfast City Council Computer Services Integrated On-line system; Apple MAC DTP; Micro-computers; CD-ROMs - Whitaker's BookBank; Financial Times Profile.
Other Equipment	Speed Copier; Photographic Equipment and Dark Room Facilities; SVHS Edit Suite and Mixing Facilities; LCD Video

Projector; OHPs; Slide Projector and
Screens; VCRs.

County Library HQ,
Dublin Road,
Mullingar,
Co. Westmeath.
Tel: Mullingar (044) 40781/40782/40783
Fax: Mullingar (044) 41322

Librarian	Mary M. Farrell
No. of Staff	20 (4 Professional, 12 Non-professional, 4 Part-time).
Branches	ATHLONE, Fr. Matthew Hall, Athlone, Co. Westmeath; Tel: (0902) 92166/94533; (Gearoid O'Brien, Assistant Librarian). CASTLEPOLLARD, Town Hall, The Square, Castlepollard, Co. Westmeath; Tel: (044) 61646; (Phyllis McCabe, Branch Librarian). KILBEGGAN, Main Street, Kilbeggan, Co. Westmeath; (Elizabeth Gorman, Branch Librarian). KILLUCAN, St. Joseph's Hall, Killucan, Co. Westmeath; (Olive Greene, Branch Librarian). MOATE, The Courthouse, Moate, Co. Westmeath; (Post vacant). MULLINGAR, Church Avenue, Mullingar, Co. Westmeath; Tel: (044) 48278; (Patricia Shaw, Senior Library Assistant).
Opening Hours	HQ: 09.30 - 13.00, 14.00 - 17.30 (Mon. - Thurs.), 09.30 - 13.00, 14.00 - 17.00 (Fri.). For opening hours of branch libraries please contact Library HQ Tel:(044) 40781/2/3.
Mobile Libraries	1 branch exchange van.
Services Offered	Adult and Children's lending; Reference and Information service; Schools Service; ILL (with restrictions on rare and o/p items); Photocopying.
Special Collections	IRISH & LOCAL STUDIES, Library HQ,

(see above), (Mr. Tony Cox, Assistant Librarian); Kirby collection; Burgess papers; Howard Bury collection; Ginnell Papers; Local Photographic collection; Michael Walsh collection; IJFR "E".

Bookstock	145,000 volumes - 140,000 available for loan and ILL (except for rare, out of print, reference, Irish and Local Studies material).
Periodicals	21 titles - available for loan and ILL; will photocopy.
A/V Stock	760 audio-cassettes, 530 compact disks, 80 multimedia packs - available for loan, but not ILL; 30 video-cassettes - not available for loan or ILL.
Other Materials	Maps; Schools Folklore collection; Lawrence collection of photographs; Local newspapers on microfilm; Paintings - not available for loan or ILL.
Catalogue	Author/title; Classified.
Classification	Dewey 20th edition.
Computer Equipment	7 PCs (1 with ENFO database); 3 laser printers; 3 dot matrix printers; BNB on CD-ROM.
Other Equipment	1 Microfilm reader/printer; 2 Microfilm readers; 3 Microfiche readers; 3 Photocopiers; TV and Video Recorder.

92 **WEXFORD COUNTY LIBRARY**
Teach Shionoid,
Abbey Street,
Wexford.
Tel: Wexford (053) 42211
Fax: Wexford (053) 23406 (County Hall)

Librarian	Catherine O'Rourke
No. of Staff	14 (4 Professional, 7 Non-professional, 3 Part-time).
Branch Libraries	BUNCLODY, 1, Irish Street, Bunclody, Co. Wexford; Tel: (054) 77467; (Lucy

Wall-Murphy, Librarian).
ENNISCORTHY, Lymington Road, Enniscorthy, Co. Wexford; Tel: (054) 36055; (Angela Parle, Librarian). GOREY, Gorey Courthouse, Upper Main Street, Gorey, Co. Wexford; Tel: (055) 21481; (Kathleen Gleeson, Librarian). NEW ROSS, Barrack Lane, New Ross, Co. Wexford; Tel: (051) 21877; (Anne Griffin, Librarian). WEXFORD Branch, Teach Shionoid, Abbey Street, Wexford; Tel: (053) 42211 ext. 355; (Jarlath Glynn, Librarian).

Departments	ACQUISITIONS/CATALOGUING, HQ (see above); (Rita O'Brien, Librarian).
Opening Hours	For opening hours, please contact HQ: Tel: (053) 42211.
Mobile Libraries	1.
Services Offered	Mobile and School Library Services, contact HQ; Library Service to Nursing Homes, Housebound and Community Centres; ILL; Photocopying.
Special Collections	Local & Irish History; Genealogy; Local Authors; Local Prints and Photographs; Archives; Local Newspapers (19th Century); IJFR "Q"; Map Collection; 1798 Collection.
Bookstock	402,359 volumes - 245, 911 available for loan and ILL except reference material.
Periodicals	50 titles - not available for loan or ILL; will photocopy.
A/V Stock	6515 audio-cassettes, 274 compact disks - available for loan and ILL; 160 video-cassettes.
Catalogue	Author; Classified (card).
Classification	Dewey. 20th Edition.
Computer Equipment	2 ENFO computers and printers.
Other Equipment	2 Microform readers/printers; 3 Photocopiers; TV; Video Recorder; Audio Cassette Player.

WICKLOW COUNTY LIBRARY
Church Road,
Greystones,
Co. Wicklow.
Tel: Greystones (01) 287 4387
Fax: Greystones (01) 287 3297

County Librarian	Gerry Maher LLB (Hons), DLIS.
No. of Staff	29 (4 Professional, 24 Non-professional, 1 Part-time).
Branch Libraries	ARKLOW, Station Road, Arklow, Co. Wicklow; Tel: (0402) 39977. BALTINGLASS, The Courthouse, Baltinglass, Co. Wicklow. BLESSINGTON. BRAY, Eglington Road, Bray, Co. Wicklow; Tel: (01) 286 2600; (Eileen Murray, Librarian). CARNEW. DUNLAVIN, Market House, Dunlavin, Co. Wicklow. ENNISKERRY; Tel: (01) 286 4339. GREYSTONES, Church Road, Greystones, Co. Wicklow; Tel: (01) 287 3548; (Una Campbell, Senior Library Assistant). RATHDRUM, 10, Gilbert's Row, Rathdrum, Co. Wicklow. TINAHELY, The Court House, Tinahely, Co. Wicklow. WICKLOW, Killmantin Hill, Wicklow; Tel: (0404) 67025.
Opening Hours	For opening hours, please contact Wicklow County Library (see above).
Mobile Libraries	1 schools vehicle.
Services Offered	Lending; Reference; Local Studies; PRISON LIBRARY SERVICE, at HQ (see above), (Mike Maguire, Librarian); SCHOOLS LIBRARY SERVICE (Primary), at HQ (see above), (Noelle Ringwood, Librarian); HOSPITALS/DAY CARE CENTRES, at HQ (see above), (Noelle Ringwood, Librarian); Adult Literacy schemes; Information on careers, business, social welfare, health; ENFO service; Photocopying.
Special Collections	Local History; J.M. Synge collection; C.S. Parnell collection; IJFR "R".

Bookstock	254,652 volumes - available for loan (except reference and local history) and ILL.
Periodicals	30 titles - not available for loan or ILL; will photocopy.
A/V Stock	1,188 audio-cassettes - available for loan and ILL.
Catalogue	Author/Class Card Catalogue; DYNIX Automated Library Systems (HQ and Bray Public Library).
Classification	Dewey.
Computer Equipment	UNIX; CD-ROM drive; 8 terminals; 2 OPACs; DYNIX software; ENFO terminal and printer.
Other Equipment	3 Microfiche readers; 1 Microfilm reader; 5 Photocopiers; TV.

94   A & L GOODBODY
1, Earlsfort Centre,
Lower Hatch Street,
Dublin 2.
Tel: Dublin (01) 661 3311 ext. 625
Fax: Dublin (01) 661 3278

Librarian	Margaret Merrick
No. of Staff	2 (2 Professional).
Opening Hours	09.00 - 17.30.
Services Offered	Reference; Enquiry; Lending; CD-ROM and On-line searching; In-house database development; Training; ILL.
Special Collections	Legal Materials: general (IRE/UK); EU Legal; Taxation.
Bookstock	5,000 volumes - 4,500 available for loan to staff only, not available for ILL.
Periodicals	60+ titles - not available for loan or ILL; will photocopy.
A/V Stock	2 compact disks - not available for loan or ILL.
Other Materials	Microfiche: EU Law.
Catalogue	TINLIB.
Classification	Moys.
Computer Equipment	IBM PCs; Windows; Novell network; CD-ROMs also networked.
Other Equipment	1 Microform reader/printer; 1 Photocopier.

95   AGE ACTION IRELAND LTD
114-116, Pearse Street,
Dublin 2.
Tel: Dublin (01) 677 9892/677 1930
Fax: Dublin (01) 677 9892

Information Officer	Tom McGuirk
No. of Staff	3 (2 Professional, 1 Non-professional).
Opening hours	09.00 - 15.30 (Mon. - Fri.).
Services Offered	Reference library; Information service; AgeInfo Database on CD-ROM (contains

	bibliographical references to over 24,000 books as well as articles from 4,000 periodicals concerned with ageing and older people).
Special Collections	The Library and Information Service's main focus is on the subject of ageing in Ireland but there is a growing amount of material from other countries both in Europe and further afield. The library has also developed links with other organisations as part of a wider information network; including the Centre for Policy on Ageing in London, CLEIRPA in Paris and Age Concern Scotland and England.
Bookstock	2,000 volumes - not available for loan or ILL.
Periodicals	60 titles - not available for loan, but available for ILL; will photocopy.
A/V Stock	10 audio-cassettes, 40 video-cassettes - not available for loan, but available for ILL.
Catalogue	Cardbox Plus.
Classification	Implementing the Centre for Policy on Ageing's classification scheme.
Computer Equipment	AgeInfo database on CD-ROM; Database of services for older people in Ireland; Database of respite care services for adults in Ireland.
Other Equipment	1 Photocopier.

AGE AND OPPORTUNITY   **96**
St. Joseph's Building,
The Marino Institute of Education,
Griffith Avenue,
Dublin 9.
Tel: Dublin (01) 837 0570
Fax: Dublin (01) 837 0591

Information Officer	John Cullen
No. of Staff	1 (Professional).
Opening Hours	10.00 - 17.00.
Services Offered	Reading room; Loans; Information files;

	Fact sheets; Information searches; ILLs.
Special Collections	Materials relating to older people and social issues.
Bookstock	1,100 volumes - 1,000 available for loan and ILL.
Periodicals	153 titles - available for loan and ILL; will photocopy.
A/V Stock	20 audio-cassettes - available for loan; 35 video-cassettes; 14 multimedia packs.
Catalogue	Filemaker Pro.
Classification	Specially developed in-house scheme.
Computer Equipment	Apple Mac Performas on a LocalTalk network; Claris software; Filemaker Pro.
Other Equipment	Photocopiers.

97   AGE CONCERN NORTHERN IRELAND
3, Lower Crescent,
Belfast BT7 1NR.
Tel: Belfast (01232) 245729

Information Manager	Mary Doonan-McCartan
No. of Staff	2 (Non-professional).
Opening Hours	09.00 - 17.00 (Mon. - Fri.) excluding Bank and Public Holidays.
Services Offered	Reference only to Age Concern Northern Ireland staff and volunteers, and to community groups; Photocopying
Subject Specialisation	Needs of the elderly and those who work with them; Welfare rights and benefits; Social services; Housing; Heating; Transport.
Bookstock	450 titles (approx.) - available for loan; 400 Information files (approx.); Press releases; Newspaper cuttings; Reports; Training material.
Periodicals	15 titles - available for loan; will photocopy.
Catalogue	Card catalogue; dictionary arrangement; author/ title/subject.
Classification	Special faceted classification scheme developed by Aslib for Age Concern and

the National Corporation for the Care of
Old People (1972).

AIB GROUP 98
Bankcentre,
Ballsbridge,
Dublin 4.
Tel: Dublin (01) 660 0311 ext. 13412
Fax: Dublin (01) 660 1696

Librarian	Mary Heslin
Opening Hours	09.30 - 13.30 (Mon. - Fri.).
Services Offered	Internal to Bank only.
Subject Specialisation	Banking.
Bookstock	350 volumes.
Periodicals	200 titles.
Catalogue	Computer - InMagic software
Classification	Own System
Computer Systems	Wang PC; InMagic software.
Other Equipment	Photocopier.

THE ALLEN LIBRARY 99
Christian Brothers,
North Richmond Street,
Dublin 1.
Tel: Dublin (01) 855 1077
Fax: Dublin (01) 855 5243

Librarian	Br. Thomas Connolly
No. of Staff	1 (Non-professional).
Opening Hours	09.00 - 17.00 (Mon. - Fri.).
Services Offered	Reference only; Available to research students and readers by appointment; Photocopying; Reading room; On-line catalogue from 1997 on. PLEASE NOTE: A FÁS Heritage Project is in progress at the present cataloguing the collection. The library will not be fully functional until 1997.
Special Collections	Book and periodicals on: Irish Social, Political and Local History; Irish

	Education; Irish Ecclesiastical History; Irish Folklore, Music and Literature; History of the Congregation of the Christian Brothers and its founder Edmund Rice; Irish Language and Literature; Archival material relating to 1916 and the War of Independence.
Bookstock	25,000 volumes - available for reference only, ILL requests are considered.
Periodicals	300 titles - available for reference only, ILL requests are considered; will photocopy.
Other Materials	Some original paintings and prints of Irish interest.
Catalogue	Heritage Library Management System (from 1997 on).
Classification	In-house.
Computer Systems	4 Tulip DT 4/665, networked, running Heritage Library Management System; 2 Macintosh Performas for Word Processing and office work; 2 Laser printers.
Other Equipment	1 Microfiche Reader; 1 Photocopier.

100   ALLIANCE FRANCAISE
1, Kildare Street
Dublin 2.
Tel: Dublin (01) 676 1732/676 7116

Librarian	Elisabeth Combeau
No. of Staff	1 (Non-professional).
Opening Hours	12.00 - 19.30 (Mon.),14.30 - 19.30 (Tues.), 10.30 - 18.30 (Wed.) 12.00 - 20.30 (Thurs.), 10.00 - 13.30 (Sat.).
Services Offered	Lending library; Tuesdays 11.00 - 12.30 reading of a novel, short stories, newspaper articles; Saturdays 11.00 - 12.30 Storytime for children (5 - 8).
Bookstock	8,000 volumes - available for loan to members (membership: students, unemployed, pensioners £5, others £10); not available for ILL.

Periodicals	8 titles - not available for loan or ILL; will photocopy.
Classification	Dewey.
Computer Equipment	Software: Biblio.

AONTAS 101
22, Earlsfort Terrace,
Dublin 2.
Tel: Dublin (01) 475 4121/475 4122
Fax: Dublin (01) 478 0064

Librarian	Mary M. Purcell
No. of Staff	1 (Professional).
Opening Hours	10.00 - 13.00, 14.00 - 17.00 (Mon. - Fri.).
Services Offered	Database of adult education courses; Telephone information service; Exhibition of adult learning opportunities; Information leaflets; Library and research facilities.
Special Collections	List of Aontas publications available.
Subject Specialisation	Adult education (some literacy material).
Bookstock	400 volumes (approx.) - not available for loan; available for ILL.
Periodicals	12 titles plus 120 (approx.) more on exchange - not available for loan or ILL; will photocopy.
A/V Stock	30 audio-cassettes - available for loan and ILL.
Catalogue	Partly computerised.
Classification	Dewey.
Computer Equipment	Inmagic (test) software for cataloguing.
Other Equipment	Canon photocopier.

APSO 102
(AGENCY FOR PERSONAL SERVICE OVERSEAS)
29/30 Fitzwilliam Square,
Dublin 2
Tel: Dublin (01) 661 4411
Fax: Dublin (01) 661 4202
E-mail: APSO@iol.ie

Resources Officer	June Carr

APSO continued

No. of Staff	2 (Non-professional).
Opening Hours	9.30 - 13.00, 14.00 - 17.30 (Mon. - Fri.).
Services Offered	Information on living and working conditions overseas through books, periodicals, videos, slides, maps. Open to the public.
Bookstock	5,840 volumes - 5,646 available for loan and ILL.
Periodicals	120 titles - not available for loan or ILL; will photocopy.
A/V Stock	100 audio-cassettes, 937 video-cassettes - available for loan and ILL; 121 multimedia packs - not available for loan or ILL.
Catalogue	Card - Author, Subject, Country
Classification	UDC.
Computer Equipment	TINLIB Software package; OPAC.
Other Equipment	1 Photocopier; TV; Video; Tape/slide Projectors.

103   ARCHBISHOP MARSH'S LIBRARY
St. Patrick's Close,
Dublin 8.
Tel: Dublin (01) 454 3511
Fax: Dublin (01) 454 3511

Keeper	Muriel McCarthy
No. of Staff	6 (4 Professional, 2 Non-professional).
Departments	DELMAS CONSERVATION BINDERY in Marsh's Library Tel: (01) 454 4609
Opening Hours	10.00 - 12.45, 14.00 - 17.00 (Mon., Wed., Thurs., Fri.), 10.30 - 12.45 (Sat.). Closed Tuesday.
Services Offered	Delmas Conservation Bindery carries out restoration of books and manuscripts to the highest international standard.
Special Collections	Books relating to the 16th, 17th, and 18th centuries.
Subject Specialisation	Irish History; Theology; Philosophy; Religious Controversy; Medicine; Law; Mathematics; Science; Travel; Literature; Music.

Bookstock	25,000 volumes - not available for loan.
Manuscripts	300 titles - not available for loan.
Catalogue	Manuscript catalogue of the entire collection; printed sectional catalogues of the manuscripts, books printed before 1641, books in French, music manuscripts and printed music books.

ARMAGH OBSERVATORY   104
College Hill,
Armagh BT61 9DG.
Tel: Armagh (01861) 522928
Fax: Armagh (01861) 527174
E-mail: [username]@star.arm.ac.uk
Web site: Http://star.arm.ac.uk

Librarian	John McFarland
Opening Hours	09.00 - 17.00 (Mon. - Fri.).
Services Offered	Library available for the use of research workers.
Subject Specialisation	Astronomy.
Bookstock	1,400 text books - for reference only.
Periodicals	15,000 volumes - for reference only.
A/V Stock	Photographs; slides (approx. 5,000).
Catalogue	Card; Computer (to limited extent).
Classification	UDC.
Computer Systems	UNIX.
Other Equipment	Photocopier; Microfiche reader.

ARMAGH (ROBINSON) PUBLIC LIBRARY   105
Abbey Street,
Armagh,
Co. Armagh BT61 7DZ
Tel: Armagh (01861) 523142
Fax: Armagh (01861) 524177

Keeper	The Dean of Armagh, Very Rev. H. Cassidy
Librarian	W. R. H. Carson.
No. of Staff	4 (1 Professional, 1 Non-professional; 2 Part-time).

105 ARMAGH (ROBINSON) PUBLIC LIBRARY continued

Opening Hours	10.00 - 12.30, 14.00 - 16.00 (Mon. - Fri.). Other times by appointment.
Services Offered	Photocopying.
Special Collections	The Library, founded in 1771, is basically the personal library of Richard Robinson, Baron Rokeby, Archbishop of Armagh, with later additions. There are 4 incunabula, 300 items printed before 1641, 12,000 items printed before 1851 (2000 Wing items), many pre-1700 books of travel and description; a copy of the first edition of "Gulliver's Travels", with emendations in Swift's own hand; Rokeby Collection of Engravings; Hogarth and Piranesi prints.
Subject Specialisation	History, with emphasis on Ireland (large collection of 18th century pamphlets dealing with the Union); Theology, especially Biblical criticism.
Bookstock	25,000 volumes (approx.) - 5,000 (approx.) available for loan at Keeper's discretion (nothing printed before 1800 available for loan).
Periodicals	10 titles - available for loan; will photocopy.
Manuscripts	40
Other Materials	Prints 1,000 (approx.); Coins 300 (approx.); Seals 2,000 (approx.).
Catalogue	Computerised; On-line BCC Computer Services, as part of Southern Education and Library board.
Computer Equipment	Digital hardware; BCC Computer system, part of Southern Education and Library Board Library Services catalogue.
Other Equipment	Photocopiers.

106 AUGHINISH ALUMINA LTD.
Askeaton,
Co. Limerick.
Tel: Askeaton (061) 604000
Fax: Askeaton (061) 604063

Librarian	Mary Sheahan
No. of Staff	450 (250 Professional, 200 Non-professional, 50 Part-time).
Opening Hours	08.00-16.30.
Services Offered	All services are offered internally; Training disks in the multimedia centre are offered to the local community.
Bookstock	600 volumes - not available for loan or ILL.
Periodicals	20 titles - not available for loan or ILL.
A/V Stock	20 audio-cassettes, 300 video-cassettes - not available for loan or ILL; 20 multimedia packs - only available for loan to the local community.
Other Equipment	1 Microform reader; 1 Microform reader/printer; 1 Photocopier.

AUSTIN CLARKE LIBRARY 107
Poetry Ireland/Éigse Éireann,
Bermingham Tower,
Upper Yard,
Dublin Castle,
Dublin 2.
Tel: Dublin (01) 671 4632
Fax: Dublin (01) 671 4634
E-mail: poetry@iol.ie

Librarian	Claire Ranson
No. of Staff	5 (Non-professional).
Opening Hours	14.00 -17.00 (Mon. - Fri.), other times by arrangement.
Services Offered	Publication: "Poetry Ireland Review"; Poetry readings; Newsletter; Writers in schools scheme.
Special Collections	Austin Clarke Collection: Clarke's own books were acquired by Poetry Ireland on his death, 6,000 volumes of poetry, prose, criticism and drama; John Jordan Collection: 2,000 volumes donated by his family, poetry; drama; fiction; criticism.
Subject Specialisation	Irish and English poetry; Irish fiction;

	Drama; Literary criticism.
Bookstock	10,000 volumes (approx.) - not available for loan or ILL.
Periodicals	600 titles (approx.) - not available for loan or ILL; will photocopy.
A/V Stock	10-20 audio-cassettes - not available for loan or ILL.
Catalogue	In progress: complete card catalogue of entire library, computer database in progress.
Equipment	Photocopiers.

108 BAR LIBRARY
Royal Courts of Justice,
P.O. Box 414,
Belfast BT1 3JP.
Tel: Belfast (01232) 241523
Fax: Belfast (01232) 231850
E-mail: dasmith@barlib.dnet.co.uk

Librarian	David Smith
No. of Staff	12 (2 Professional, 9 Non-professional, 2.5 Part-time).
Opening Hours	09.15 - 17.15 (Mon. - Fri.). Access available to members at all times.
Services Offered	Library and information services solely for barristers in Northern Ireland.
Special Collections	NI caselaw; NI legislation.
Bookstock	75,000 volumes - almost everything available for loan to members only (barristers).
Periodicals	50 titles - not available for loan or ILL; will photocopy.
A/V Stock	6 CD-ROMs - not available for loan or ILL.
Other Materials	Historic collection of portraits and photographs of NI Judiciary and Bar.
Catalogue	Card + Idealist. Due to fully automatic this year - currently selecting system.
Classification	Moys.
Computer Equipment	Novell Network running 486 + Pontim

| | PCs; Microsoft Office Professional; Pegasus opera accounts; Idealist: library database, catalogue, index to NI law; CD-ROM: All England law reports, Celex, Weekly law reports, Industrial cases, etc.; Databases: Legal Journals Index, Daily law reports, Financial journals index, Badger, current law. External: Lexis & Nexis. |
| Other Equipment | 2 Photocopiers; 4 Faxes. |

BBC NORTHERN IRELAND   **109**
News Information and Research Centre (NIRC),
Rooms 106/109 Broadcasting House,
Ormeau Avenue,
Belfast BT2 8HQ.
Tel: Belfast (01232) 338648
Fax: Belfast (01232) 338800
E-mail: mark.cox@bbc.co.uk

Library Manager	Marshall Hopley
No. of Staff	10.
Opening Hours	09.30 - 17.30.
Services Offered	Loans; Research; Intended primarily for BBC NI personnel; external libraries and bona fide students and researchers assisted as time permits. Organisations and other commercial customers may apply for a rate card for services.
Special Collections	A selection of regional and national newspapers kept uncut for 6 weeks; Selected papers cut for stories of regional and BBC NI interest; Cuttings files date from 1969 and cover a very wide range of subjects; An in-house records service related to BBC NI management and programme output is maintained.
Subject Specialisation	Book specialisations include Local studies (especially History and Politics) and broadcasting/the media.
Bookstock	2,000 volumes - 90% available for loan to BBC personnel and local libraries on a per occasion basis.

Periodicals	15 titles (2 copies purchased, one for reference only, one for distribution within BBC NI) - available for ILL per occasion basis; will photocopy on a per occasion basis.
A/V Stock	Film/VT Library Stock: 5,000 film cans (1960s to date); 5,000 spools of 1" videotape (1984 to date); 480 spools of 2" videotape (1970 -1984); 10,600 3/4" video-cassette; 11,000 ½ " video-cassette. Radio Programmes: 12,000 1/4" open reel tapes. Gramophone Library: 18,000 vinyl/CDs. The same conditions for access apply throughout the Library Services department. In the first instance, contact Library Manager, Marshall Hopley, Tel: (01232) 3383223.
Catalogue	At present card catalogue of author and title. Shortly to computerise classification and circulation system.
Classification	Dewey - to become categorisation based on customer needs.
Computer Equipment	NIRC (Ref) has at present stand alone computer and Systems system for keeping track of periodicals and general administration. Shortly to join a LAN comprising Queen's University Belfast and the Linen Hall Library for exchange of bibliographic information. Using dBase IV at present for in-house housekeeping. Radio Programmes/ Gramophone Library: stand-alone system for CD collection using dBase IV; online access to BBC Echo system for stock control of radio tapes. Shortly to acquire CD-ROMs of Gramophone Library London (BBC) catalogue. Film/VT Library: on-line access to BBC VTOL system for stock control of BBC film and videotape material; Shortly to upgrade to IBM PC network comprising access to VTOL and local processing.

| Other Equipment | Microfilm material relates to in-house records, e.g. policy papers of BBC NI and programme files now in abeyance; Microfile of Whitakers BIP and BBC Reference Libraries in London Book Collections; NIRC (News Information). |

AN BORD ALTRANAIS (NURSING BOARD)   110
31-32, Fitzwilliam Square,
Dublin 2.
Tel: Dublin (01) 676 0226
Fax: Dublin (01) 676 3348

Librarian	Muriel Haire
No. of Staff	2 (1 Professional, 1 Non-professional).
Opening Hours	10.30 - 12.30, 14.00 - 17.00 (Mon. - Fri.).
Services Offered	Information retrieval service; Reading room; Access to a wide range of Nursing/Medical journals; Book collection; Information files; Reference service; Photocopy/Document supply service; Video rental; Current awareness service.
Special Collections	Professional Nursing journals/books/reports.
Bookstock	1,800 volumes - reference only.
Periodicals	110 titles - reference only; will photocopy.
A/V Stock	2 compact disks (CINAHL & RCN Nurse ROM); 130 video-cassettes - available for loan and ILL.
Catalogue	Inmagic - DB Textworks.
Classification	Royal College of Nursing classification system.
Computer Equipment	3 PCs; 2 Printers; DB - Textworks; WordStar; Ventura; Access On-line DataStar; Internet; 2 CD-ROM drives.
Other Equipment	1 Microfiche reader; 2 Photocopiers.

BORD NA MONA   111
Technical Information Office,
Droichead Nua,
Co. Kildare.

BORD NA MONA continued
Tel: Newbridge (045) 431201
Fax: Newbridge (045) 433240

Information Officer	Tony McKenna
No. of Staff	1 (Non-professional).
Opening Hours	By appointment only.
Special Collections	2,600 translations (mainly Russian and German), peat-related.
Bookstock	16,500 volumes - most available for loan (except rare books) and ILL.
Periodicals	12 titles - available for ILL; will photocopy.
Catalogue	On PC with on-line searches on keyword, author, etc. Print-out of holdings.
Classification	Own.
Computer Equipment	AST SVA PC; Librarian Information Retrieval System; On-line database connection to CORDIS, Dialog, ESA, Databank GlobalScan and Newsline databases.
Other Equipment	Photocopier; Microfiche reader/printer.

112 **AN BORD TRÁCHTÁLA/THE IRISH TRADE BOARD**
Merrion Hall,
Strand Road,
Sandymount,
Dublin 4.
Tel: Dublin (01) 206 6000
Fax: Dublin (01) 206 6367

Librarian	Margaret Hogan
No. of Staff	13 (5 Professional, 8 Non-professional).
Opening Hours	09.00 - 13.00, 14.00 - 17.00 (Mon. - Fri.). Appointment necessary.
Services Offered	Enquiry Service; On-line searching.
Special Collections	EU business related official documentation.
Subject Specialisation	Market research; Marketing.
Bookstock	15,000 volumes - not available for loan, restricted ILL.
Periodicals	600 titles - not available for loan or ILL; will photocopy.

A/V Stock	10 compact disks - not available for loan or ILL.
Classification	UDC
Computer Equipment	UNICORN collection management system (SIRS Corp.); ICL and Wang Hardware; Access to following on-line hosts: DIALOG, Datastar, FT Profile, Leatherhead Food RA, Business Eye, Cognotec; Minitel Catalogue; Market Information Database (MIDB)
Other Equipment	Microform reader/printer; FUJI FMRP 30AU; Canon Photocopier NP 3225 AF

BRYSON HOUSE 113
28 Bedford Street,
Belfast BT2 7FE
Tel: Belfast (01232) 325835

Librarian	Liz White
No. of Staff	1 (Non-professional).
Opening Hours	Student Unit Library, 09.00 - 16.30 (Mon. - Thurs.), 09.00 - 15.30 (Fri.).
Other Services	There is a small library in the Multicultural Resource Centre in Bryson House, which deals with educational and social issues relating to ethnic minorities.
Subject Specialisation	Social Welfare; Social Work; Community.
Bookstock	250 volumes - available for loan to staff, students/volunteers based in Bryson House and members of local voluntary/community groups.
Periodicals	Magazines relating to Social Work; will photocopy.
A/V Stock	20 audio-cassettes, 20 video-cassettes, 10-20 multimedia packs - lending facility as per bookstock.
Catalogue	Author catalogue; subject catalogue

CAPPAGH ORTHOPAEDIC HOSPITAL 114
Medical Library,
Finglas,

114 CAPPAGH ORTHOPAEDIC HOSPITAL continued
Dublin 11.
Tel: Dublin (01) 834 1211
Fax: Dublin (01) 864 0294
E-mail: rcsiorth@iol.ie

Librarian	None
No. of Staff	1 (1 Part-time).
Opening Hours	09.30 - 12.00, 12.45 - 17.00.
Services Offered	OVID Medline; Video facilities; Unique collection of Orthopaedic Texts.
Special Collections	Journal of Bone & Joint Surgery (American & British commenced 1927); Clinical Orthopaedics & Related Research (commenced 1972); only sources in Republic of Ireland.
Bookstock	400+ volumes - not available for loan or ILL.
Periodicals	42 titles - not available for loan or ILL; will photocopy.
A/V Stock	6 compact disks, 10 video-cassettes - not available for loan or ILL.
Computer Equipment	1 stand alone PC; CD-ROM facility (3 CD drives).

115 CAVAN GENERAL HOSPITAL LIBRARY C
Cavan General Hospital
Cavan.
Tel: Cavan (049) 61399
Fax: Cavan (049) 61065

Librarian	Jean Harrison
No. of Staff	2 (1 Professional, 1 Non-professional).
Opening Hours	10.30 - 17.00 (Mon.),18.30 -20.30 (Tues.) 14.00 - 17.00 (Wed., Thurs).
Services Offered	Lend books and videos; Photocopies available of journal articles; Computerised searches on Medline, CINAHL; ILL.
Special Collections	Medical; Nursing; Midwifery; Disability healthcare; Management; General healthcare.
Bookstock	500 volumes - not available for loan except

	to staff; available for ILL.
Periodicals	50 titles - not available for loan or ILL; will photocopy.
A/V Stock	3 compact disks - not available for loan or ILL; 4 video-cassettes - available for loan and ILL.
Classification	Dewey.
Computer Equipment	Heritage library system; 1 CD-ROM; 1 PC; Software: Medline; CINAHL.
Other Equipment	1 Photocopier, charge-card system.

CENTRAL BANK OF IRELAND   **116**
PO Box 559,
Dame Street,
Dublin 2.
Tel: Dublin (01) 671 6666
Fax: Dublin (01) 671 6561

Librarian	Mairéad Ní Bhriain
No. of Staff	6 (6 Non-professional, 2 Part-time).
Opening Hours	09.30 - 17.00 (Mon. - Fri.).
Services Offered	Information and Library Services for Staff; ILL.
Special Collections	Economics and Central Banking.
Bookstock	7,000 volumes - 6,500 available for loan; available for ILL if not in use.
Periodicals	2,000 titles - not available for loan or ILL.
Catalogue	Classified.
Classification	Dewey Decimal Classification.
Computer Equipment	PC; Microsoft Word 6.0; FT Profile; IRIS; Minitel.
Other Equipment	1 Microform reader; 1 Photocopier.

CENTRAL CATHOLIC LIBRARY   **117**
74, Merrion Square,
Dublin 2.
Tel: Dublin (01) 676 1264

Honorary Librarian	Peter Costello
Librarian	Deirdre Quinn
No. of Staff	2 (1 Professional, 1 Non-professional).

117 CENTRAL CATHOLIC LIBRARY continued

Opening Hours	11.00 - 19.00 (Mon. - Fri.), 11.00 - 17.30 (Sat.).
Services Offered	Lending and reference facilities; Postal information service; Reading rooms; ILL; Photocopying.
Special Collections	Irish History; Art; Architecture; Philosophy; Theology; Rare Books 1522 onwards.
Subject Specialisation	Catholicism.
Bookstock	90,000 volumes - 14,000 available for loan (to members of Library) and ILL.
Periodicals	470 titles - not available for loan or ILL; will photocopy.
A/V Stock	100 audio-cassettes, 40 video-cassettes, 40 compact disks - available for loan and ILL.
Catalogue	Author and Title.
Classification	Special.
Other Equipment	Photocopier.

118 CENTRAL REMEDIAL CLINIC
Vernon Avenue,
Clontarf,
Dublin 3.
Tel: Dublin (01) 833 2206
Fax: Dublin (01) 833 5496
E-mail: tdcrc@iol.ie

Librarian	Patricia Mac Keogh
No. of Staff	2 (1 Professional, 1 Non-professional).
Opening Hours	By appointment only.
Services Offered	On-line searching service; ILL; Provision of articles through BLLD.
Special Collections	Medical; Rehabilitation; Psychology; Paramedical; Education.
Bookstock	16,000 volumes - available for loan (only on request) and ILL.
Periodicals	20 titles - will photocopy.
A/V Stock	2 video-cassettes: "Information on Cerebral Palsy", "Measurement of Movement in the Joints of Lower Limbs" - available for loan, purchase and ILL; Set of booklets:

"Information on Cerebral Palsy";
Multimedia packs - video and booklets can
come as pack.

Catalogue	Computerised Catalogue.
Classification	Dewey (modified).
Computer Equipment	IBM PC; Medline on CD-ROM; CO-NET (Assistive Technology); REHADAT (Technical Aids); Handynet.
Other Equipment	2 Photocopiers

CHESTER BEATTY LIBRARY 119
20, Shrewsbury Road,
Dublin 4.
(will move to Dublin Castle in 1997)
Tel: Dublin (01) 269 2386/269 5187
Fax: Dublin (01) 283 0983

Director	Dr. Michael Ryan
No. of Staff	12 (4 Professional, 2 Part-time).
Opening Hours	09.30 - 17.00 (Tues. - Fri.), 14.00 - 17.00 (Sat.).
Services Offered	By appointment with the Director; Photocopying; Photographic orders; Shop; Lectures; Free guided tours on Wednesdays and Saturdays at 2.30pm.
Special Collections	Islamic, Oriental and Western books and mss.
Bookstock	6,000 rare books, 13,000 manuscripts - not available for loan or ILL.
Periodicals	6 titles - not available for loan or ILL; will photocopy.
A/V Stock	20 video-cassettes - not available for loan or ILL.
Other Materials	Paintings, furniture and some ceramics from China; Coins, bronze statues (16th-17th century); Costumes (18-19th century China); Slide library: c.7000 images.
Catalogue	Card and 60 printed volumes.
Classification	In-house
Computer Equipment	LAN using WordPerfect and database.
Other Equipment	Microform readers; Photocopiers; In-house microfilm camera.

120   CHILD ACCIDENT PREVENTION TRUST
Department of Epidemiology,
Mulhouse Building,
Grosvenor Road,
Belfast BT12 6BJ.
Tel: Belfast (01232) 240503 ext. 2588
Fax: Belfast (01232) 231907
E-mail: mercer@v1.eph.qub.ac.uk

Information Manager	Rosie Mercer.
No. of Staff	1 (Professional).
Opening Hours	09.00 - 17.00.
Services Offered	Information; Training; Literature searches; Research Consultancy; Photocopying.
Special Collections	All materials relate to issues on Child Health - Housing, Play, but particularly Accidents and their prevention.

121   COMBAT POVERTY AGENCY
8, Charlemont Street,
Dublin 2.
Tel: Dublin (01) 478 3355
Fax: Dublin (01) 478 3731

Information Officer	Joan O'Flynn.
No. of Staff	5.
Opening Hours	09.30 - 13.00, 14.00 - 17.00 (Mon. - Fri.).
Services Offered	Bibliographies; Current awareness bulletins; ILLs. Outside readers welcome to use material on premises; photocopying available.
Special Collections	Publications on Poverty and Social Issues in Community Development; In-house publications for sale.
Bookstock	3,000 volumes - available for loan (to staff only) and ILL.
Periodicals	200 titles - not available for loan or ILL; will photocopy.
A/V Stock	60 video-cassettes - available for loan and ILL.
Other Materials	Sales of agency publications.
Catalogue	TINLIB.

Classification	Own system.
Computer Equipment	IBM PC 12 Model 50; TINLIB software.
Other Equipment	Microfiche reader; Photocopier.

COMMUNITY RELATIONS INFORMATION CENTRE 122
31, Castle Lane,
Belfast BT1 5DB.
Tel: Belfast (01232) 311881
Fax: Belfast (01232) 244364
E-mail: mark@nicrc.thegap.com
Web site: Http://www.gpl.net/customers/nicrc/

Centre Manager	Mark McCann
No. of Staff	2 (Professional).
Opening Hours	09.00 - 17.00 (Mon. - Sat.).
Services Offered	Enquiry service concerning all aspects of community relations work; Referral service; Publications - free and for sale. We display material from all of Northern Ireland's community relations organisations.
Special Collections	Database of community relations (related stories) from 1992 to present.
Bookstock	374 volumes - not available for loan or ILL.
A/V Stock	3 video-cassettes - not available for loan or ILL.

CONTEMPORARY MUSIC CENTRE 123
95, Lower Baggot Street,
Dublin 2.
Tel: Dublin (01) 661 2105
Fax: Dublin (01) 676 2639
E-mail: info@cmc.ie

Librarian	Roísín Maher
No. of Staff	5 (3 Professional, 2 Non-professional) 2 Part-time.
Opening Hours	09.30 - 01.00, 14.00 - 17.30 (Mon. - Fri.).
Services Offered	The Contemporary Music Centre is an all-Ireland archive and resource centre which

	promotes and documents the music of modern Irish classical composers.
Special Collection	Major library of music scores by twentieth-century Irish composers; Sound archive; biographical and research material relating to Irish contemporary music; Information service.
Bookstock	250 volumes - not available for loan or ILL.
Periodicals	20 titles - not available for loan or ILL; will photocopy.
A/V Stock	650 audio-cassettes, 205 compact disks - not available for loan or ILL.
Music Scores	1,926 scores by Irish composers - not available for loan or ILL, available for purchase.
Catalogue	Special music score catalogue.
Computer Equipment	Macintosh computer network including CD-ROM facility. Software: FileMaker Pro 3.0.
Other Equipment	Microform readers; 1 Photocopier; Scanner.

124   COUNCIL FOR THE HOMELESS (NORTHERN IRELAND)
153, University Street,
Belfast, BT7 1HR.
Tel: Belfast (01232) 246440
Fax: Belfast (01232) 241266

Librarian	Tim Watt
No. of Staff	3.
Opening Hours	09.00 - 17.00 (Mon. - Fri.) closed Bank Holidays.
Services Offered	Specialising in Homelessness and related topics; Health; Housing Policy; Young People; Advice; European; Republic of Ireland; Britain; Northern Ireland; also Journals, Annual Reports, Paper cuttings and Briefing papers.
Special Collections	Research documents on the aspects of Homelessness and statistics in relation to

	Northern Ireland.
Bookstock	1,500 volumes (approx.) - most available for loan, but not ILL.
Periodicals	30 titles - not available for loan or ILL; will photocopy.

CRAIG GARDNER/PRICE WATERHOUSE 125
Gardner House,
Wilton Place,
Dublin 2.
Tel: Dublin (01) 662 6000
Fax: Dublin (01) 662 6200
E-mail: Susan_Creedon@Europe.notes.pw.com

Librarian	Susan Creedon
No. of Staff	3 (2 Professional, 1 Non-professional).
Opening Hours	09.00 - 17.30 (Mon. - Fri.).
Services Offered	To staff members only.
Special Collections	Taxation; Accounting; Business.
Bookstock	9,000 volumes - not available for loan or ILL.
Periodicals	70 titles - not available for loan or ILL; will photocopy.
A/V Stock	3 compact disks - not available for loan or ILL.
Catalogue	Database on BRS/SEARCH.
Classification	Internal.
Computer Equipment	BRS/SEARCH (full text retrieval); Access to on-line databases.
Other Equipment	Microfiche reader/printer.

CRH 126
Belgard Castle,
Clondalkin,
Dublin 22.
Tel: Dublin (01) 404 1000
Fax: Dublin (01) 404 1007

Librarian	Martina Kealy
Bookstock	300 volumes - not available for loan or ILL.
Periodicals	60 titles - not available for loan or ILL.

127 DIOCESAN LIBRARY OF DOWN AND DROMORE AND CONNOR

Church of Ireland Diocesan Office,
12, Talbot Street,
Belfast BT1.
Tel: Belfast (01232) 322268

Librarian	J.F. Rankin, Secretary to Library Committee.
Services Offered	Open to Church of Ireland Clergy and Lay enquirers. Others by appointment through Miss Sheila Regan, Diocesan Office.
Special Collections	Charles Parsons Reichel Collection; Bishop Reeves manuscripts (deposited in Public Records Office, Northern Ireland).
Subject Specialisation	Theology and biography.
Bookstock	2,000 volumes.

128 DISABILITY ACTION

2, Annadale Avenue,
Belfast BT7 3JR.
Tel: Belfast (01232) 491011
Fax: Belfast (01232) 491627

Information Officer	Brigid Heggarty
No. of Staff	1 (Non-professional).
Opening Hours	09.00 - 17.00 (Mon. - Fri.); Telephone enquiry line: 14.00 - 17.00 (Mon. - Fri.). Library visits by appointment.
Services Offered	Library service for staff and other professionals; Information service for disabled persons, carers and service providers.
Special Collections	Disability related material.
Bookstock	2000 books and articles - available for loan (to professionals, other agencies, interested individuals) and ILL.
Periodicals	80 titles - not available for loan or ILL; will photocopy (10p per sheet).
A/V Stock	20 video-cassettes.
Catalogue	Computerised catalogue using Heritage Library Management software.

Classification	Special in-house classification with fifteen top level categories.
Computer Equipment	IBM compatible PC; Heritage Library Management software; Microsoft Word; dBase IV; laser printer.
Other Equipment	Photocopier; Overhead Projector; Television and Video.

DUBLIN AIDS ALLIANCE 129
The Eriu Centre,
53, Parnell Square West,
Dublin 1.
Tel: Dublin (01) 873 3799
Fax: Dublin (01) 873 3174

No. of Staff	1 (1 Professional part-time).
Opening Hours	11.00 - 16.30 (Mon., Wed., Fri.).
Services Offered	Information from the Social and Health Sciences; Historical Information; Posters and leaflets available; Education training resources; Press cuttings; Profile of Irish, English and US organisations; Global statistics and general histories of European countries; Medical journals; Holistic magazines including magazines published by various organisations (Aids-related).
Special Collections	Video library.
Bookstock	55 volumes - available for loan and ILL.
A/V Stock	47 video-cassettes available for loan and ILL.
Other Materials	Posters, leaflets, badges.

DUBLIN DENTAL HOSPITAL LIBRARY 130
Dunlop/Oriel House,
Lincoln Place,
Dublin 2.
Tel: Dublin (01) 662 0766 ext. 205
Fax: Dublin (01) 661 2072

| Librarian | Anne M. O'Byrne. |
| No. of Staff | 2 (1 Professional, 1 Non-professional). |

130 DUBLIN DENTAL HOSPITAL LIBRARY continued

Opening Hours	Term: 10.00 - 13.00, 14.00 - 22.00 (Mon. - Fri.), 10.00 - 12.30 (Sat.); Inter-term: 10.00 - 13.00, 14.00 - 17.00 (Mon. - Fri.).
Services Offered	Library service to staff and students of Dublin Dental Hospital: Postgraduates and Undergraduates; Secondary reference facilities (on application) per extern readers; Dental professionals and allied medical and academic personnel.
Special Collections	Early archival works in Surgery, Medicine and Dentistry. Sheldon Friel Collection; RB Dockrell Collection.
Subject Specialisation	Dentistry.
Bookstock	2,200 volumes - not available for loan; available for ILL; photocopy service to other libraries - in accordance with copyright regulations.
Periodicals	80 titles plus back files (3,500 journals) - not available for loan or ILL; will photocopy in accordance with copyright regulations.
A/V Stock	Video-cassettes - not available for loan or ILL; 2 Cal packages.
Manuscripts	Thesis material (35 held) - not available for loan.
Catalogue	Author/Subject; Audio-visual: Author, Subject, Title
Classification	Black's Medical and Dental Classification (derivative of Dewey).
Computer Equipment	CD Plus (Medline).
Other Equipment	Microfiche reader - Shirl; printing and photocopying service provided to Library centrally; Student copier:copyright regulations applied by Library Staff.

131 DUNSINK OBSERVATORY
Castleknock,
Dublin 15.
Tel: Dublin (01) 838 7911
Fax: Dublin (01) 838 7090
E-mail: astro@dunsink.dias.ie

Librarian	Mary Callanan
No. of Staff	0.5
Opening Hours	09.30 - 13.00, 14.30 - 17.30 (Mon. - Fri.).
Services Offered	Restricted access; Photocopying; ILL (to academic libraries only).
Subject Specialisation	Astronomy.
Bookstock	2,000 volumes.
A/V Stock	Slides.
Catalogue	Classified.
Classification	Special.
Equipment	Access to microfiche reader/printer.

DUPONT (UK) LTD. 132
Maydown Works,
P.O. Box 15,
Londonderry BT47 1TU.
Tel: Londonderry (01504) 860860
Fax: Londonderry (01504) 860244

Librarian	S.T. McDowell
No. of Staff	1 (Non-professional, Part-time).
Opening Hours	08.00 - 16.30 (Mon. - Fri.).
Services Offered	To members of staff; Photocopying.
Subject Specialisation	Polymer science; Chemistry.
Bookstock	1,200 volumes - 1,000 available for loan to employees only; not available for ILL.
Equipment	Microform reader.

ECONOMIC AND SOCIAL RESEARCH INSTITUTE 133
4, Burlington Road,
Dublin 4.
Tel: Dublin (01) 667 1525
Fax: Dublin (01) 668 6231
E-mail: mromsc@esri.ie

Librarian	Maura Rohan
No. of Staff	2.
Opening Hours	10.00 - 13.00, 14.30 - 17.00 (Mon. - Fri.).
Services Offered	Bookstock and periodicals available for consultation to members of the Institute; Loans and photocopies to other libraries by

	arrangement.
Special Collections	CSO Publications; Journals in Economics and Sociology.
Subject Specialisation	Economics; Sociology; Statistics.
Bookstock	20,000 items (books and reports) - available for loan (depending on staff members needs) and ILL.
Periodicals	150 titles - not available for lending or ILL; will photocopy.
Catalogue	Computerisation in progress.
Classification	Dewey.
Computer Equipment	2 networked 486 PCs; CAIRS IMS; Windows 3.1; AMI-PRO 3.1; Deskjet printer; CD-ROMs: Econlit, Sociofile.
Other Equipment	Microfiche reader, photocopier.

134 EDUCATIONAL GUIDANCE SERVICE FOR ADULTS
2nd Floor,
Glendinning House,
6, Murray Street,
Belfast BTI 6DN.
Tel: Belfast (01232) 244274
Fax: Belfast (01232) 240892

Librarian	Mary Blair/Anne Levi
No. of Staff	1 (Professional, Jobshare).
Opening Hours	09.00 - 13.00, 14.00 - 17.00 (Mon. - Thurs.), 09.00 - 13.00, 14.00 - 16.00 (Fri.).
Services offered	Telephone, postal and personal enquiries; Photocopies and database printout for individual clients; Information searches for other organisations; Leaflets on particular subject areas, e.g. training in media/counselling/management.
Special Collections	Books and periodicals relevant to adult education; Careers files and detailed information on local course provision.
Bookstock	c.400 reports - books available for reference.
Periodicals	65 titles - not available for loan or ILL;

	will photocopy moderate quantities.
Catalogue	Computer database in preparation.
Classification	Own.
Computer Equipment	CD-ROM databases: ECCTIS, PICKUP, TAP, NCVQ, Adult Directions.
Other Equipment	Photocopiers.

EQUAL OPPORTUNITIES COMMISSION FOR NORTHERN IRELAND 135
Chamber of Commerce House,
22, Great Victoria Street,
Belfast BT2 7BA.
Tel: Belfast (01232) 242752
Fax: Belfast (01232) 331047

Senior Information Officer	Irene Kingston
Information Officer	Lyn Mackender
No. of Staff	2 (2 Professional).
Opening Hours	09.00 - 17.00 (Mon. - Fri.)
Services Offered	Reference library services to the general public; Information service; Answering enquiries; Information on equal opportunities issues and assistance on directing researchers to appropriate sources of information.
Special Collections	Comprehensive collection of newspaper articles relating to equal opportunities issues; Legal material; Case law; Legislation, etc.
Bookstock	1,000 + volumes - not available for loan or ILL.
Periodicals	100 + titles - not available for loan or ILL; will photocopy if requested.
A/V Stock	30 audio-cassettes - not available for loan or ILL; 35 video-cassettes - available for consultation by training organisations only, and at the discretion of the staff; not available for ILL.
Catalogue	Card Catalogue: Author and Title.
Classification	Own.
Computer Equipment	Library is not computerised as yet.
Other Equipment	Photocopying services available; Facilities for viewing audio-visual material.

EUROPEAN BUSINESS INFORMATION CENTRE
Local Enterprise Development Unit,
LEDU House,
Upper Galwally,
Belfast BT8 4TB
Tel: Belfast (01232) 491031
Fax: Belfast (01232) 691432
E-mail: ebic.ledu@nics.gov.uk

Librarian	Brigid Donnelly
No. of Staff	5.5 (3 Professional, 3 Non-professional, 1 Part-time).
Departments	4 Regional/information Centres: Londonderry, Newry, Omagh, Ballymena.
Opening Hours	09.00 - 17.15 (Mon. - Fri.).
Services Offered	Business information for small companies only (up to 250 employees). European information: legislation, market research; Business information: trade, product, market research.
Special Collections	Official Journal; Minitel; Keynote; Kompass Europe; Market research collection.
Bookstock	5,000 volumes (mainly reference) - available for ILL only if unavailable elsewhere.
Periodicals	230 titles - not available for loan, available for ILL only if unavailable elsewhere.
A/V Stock	20 audio-cassettes, 6 compact disks - not available for loan or ILL; 100 video-cassettes - available for loan to businesses.
Catalogue	CALM 2000.
Classification	Superlink.
Computer Equipment	6 486 PCs; 2 laser printers; On-line access to: FT Profile, MAID Profound, Knight-Ridder, Datastar. CD-ROMs: Eurolaw, Minitel, Keynote, Factfinder, Kompass Europe.
Other Equipment	Canon Microfiche reader/printer; Photocopier.

Loughlinstown,
Shankill,
Dublin 18.
Tel: Dublin (01) 204 3100
Fax: Dublin (01) 282 6456
E-mail: fmurray@iol.ie

Information Officer	Fiona Murray
No. of Staff	4 (2 Professional, 2 Non-professional).
Office Hours	09.00 - 17.00 (Mon. - Fri.). For external users by appointment only.
Services Offered	Open to all for reference/consultation by appointment; loans only to other libraries
Special Collections	Foundation's own publications; Research reports on aspects of living and working conditions in Europe.
Bookstock	7,000 volumes - available for loan (to foundation staff) and ILL.
Periodicals	300 titles - not available for loan or ILL; will photocopy.
A/V Stock	Few items - available for loan (to foundation staff); few compact disks - not available for loan or ILL
Catalogue	UNICORN.
Classification	UDC
Computer Equipment	PC network; 1 CD-ROM Drive; UNIX system in Foundation: used in library for word processing, E-mail and access to external online databases; Hosts include: ESA-IRS, Eurobases, ECHO, European Parliament, EMIRE Database, Employment and Industrial Relations in Europe; Hosted on ECHO, produced by European Foundation.
Other Equipment	1 Microform reader; 1 Microform reader/printer; 2 Photocopiers.

Graham House,
1-5, Albert Square,
Belfast, BT1 3EQ.

138   **THE EXTERN ORGANISATION continued**
Tel: Belfast (01232) 240900
Fax: Belfast (01232) 331498
E-mail: info@extern.cinni.org

Information Officer	Stephanie Mallon
No. of Staff	4 (Professional).
Opening Hours	09.00 - 17.00 (Mon. - Fri.).
Services Offered	Lending facilities specifically to staff, students and those working in the criminal justice fields but also to the general public enquiries. The library is being re-assembled at present.
Special Collections	Centre of Independent Research & Analysis of Crime - research documents in the Northern Ireland Criminal Justice field.

139   **FORFÁS**
Wilton Park House,
Wilton Place,
Dublin 2.
Tel: Dublin (01) 607 3000
Fax: Dublin (01) 660 3703
E-mail: forfas@forfas.ie

Information Officer	Jim Burke
Bookstock	Information for staff use only; ILL from time to time.
Periodicals	Not usually available for lending or ILL; will photocopy a few requests.
A/V Stock	10 compact disks - not available for loan.

140   **FORUM FOR COMMUNITY WORK EDUCATION NI**
123-137, York Street,
Belfast BT15 1AB.
Tel: Belfast (01232) 232587
Fax: Belfast (01232) 312216

Librarian	Freda Browne.
No. of Staff	1 (Part-time).
Opening Hours	09.00 - 17.00 (Mon. - Fri.).

Services Offered	Lending facility for Community Groups, most Information Centres and Community work.
Special Collections	NI IDEAs annual; training manuals.

FRANCISCAN LIBRARY 141
Dún Mhuire,
Seafield Road,
Killiney,
Co. Dublin.
Tel: Dublin (01) 282 6760/282 6091
Fax: Dublin (01) 282 6993

Information Officer	Fr. Ignatius Fennessy
No. of Staff	1 (Non-professional).
Opening Hours	10.00 - 17.00.
Services Offered	Research; Photocopying.
Special Collections	Eamon de Valera papers; Seán MacEóin papers; Gaelic Mss. (11-19th centuries); Irish Franciscan Mss.; Latin (& other languages) Mss. (11-20th centuries); Old books (16-19th centuries); Incunabula (24).
Bookstock	c.20,000 volumes.
Periodicals	c.250 titles.
Catalogue	Computerised: Cardbox-Plus.
Classification	Vatican library, modified.
Computer Equipment	Hardware: AST 386SX PC, HP Laserjet III printer. Software: Cardbox-Plus: books, journals, articles; WordPerfect: word processor.
Other Equipment	1 PC Printer 80 (Canon); 2 Photocopiers: 526 3M, SF 8260 Sharpe.

GENERAL CONSUMER COUNCIL FOR NORTHERN 142
IRELAND
Elizabeth House,
116, Holywood Road,
Belfast BT4 1NY.
Tel: Belfast (01232) 672488
Fax: Belfast (01232) 657701

GENERAL CONSUMER COUNCIL FOR NORTHERN IRELAND continued

Librarian	Alan Walker
No. of Staff	11 (7 Professional, 4 Non-professional, 3 Part-time).
Opening Hours	09.00 - 17.00 (Mon. - Fri.).
Services Offered	The Council has a small reference library which contains information on areas within the Council's remit namely Energy, Food and Transport. The library also contains publications from the main consumer organisations. The library is open to the public for reference, however, while some publications are available to public, we are unable to lend any of the material out at present.
Sepcial Collections	All publications of the General Consumer Council for Northern Ireland.
Periodicals	20 titles - not available for loan, reference only.
A/V Stock	Audio-cassettes, video-cassettes - reference only.
Other Equipment	Photocopiers.

143 GEOGRAPHICAL SOCIETY OF IRELAND
c/o Freeman Library,
Geography Department,
Trinity College,
Dublin 2.
Tel: Dublin (01) 608 1454
Fax: Dublin (01) 671 3397

Hon. Librarian	Richard Haworth
Opening Hours	09.00 - 13.00, 14.00 - 17.00 (Mon. - Fri.).
Services Offered	Photocopying.
Subject Specialisation	Geography Serials.
Bookstock	500 volumes - not available for loan or ILL.
Periodicals	c.100 Geography serials - not available for loan or ILL; will photocopy.
Catalogue	Guard Book.
Classification	Own system.
Other Equipment	Photocopier.

GLENSTAL ABBEY
Murroe,
Co. Limerick.
Tel: Limerick (061) 386103
Fax: Limerick (061) 386328

Librarian	Fr. Mark Tierney OSB, Br. Colmán Ó Clabaigh OSB.
Opening Hours	By appointment.
Services Offered	Private monastic library willing to facilitate scholars and students on an occasional basis.
Special Collections	Ecclesiastical, monastic and liturgical reviews - Irish, English, European and American.
Subject Specialisation	Religion; Liturgy; Irish History.
Bookstock	27,000 volumes - not available for loan or ILL except in very exceptional circumstances.
Periodicals	Not available for loan or ILL; will photocopy.
Catalogue	Card Index.
Classification	Modification of Dewey.
Equipment	Photocopier.

GOETHE INSTITUT LIBRARY
37, Merrion Square,
Dublin 2.
Tel: Dublin (01) 661 1155
Fax: Dublin (01) 661 1358

Information Officer	Ursula Moeller
No. of Staff	2 (1 Professional, 1 Non-professional).
Departmental Library	LIBRARY FOR TEACHERS AND STUDENTS OF GERMAN, 62, Fitzwilliam Square, Dublin 2; Tel: (01) 661 8506, Fax: (01) 676 2213; (Susi Dockrell and Bea Schlitzer, Teachers).
Opening Hours	10.00 - 13.00 (Tues., Thurs., Fri., Sat.), 14.00 - 19.00 (Tues., Wed., Thurs.).
Services Offered	Lending Library available to the general public; Photocopying; ILL; Information on

	German issues.
Special Collections	Complete stock is a special collection of German books and English translations relating to German issues; The Goethe-Institute Libraries worldwide serve as information centres for the Federal Republic of Germany.
Special Services	ILL FOR LIBRARIES IN GERMANY, contact HQ (see above).
Bookstock	10,000 volumes - 9,200 available for loan (to personal members) and ILL.
Periodicals	45 titles - available for loan and ILL; will photocopy.
A/V Stock	800 audio-cassettes, 220 compact disks, 600 video-cassettes - available for lending and ILL.
Other Materials	Information brochures and leaflets; posters.
Catalogue	Author; Classified; (card catalogue).
Classification	UDC.
Computer Equipment	For Internal use only: 1 PC, Word, Windows, Address Plus; Catalogue programme: Allegro.
Other Equipment	1 Photocopier.

146   GPA-BOLTON LIBRARY
John Street,
Cashel,
Co. Tipperary
Tel: Tipperary (062) 61944

Custodian	Very Revd. The Dean of Cashel
No. of Staff	3 .
Opening Hours	By appointment only, contact: Dean Philip Knowles, The Deanery, Cashel, Co. Tipperary; Tel: (062) 61232 or Mary Mulvey, Tourist Office, City Hall, Cashel, Co. Tipperary; Tel: (062) 61333.
Services Offered	Scholars/students welcome, but preferably with references: a contribution will be expected. Genealogical resources on computer, 1668 to present day (15,000

	entries)
Special Collections	Antiquarian books (printing from 1473 to present); Archbishop King's Books (pre-1730); Archbishop Bolton's Books (pre-1744); approx. 11,500 titles.
Bookstock	12,000 + - not available for loan.
Periodicals	100 + (17th - 19th century newspapers) - not available for loan; will photocopy.
Manuscripts	25, plus codices, letters, maps, documents from 1700 - not available for loan.
Catalogue	Printed and published in 1973.
Classification	By shelf position.
Computer Equipment	ITT XTRA XL with 40 Mb RAM (640 Kb ROM);Laser printer. Software: word-processing, dBase III, spreadsheet; used for genealogy, cataloguing, exhibition notes.
Other Equipment	Photocopier

GRAND LODGE OF FREEMASONS OF IRELAND 147
17, Molesworth Street,
Dublin 2.
Tel: Dublin (01) 676 1337/679 5465
Fax: Dublin (01) 660 9089

Librarian	Barry Lyons
Opening Hours	By appointment.
Services Offered	Exhibitions and guided tours of the building.
Special Collections	Chetwode Crawley Collection (c.500 Masonic items pre-1851).
Subject Specialisation	Freemasonry.
Bookstock	10,000 - 12,000 volumes - available for loan (to members of the Order only)and ILL only in special circumstances (Academic libraries, etc.).
Periodicals	A small number (Masonic) - not available for loan; will photocopy in special circumstances on request.
Manuscripts	18 - 20th century Mss.
Catalogue	Author; Classified; (card).
Classification	Special.
Equipment	Microfilm reader; Photocopier.

148 GUINNESS IRELAND GROUP LTD.
Library and Information Service,
St. James's Gate,
Dublin 8.
Tel: Dublin (01) 453 6700 ext. 5528/5495
Fax: Dublin (01) 453 7804
E-mail: mooneye@guinness2.team400.ie or
mooneyhm@guinness2.team400.ie

Manager	Eithne Mooney
No. of Staff	2 (Professional).
Opening Hours	09.00 - 17.00 (Mon. - Fri.).
Services Offered	Services to organisations in Ireland and UK; Access to bonafide enquirers
Special Collections	Periodicals, books and reference material relating to Brewing Science and the history of brewing; Chemistry, Biochemistry, Biotechnology, Microbiology as related to brewing.
Subject Specialisation	Brewing science.
Bookstock	5,000 volumes.
Periodicals	150 titles - not available for loan or ILL; will photocopy.
Computer Equipment	Library management functions computerised with CAIRS IMS/LMS software on 2 networked PCs using Novell communications software; On-line access to Brewing Research Foundation Int. database, Dialog, Datastar, Orbit; Factfinder. CD-ROMs: Anbar, Eurolaw.
Other Equipment	Microform reader/printers; Photocopiers.

149 HEALTH AND SAFETY AUTHORITY
10, Hogan Place,
Dublin 2.
Tel: Dublin (01) 662 0400
Fax: Dublin (01) 662 3560
E-mail: information@hsa.ie

Librarian	Valerie Robinson.
No. of Staff	3 (1 Professional, 2 Non-professional).
Opening Hours	09.15 - 13.00, 14.15 - 17.00.

Services Offered	Full library service to Health and Safety Authority Staff; limited service to the public by appointment (for reference purposes only).
Special Collections	Occupational Health and Safety.
Bookstock	5,000 volumes - available for loan (to staff only) and ILL.
Periodicals	110 titles - not available for loan or ILL; will photocopy.
A/V Stock	30 video-cassettes - not available for loan or ILL.
Catalogue	Computerised - UNICORN.
Computer Equipment	5 CD-ROMs: OSHCD; OSHROM; CHEMBANK; EINECS; PESTBANK.
Other Equipment	1 Microform reader; 1 Photocopier.

HERITAGE LIBRARY (INNER CITY TRUST) 150
Hegarty House,
14, Bishop Street,
Derry BT48 6PW.
Tel: Derry (01504) 351228
Fax: Derry (01504) 360921

Contact	Patricia Ann Griffin
No. of Staff	6 (6 Non-professional) 3 Part-time.
Opening Hours	09.00 - 17.00 (Mon. - Fr.i).
Services Offered	Oral History Research; Facilities to record memoirs of local people covering personal, social, historical, economic and political aspects of local life; Reference library service (Irish interest with a special section on local interest); Public Gallery and Conference Room.
Special Collections	Oral History Collection: an ongoing collection of recordings and accompanying transcripts from local people on various aspects of life from the 1920s onwards, available for loan to local projects and open for public access but not available for ILL; Past issues of London Illustrated News (later London News), Irish Telegraph (later Irish Daily Telegraph), Belfast Newsletter

150   HERITAGE LIBRARY (INNER CITY TRUST) continued

	(mostly dating c.1850-1940); The Capuchin Annual (c.1920-1970).
Bookstock	2,400 volumes - not available for loan, available for ILL.
Periodicals	4 titles - available for loan (to local projects) and ILL.
A/V Stock	400 Oral History recordings complete with transcripts - available for loan (to local projects); not available for ILL.
Computer Equipment	Olivetti PCs 286.
Other Equipment	Recording and listening equipment.

151   HOUSING RIGHTS SERVICE
72, North Street,
Belfast, BT1 1LD.
Tel: Belfast (01232) 245640
Fax: Belfast (01232) 312200

Information Officer	Nicola McCrudden
No. of Staff	3 (Non-professional).
Opening Hours	09.00 - 17.00 (Mon. - Fri.).
Services Offered	Reference material on various aspects of housing including the private rented sector, homelessness, housing debt and the Northern Ireland Housing Executive; Photocopying; Membership services (includes briefing papers and "Housing Update" newsletter); Information sessions.
Bookstock	Under review, reference only, no ILL at present.
Periodicals	Under review, reference only, no ILL at present; will photocopy subject to copyright laws.
Catalogue	Under review at present.
Classification	Own system.
Computer Equipment	PCs (486s); MS Office (Word, Excel, Access, PowerPoint).
Other Equipment	1 Cannon MP6030 Photocopier; Scanner (Scanjet 3C).

IBM IRELAND LTD.
2, Burlington Road,
Dublin 4.
Tel: Dublin (01) 660 3744
Fax: Dublin (01) 660 0638

Librarian	Rose Mary Cahill
No. of Staff	1 (Professional).
Opening Hours	09.00 - 17.15 (Mon. - Fri.).
Services Offered	In-house only.
Special Collections	IBM Technical Material.
Bookstock	140 volumes - staff members have priority, available for ILL on direct request (subject to recall if staff member requires it).
Periodicals	50 titles - available for loan (to staff only) and ILL; will photocopy.

ICC BANK PLC.
72-74 Harcourt Street,
Dublin 2.
Tel: Dublin (01) 475 5700
Fax: Dublin (01) 671 7797
E-mail: doylem@ICC.ie

Information Officer	Mary Doyle.
No. of Staff	2 (Non-professional, Part-time).
Opening Hours	09.15 - 17.00 (Mon. - Fri.).
Services Offered	Our library provides a business information service primarily for the Bank. Material held includes annual reports, periodicals, statistics, books and other publications relating to business, banking, economic and fiscal matters.
Bookstock	400 volumes (approx.) - available for loan (to staff only); not usually available for ILL.
Periodicals	40 titles - available for loan (to staff only); not usually available for ILL; will photocopy.
Catalogue	Inmagic - DB Textworks.
Computer Systems	2 On-line Databases: FT Profile & Business Eye (Irish Based); Internet.
Other Equipment	1 Photocopier.

154 INDUSTRIAL DEVELOPMENT BOARD FOR NORTHERN IRELAND (IDB)

Export Information Centre,
IDB House,
64, Chichester Street,
Belfast, BT1 4JX.
Tel: Belfast (01232) 233233
Fax: Belfast (01232) 545300

Librarian	Lynne Crowe
No. of Staff	4 (Non-professional).
Departments	EXPORT INFORMATION CENTRE, Room 327 (see above). ADMINISTRATION OF DTI OVERSEAS TRADE SERVICES (see above).
Opening Hours	09.00 - 17.00 (Mon. - Fri.).
Services Offered	Export information; Marketing information; Overseas Trade Services; We act as the regional office for the UK Department of Trade and Industry.
Bookstock	1,700 volumes (approx.) - not available for loan or ILL.
Periodicals	30 titles (approx.) - not available for loan or ILL; will photocopy.
A/V Stock	10 compact disks - not available for loan or ILL.
Computer Equipment	1 CD-ROM: 10 various business titles; 1 On-line database: "Profound", provided by Market Analysis and Information Database.

155 INSTITIÚID TEANGEOLAÍOCHTA ÉIREANN (ITÉ)

(The Linguistics Institute of Ireland),
31, Fitzwilliam Place,
Dublin 2.
Tel: Dublin (01) 676 5489
Fax: Dublin (01) 661 0004

Librarian	Íosold Ó Deirg
No. of Staff	2 (1 Professional, 1 Non-professional).
Opening Hours	09.30 - 12.30, 14.30 - 17.00 (Mon. - Fri.).
Services Offered	Lending and ILL to registered readers only; Reference.

Subject Specialisation	Applied and theoretical linguistics; Language learning and teaching; Irish and other modern languages.
Bookstock	10,000 volumes - available for loan (except to undergraduates) and ILL.
Periodicals	184 titles - not available for loan but available for ILL; will photocopy.
A/V Stock	485 audio-cassettes - not available for loan but available for ILL; 2 compact disks - not available for loan or ILL.
Catalogue	Computerised.
Classification	ETIC classification (adapted).
Computer Systems	Heritage, Microsoft, CD-ROM.
Other Equipment	Microform reader; Photocopier

INSTITUTE OF CHARTERED ACCOUNTANTS   **156**
IN IRELAND
Chartered Accountants House,
87-89, Pembroke Road,
Ballsbridge,
Dublin 4.
Tel: Dublin (01) 668 0400
Fax: Dublin (01) 668 5685
E-mail: ddownes@icai.ie
Web site: Http://www.icai.ie

Librarian	Daisy Downes
No. of Staff	2.5 (1 Professional; 3 Part-time).
Departmental Library	INSTITUTE OF CHARTERED ACCOUNTANTS IN IRELAND - BELFAST LIBRARY, 11, Donegall Square South, Belfast BT1 5JE; Tel: (01232) 321600, Fax: (01232) 230071, E-mail: icai@icai.dnet.co.uk; (Anne Woods, Assistant Librarian).
Opening Hours	Dublin: 09.30 - 21.00 (Mon.), 9.30-17.30 (Tues. - Fri.); Belfast: 09.30 - 17.30 (Mon. - Fri.).
Services Offered	Lending and Reference free of charge to ICAI and IATI members and students; Non-members may join on payment of £30 registration fee.

INSTITUTE OF CHARTERED ACCOUNTANTS IN IRELAND continued

Special Collections	CPD course papers; Irish Co. Annual Reports.
Subject Specialisation	Accountancy.
Bookstock	20,000 volumes - 18,000 available for loan (to library members only); not available for ILL.
Periodicals	160 titles - not available for loan or ILL; will photocopy subject to copyright restrictions.
A/V Stock	100 audio-cassettes - available for loan but not ILL; 5 compact disks, 20 video-cassettes - not available for loan or ILL.
Catalogue	TINLIB with OPAC terminals.
Classification	UDC.
Computer Equipment	5 ICL PCs; Toshiba CD-ROM drive; 1 Multimedia PC; TINLIB Library System software (Catalogue, Circulation, Acquisitions and Serials); ABI Inform & ATO Accountancy on CD-ROM; Minitel; Cognotec; File server with modem for internet access; Word processing; Spreadsheets; DTP; E-mail, etc.
Other Equipment	Photocopier; Cassette recorder.

157 INSTITUTE OF PUBLIC ADMINISTRATION (IPA)
57-61, Lansdowne Road,
Dublin 4.
Tel: Dublin (01) 668 6233
Fax: Dublin (01) 668 9135
Telex: 90533

Librarian	Mary J. Prendergast
No. of Staff	6 (2 Professional, 4 Non-professional).
Opening Hours	09.15 - 13.00, 14.15 - 17.30 (Mon. - Fri.); In term time open to 22.00 (Mon. - Thurs.).
Services Offered	Information, reference and lending facilities for members, students and staff of the Institute.
Special Collections	Public Management and related material on

	Sociology, Politics, Economics, Law, Public Service, Local Government, Social policy, Health Services, Finance, Accountancy, Personnel and Management.
Bookstock	40,000 volumes (approx.) - available for loan (to members, students and staff of the Institute) and ILL.
Periodicals	330 titles - not available for loan or ILL; will photocopy.
Catalogue	Computerised.
Classification	Dewey.
Computer Equipment	"Bookshelf" Software on IBM Hardware.
Other Equipment	Microfiche reader; Photocopier.

INSTITUTION OF ENGINEERS OF IRELAND 158
22, Clyde Road,
Ballsbridge,
Dublin 4.
Tel: Dublin (01) 668 4341
Fax: Dublin (01) 668 5508
E-mail: iei@iol.ie

Librarian	John Callanan
Opening Hours	9.30 - 13.00, 14.00 - 17.00 (Mon. - Fri.).
Subject Specialisation	Historical Engineering.
Bookstock	5,000 volumes - available for loan to members through ILL.
Periodicals	75 titles - available to members through ILL; will photocopy.
Manuscripts	Manuscript papers of John MacNeill - not available for loan.
Catalogue	Author, Classified, Subject, (Card); Q&A database.
Classification	UDC.

INSTITUTO CERVANTES 159
(Formerly Spanish Cultural Institute),
58, Northumberland Road,
Dublin 4.
Tel: Dublin (01) 668 2024
Fax: Dublin (01) 668 8416

Librarian	Mabel Lopez
No. of Staff	2 (1 Professional, 1 Non-professional).
Opening Hours	11.00 - 20.00 (Mon. - Thurs.), 10.00 - 14.00 (Fri.).
Services Offered	Information and Reference; Lending; ILL in co-operation with Spanish National Library; Photocopying; Searching through the main Spanish Databases (Spanish National Bibliography, ISBN, Spanish Books in Print, Spanish courses in Spain; University Information Programme etc.).
Special Collections	Contemporary Spanish language authors; Resource Centre: methods and texts for the teaching of Spanish; Spanish Music on CD; Spanish cinema.
Bookstock	10,000 volumes - 6,000 available for loan (to members and students) and ILL.
Periodicals	60 titles - available for loan and ILL; will photocopy.
A/V Stock	300 audio-cassettes, 300 compact disks, 1,000 video-cassettes - available for loan and ILL.
Catalogue	ISBD, computerised.
Classification	UDC.
Computer Equipment	4 PCs (Windows, WordPerfect, Dbase, etc.); Databases on CD-ROM: Spanish National Bibliography, National Library, ISBN, Spanish Books in Print, CSIC Databases (Superior Council for Scientific Research), Libraries without Frontiers (Latin American holdings in Spanish Libraries), Queen Sophia Centre for the Arts. (graphic database with over 500 colour images of paintings), Spanish Courses in Spain, University Information Programme, La Langua Espanola interactive CD-ROM.
Other Equipment	1 Photocopier

46-49, Molesworth Street,
Dublin 2.
Tel: Dublin (01) 677 2582/677 2753
Fax: Dublin (01) 677 2621

Hon. Librarian	Patrick F. McGovern
Chief Executive	Denis Hevey
Branch Libraries	Cork, Dundalk, Galway, Limerick and Sligo.
Opening Hours	09.00 - 17.30 (Mon. - Fri.).
Services Offered	To Institute members; others on application.
Bookstock	600 volumes - available for loan to members and others on application; not available for ILL.
Periodicals	2 titles - available for loan but not ILL; will photocopy.
Subject Specialisation	Insurance; Insurance law
Computer Equipment	6 PCs; 3 Laser printers; Microsoft Office.
Other Equipment	Rank Xerox Photocopier.

73, Merrion Square,
Dublin 2.
Tel: Dublin (01) 676 3430
Fax: Dublin (01) 661 6309

Archive Director	David J. Griffin
No. of Staff	6.
Opening Hours	10.00 - 13.00, 14.30 - 17.00 (Tues. - Fri.). Closed for the month of August.
Services Offered	The Irish Architectural Archive is a charitable company established in Dublin in 1976 to collect and preserve photographs, drawings, models and other documents relating to the historic architecture of Ireland. Architectural drawings, photographs, documents and models are available for consultation in the public reading room; No lending facilities.
Special Collections	350,000 Photographs; 75,000 Architectural

drawings; Books; Pamphlets; Newspaper cuttings; Engravings; Documentary records of over 20,000 buildings in Ireland; Ashlin & Coleman Collection; Dublin Artisans' Dwellings Co. Collection; Emo Court Collection; Green Studio Collection; Alan Hope Collection; Alfred Jones Collection; McCurdy & Mitchell Collection; Raymond McGrath Collection; Ormonde Loan Collection; RIAI Murray Collection; Scott Tallon Walker Collection, Workhouse Drawings Collection.

Subject Specialisation	Historic Architecture of Ireland.
Catalogue	Card Index.
Equipment	Photocopiers.

162 IRISH BUSINESS AND EMPLOYERS CONFEDERATION (IBEC)
Confederation House,
84-86, Lower Baggot Street,
Dublin 2.
Tel: Dublin (01) 660 1011
Fax: Dublin (01) 660 1717
E-mail: kevin.reid@ibec.team400.ie

Librarian	Kevin Reid
No. of Staff	2 (1 Professional, 1 Non-professional).
Opening Hours	9.30 - 12.45, 14.00 - 17.30 (Mon. - Fri.).
Services Offered	The Library/Information Unit is available only to staff, but service is given to IBEC members and general public.
Special Collections	CII/FIE Reference material (1965 to date); CII/FIE Annual reports; EC Official Journals on CD-ROM/Microfiche; ILO, OECD, EIS, IDS, Croners; Complete CSO collection; Acts (1948 to date); Bills (1970 to date); S.I.s (1930 to date).
Bookstock	3,000 volumes - not available for loan but available for ILL.
Periodicals	150 titles (approx.) - not available for loan, but available for ILL; will photocopy.

AV Stock	1 compact disk - not available for loan or ILL.
Catalogue	Computerised (In-house design).
Classification	Dewey.
Computer Equipment	Wang PC DT4/50 with CD-ROM drive; Trade statistics database 1994-95 (in-house design); IBEC Publications on in-house design database; Business Eye; Rapid.
Other Equipment	Microfiche reader/printer; Photocopier; 2 dedicated incoming fax machines.

IRISH DEAF SOCIETY 163
Carmichael House,
North Brunswick Street,
Dublin 7.
Tel: Dublin (01) 872 5748
Fax: Dublin (01) 872 5748
E-mail: irideaso@indigo.ie

Librarian	David Breslin
No. of Staff	20 (4 Professional, 16 Part-time).
Opening Hours	09.00 - 23.00.
Services Offered	Reference library; Counselling; Translating; Interpreter services; Information about and the supply of technical aids; Classes in Irish sign language; Seminars, lectures and workshops which deal with deaf issues; Publications: The Irish Deaf Journal (national and international news).
Special Collections	Reference library which contains periodicals and books on deaf issues.
Bookstock	200 volumes - available for loan and ILL.
Periodicals	450 titles - available for loan and ILL; will photocopy.
A/V Stock	30 video-cassettes - available for loan and ILL.

IRISH FILM INSTITUTE 164
6, Eustace Street,
Dublin 2.

IRISH FILM INSTITUTE continued
Tel: Dublin (01) 679 5744
Fax: Dublin (01) 677 8755
E-mail: ifc@iol.ie

Information Officer	Sarah McCarthy
No. of Staff	2 (2 Non-professional, 1 Part-time).
Opening Hours	11.00 - 13.00, 14.00 - 19.00 (Tues., Wed., Fri.), 11.00 - 13.00, 14.00 - 20.00 (Thurs.), 11.00 - 14.00 (Sat.). Closed on Mondays.
Services Offered	Reference library; Photocopying facilities; Postal and phone queries dealt with.
Special Collections	Books on film (all aspects); Aim is to build up an extensive collection of articles, books and information relating to Irish Cinema.
Bookstock	1,500 - 2,000 (approx.) - available for reference only.
Periodicals	23 titles, 10 current subscriptions - will photocopy.
Other Materials	Teachers Packs; Media Education.
Catalogue	AACR Author, Title, Subject.
Classification	UDC.
Other Equipment	Photocopier.

165   IRISH LINEN CENTRE AND LISBURN MUSEUM
Market Square,
Lisburn,
Co. Antrim, BT28 1AG.
Tel: Lisburn (01846) 663377
Fax: Lisburn (01846) 672624

Librarian	Breda Collins (Research and Publications Officer)
No. of Staff	2 (2 Non-professional, 2 Part-time).
Opening Hours	09.00 - 17.00 (Mon. - Fri.).
Services Offered	Reference library only.
Subject Specialisation	Irish history, especially Ulster, the history of Lisburn and the Lagan Valley; Linen technology; Costume and fabrics.
Special Collections	Library holdings of the former Lambeg Industrial Research Association (LIRA)

	comprising approximately 2,000 books, journals, manuscripts, technical reports and photographs on all aspects of the linen industry.
Bookstock	c.2,000 - available for reference only, ILL under consideration.
Periodicals	c.30 titles - not available for loan or ILL, but will photocopy.
A/V Stock	50 audio-cassettes; 60 video-cassettes.
Other Materials	Newspapers: Lisburn Standard and Lisburn Herald (partial coverage 1898-1964); Maps and plans; 1901 Census enumeration schedules of Lisburn (microfilm); Photographs and slides.
Catalogue	Card catalogue. LIRA Library awaiting cataloguing. Computerisation under review.
Classification	Own classification.
Other Equipment	1 Regma RA; 4 Reader/printers; Photocopiers; Orders for reproduction of photographs/slides can be made through the keeper of Collections.

IRISH MANAGEMENT INSTITUTE   166
National Management Centre,
Sandyford Road
Dublin 16
Tel: Dublin (01) 295 6911
Fax: Dublin (01) 295 9479
E-mail: library @imi.ie

Librarian	Mary Turner BA, Dip. Lib., BL.
No. of Staff	2 (1 Professional, 1 Non-professional).
Opening Hours	09.00 - 19.00 (Mon.), 09.00 - 17.30 (Tues. - Fri.).
Services Offered	Reference; Inquiry; Lending; Document delivery; Services to members of the Institute; Photocopying and ILL to external users.
Special Collections	Management Literature and Information.
Bookstock	12,000 volumes - 11,500 available for loan (to members only) and ILL.

IRISH MANAGEMENT INSTITUTE continued

Periodicals	300 current titles - not available for loan or ILL; will photocopy.
Classification	UDC
Computer Equipment	Fully integrated library network including CD-ROM.
Other Equipment	Microform reader; 2 Photocopiers.

167 **IRISH NURSES ORGANISATION**
11, Fitzwilliam Place,
Dublin 2.
Tel: Dublin (01) 676 0137
Fax: Dublin (01) 661 0466

Education Officer	Annette Kennedy
No. of Staff	2 (2 Non-professional, Part-time). Two staff members from the Education department handle library enquiries.
Services Offered	Service restricted to INO members, exceptions for non-members made with prior permission. We are in the process of developing a library service for our members, however we do not as yet have a librarian so our service is limited at present.
Special Collections	Nursing Journals; Nursing Books; Microfiche; CD-ROM Databases (Nursing and Medical) (available late 1996 - contact library for details).
Bookstock	130 volumes (approx.) - not available for loan or ILL.
Periodicals	20 titles (approx.) - not available for loan of ILL; will photocopy.
Computer Equipment	1 PC 486 with CD-ROM drive; Software includes Microsoft Office; Inkjet printer.
Other Equipment	Microform reader/printer; Photocopier.

168 **IRISH RAILWAY RECORD SOCIETY**
Library and Headquarters,
Box 9, Main Hall,
Heuston Station,
Dublin 8.

Librarian	Tim Moriarty
No. of Staff	All staff are volunteers and non-professional.
Opening Hours	20.00 - 22.00 (Tues. only, September - June).
Services Offered	Private members library - study facility may be granted to non-members for educational purposes, i.e., Theses, Projects etc. Application to read in the library should be made in person or in writing to the Honorary Librarian; Learned Journal (3 times per year) available on subscription.
Special Collections	Irish Railway timetables; Irish Railway tickets; Railway law literature; Archival Collection; Small exhibits: Museum of Railway relics and memorabilia including ticket printing machinery and railway heraldry.
Subject Specialisation	Railway History and Operations.
Bookstock	16,000 volumes (books, pamphlets) - available for loan to members only.
Periodicals	30 current titles, large holding of non-current transport periodicals.
A/V Stock	Photographic Collection (Irish Railways and Transport).
Catalogue	Card; Author and Subject; Specialised Irish indices.
Classification	Dewey 18th edition.
Computer Equipment	In-house database management software running on a Commodore Amiga A3000/20. Databases available for: Book borrowing system, Timetables, Periodicals, Railway law, General reading, Accessions (1993 -). Work is ongoing on the computer conversion of card catalogues and indices.

THE IRISH TIMES LTD.   **169**
11-15, D'Olier Street,
Dublin 2.
Tel: Dublin (01) 679 2022
Fax: Dublin (01) 676 0430
E-mail: jgibson@irish-times.ie

169   **THE IRISH TIMES LTD. continued**

Librarian	John Gibson
No. of Staff	5 (Professional).
Opening Hours	10.00 - 18.00.
Services Offered	Access to library by arrangement only; Photocopying.
Special Collections	Newspaper cuttings; Microfilm (Irish Times 1859-to present); Microfiche; 300,000 Photographs.
Bookstock	500 volumes - not available for loan, reference only (Dail/Seanad Debates, 1930-to present).

170   **IRISH TRADITIONAL MUSIC ARCHIVE/TAISCE CHEOL DÚCHAIS ÉIREANN**
63, Merrion Square,
Dublin 2.
Tel: Dublin (01) 661 9699
Fax: Dublin (01) 662 4585

Librarian	Nicholas Carolan
No. of Staff	4 (1 Part-time).
Opening Hours	10.00 - 13.00, 14.00 - 17.00 (Mon. - Fri.).
Services Offered	Public access; Consultancy; Copying.
Special Collections	Breandán Breathnach Collection; Diane Hamilton Collection; Proinsias Ó Conluain Collection.
Bookstock	6,000 volumes - not available for loan or ILL.
Periodicals	55 titles - not available for loan or ILL; will photocopy as per copyright law.
A/V Stock	3,000 audio-cassettes, 2,000 compact disks, 150 video-cassettes, 100 multimedia packs - not available for loan or ILL.
Other Materials	Photographs; Sheet Music; Ballad Sheets; 78 Records; LP Records; Ephemera.
Catalogue	Computerised, created In-house using InMagic.
Classification	UDC-based, created in-house.
Computer Equipment	6 PCs; CD-ROM drive; InMagic; SearchMagic; Score, Omnipage; Photoshop; WordPerfect software.
Other Equipment	Photocopier.

IRTU

(INDUSTRIAL RESEARCH AND TECHNOLOGY UNIT)
Industrial Science Centre,
17, Antrim Road,
Lisburn, BT28 3AL.
Tel: Lisburn (01846) 623000
Fax: Lisburn (01846) 676054
E-mail: superhighway.irtu@nics.gov.uk

Contact	Roisin Goodwin/Alan Boyd/Trevor Forsythe
Opening Hours	09.00 - 17.10 (Mon. - Fri.).
Services Offered	Information Centre; Commercial Databases; Scientific information service; On-line search service of 1,700 commercial information databases covering Science, Technology, Patents, Engineering, Economics and Business; Resource Centre and Document Support Service; Technical advisory service using CD-ROM; Environmental Enquiry Point freephone 0800-262227; Mobile Information Unit; Information Superhighway Centre 0800-515319.
Special Collection	Publications: IRTU's Environmental Magazine and Waste Exchange Bulletin published quarterly.

LAKE COMMUNICATIONS LTD.

Beech House,
Greenhills Road,
Tallaght,
Dublin 24.
Tel: Dublin (01) 451 5422
Fax: Dublin (01) 452 0826

Librarian	M. Nolan
Opening Hours	09.00 - 17.00 (Mon. - Fri.).
Service Offered	Library contains small number of textbooks relating to Telecommunications; Engineering; Marketing and Management. Most of the library contains Data books

	from electronic component manufacturers.
Bookstock	c.100 volumes - not available for loan or ILL.
Periodicals	c.20 titles - not available for loan or ILL.

173 **LAW LIBRARY**
PO Box 2424,
Dublin 7.
Tel: Dublin (01) 872 0622
Fax: Dublin (01) 872 0455
Web site: Http://www.indigo.ie/lawlibrary.ie

Librarian	Jennefer Aston
No. of Staff	13.5 (4 Professional, 11 Non-professional, 3 Part-time).
Opening Hours	09.00 - 17.30 (Mon. - Fri.).
Services Offered	Indexes to: Irish Legal Periodical articles, Statutory Instruments, Implementation of EU Directives on OPAC. In-house databases of Judgements. Monthly current awareness service to members on legal developments.
Subject Specialisation	Law.
Bookstock	105,000 volumes - available for loan to subscribing members of the Bar only.
Periodicals	250 - 300 current titles - available for loan to members only; will photocopy only by arrangement.
A/V Stock	10 compact disks - not available for loan or ILL.
Other Materials	Notebook computers for loan to members.
Catalogue	OPAC - URICA.
Classification	Moys.
Computer Equipment	MDISL Equipment; URICA software; 2 Novell LANs providing access to in-house databases (Software: Textmaster), a range of CD-ROMs and OPAC.
Other Equipment	Microform reader/printers; Photocopiers; Velobinding machine; Fax machines.

LAW SOCIETY OF IRELAND
Blackhall Place,
Dublin 7.
Tel: Dublin (01) 671 0711
Fax: Dublin (01) 677 0511
E-mail: lawsoclb@iol.ie

Librarian	Margaret Byrne
No. of Staff	2 (Professional, 1 Part-time).
Opening Hours	09.00 - 17.00 (Mon. - Fri.).
Services Offered	Lending, reference and information services to Law Society members and students.
Subject Specialisation	Law.
Bookstock	15,000 volumes - 4000 available for loan (to Law Society members and students); not available for ILL.
Periodicals	120 current titles - not available for loan or ILL; will photocopy.
Catalogue	Card.
Classification	Moys Dewey.
Computer Systems	PCs; Access to LEXIS on-line legal database; CELEX and Legal Journal Index Database available on CD-ROM.
Other Equipment	Microfiche reader/printer; Photocopier; Fax machine.

LAW SOCIETY OF NORTHERN IRELAND
98, Victoria Street,
Belfast BT1 3JZ.
Tel: Belfast (01232) 231614
Fax: Belfast (01232) 232606

Librarian	Mandy McIlveen
No. of Staff	3 (2 Professional , 1 Non-professional).
Opening Hours	09.00 - 17.00 (Mon. - Fri.).
Services Offered	Photocopying; Reference and Information to solicitors; Others by appointment.
Subject Specialisation	Law.
Bookstock	5,000 volumes - not available for loan or ILL.
Periodicals	30 titles (approx.) - not available for loan

LAW SOCIETY OF NORTHERN IRELAND continued

	or ILL; will photocopy.
Catalogue	Computerised.
Classification	Moys.
Computer Equipment	Fortune Microcomputer; CD-ROM; On-line database.
Other Equipment	Photocopier; Fax machine.

176 LEGAL AID BOARD
St. Stephen's Green House,
Earlsfort Terrace,
Dublin 2.
Tel: Dublin (01) 661 5811
Fax: Dublin (01) 676 3426

Opening Hours	Law centres: 10.00 - 12.30, 14.00 - 16.00.
Services Offered	Legal services to persons of modest means at little cost under the Scheme of Civil Legal Aid and Advice through 26 Law Centres located throughout the country.

177 LEPROSY MISSION
44, Ulsterville Avenue,
Belfast BT9 7AQ
Tel: Belfast (01232) 381937
Fax: Belfast (01232) 381842

Director	A. Colin Ferguson
Services Offered	Enquiries to Director; Photocopying.
Special Collections	Reference collection on history and treatment of leprosy sufferers world-wide.
Subject Specialisation	Leprosy.
A/V Stock	Videos; Slide sets; 16mm films - available for loan.

178 LINEN HALL LIBRARY
17, Donegall Square North,
Belfast BT1 5GD.
Tel: Belfast (01232) 321707
Fax: Belfast (01232) 438586

Librarian	John Gray
No. of Staff	20 (5 Professional, 15 Non-professional).
Opening Hours	09.30 - 17.30 (Mon., Tues., Wed., Fri.), 09.30 - 20.30 (Thurs.), 09.30 - 16.00 (Sat.).
Services Offered	General lending; Irish and Local Studies; Photocopying; Fax; Telephone.
Special Collections	Specialisation in Irish and local studies with particular emphasis on Antrim, Down and Belfast; Early Ulster writing; Maps; Poetry; Theatre; Postcards; Northern Ireland political literature collection (1968 to date); Genealogical material.
Subject Specialisation	Irish and local history.
Bookstock	200,000 volumes - 150,000 available for loan (to members only) and ILL.
Periodicals	1,000 titles - not available for loan or ILL; will photocopy.
Catalogue	Dictionary.
Classification	Dewey (Amended).
Computer Equipment	BLCMP.
Other Equipment	Microform reader/printer, Photocopiers.

MARITIME INSTITUTE OF IRELAND 179
Haigh Terrace,
Dun Laoghaire,
Co. Dublin.
Tel: Dublin (01) 280 0969

Librarian	Beatrice Rush, Dip. Lib., Geneva.
No. of Staff	3 (1 Professional, 2 Non-professional) 3 Part-time.
Opening Hours	By appointment only.
Services Offered	Reference library; Books lent only to members of the Maritime Institute.
Special Collections	Lloyds Register of Ships (1842 to date); Charts; Postcards of ships and boats.
Subject Specialisation	Maritime subjects.
Bookstock	4,500 volumes - available for loan to members only; not available for ILL
Periodicals	60 titles - not available for loan or ILL; will photocopy.

179 MARITIME INSTITUTE OF IRELAND continued

Other Materials	Newspaper cuttings books from late 1950s.
Catalogue	By author.
Classification	Dewey.
Computer Equipment	Soon available.
Other Equipment	Microform readers/printers soon available; Photocopiers.

180 MATER MISERICORDIAE HOSPITAL
Eccles Street,
Dublin 7.
Tel: Dublin (01) 830 1122/830 8788

Librarian	Patricia McCarthy/Sr. Delourdes Cooney
No. of Staff	2 (Non-professional).
Opening Hours	Office Desk: 09.00 - 17.00 (Mon. - Fri.); Reading Areas: 09.00 - 23.00.
Services Offered	Library Services; Photocopying Services; CD-ROM Services; Typing if required; Bookings for lecture/conference facilities and preparation of same; Searches on computer and instruction of same; Obtaining information on different topics for papers/dissertations etc.
Bookstock	1,066 volumes - available for loan to all members of the Medical Library; not available for ILL.
Periodicals	95 titles - available for short period loan; not available for ILL; will photocopy.
A/V Stock	20 a/v-cassettes and 3 display units; 16 sets of lecture slides; 113 tapes - not available for loan or ILL.
Catalogue	Computerised; Printed.
Computer Equipment	CD-ROM ; Windows 95.
Other Equipment	1 Rank Xerox photocopier.

181 MEATH HOSPITAL LIBRARY
Heytesbury Street,
Dublin 8.
Tel: Dublin (01) 453 6555 ext. 2674
Fax: Dublin (01) 453 6570
E-mail: meathlib@iol.ie

Librarian	Anne Murphy
No. of Staff	2 (1 Professional, 1 Part-time).
Opening Hours	08.30 - 12.30, 13.30 - 16.30.
Services Offered	Book borrowing; Daily newspapers; Information Service; ILL; On-line searching; Photocopying facilities; Internet (mediated by librarian); Access to bibliographic, full text and CDI databases on CD-ROM; Access to "teach yourself typing", word-processing, spreadsheet and presentation software; Book catalogue; Guides; Library tours; User Education programme for nurses; Accession list - monthly; "Current journals" list - six monthly. The libraries of the Meath, Adelaide, National Children's Hospital and St. Loman's Hospitals will form the new Tallaght Hospital Library with a planned opening date for July 1997.
Bookstock	1,400 volumes - 1,300 available for loan to staff and students of the hospital; not available for ILL.
Periodicals	80+ titles - not available for loan of ILL; will photocopy.
A/V Stock	6 compact disks, 2 multimedia packs not available for loan or ILL; 8 video-cassettes - available for loan (overnight); not available for ILL.
Catalogue	Computerised using InMagic.
Classification	DDC20, AACR2, MeSH subject headings.
Computer Equipment	Dell: Optiplex XL575, 433s/L with CD-ROM drive; Dell 4100 DL Dimension; InMagic database package; Microsoft Office, "Mavis Beacon" Typing; CD-ROMs: Medline (1992 to date), CINAHL (1983 to date), Healthplan, New England Journal of Medicine - full-text, Journal of Bone and Joint Surgery - full-text; DATASTAR access using Knight-Ridder; Internet access using Ireland On-line; Fax modem: 14,400.
Other Equipment	Photocopier; Projection panel; Overhead projector; Fax; Answering machine.

MEDICAL LIBRARY
St. Vincent's Hospital,
Elm Park,
Dublin 4.
Tel: Dublin (01) 209 4921
Fax: Dublin (01) 283 8123
E-mail: seanl@svherc.ucd.ie

Librarian	Seán Love
No. of Staff	2 (1 Professional) 1 Part-time.
Opening Hours	09.30 - 17.30 (Mon., Fri.), 09.30 - 21.00 (Tues., Thurs.).
Services Offered	Computer network offering complete Medline (1966 -); Internet: E-mail and multiple applications; Also linked to UCD mainframe directly with access to UCD fileservers; Mix of Apple and IBM workstations; Laser printing; Scanning; Slide-making; Books; Journals; Video; Audio; CDs; Photocopying; ILL; Member of Council of International Hospitals (Research Resource).
Special Collections	General Medical; Surgical; Nursing.
Bookstock	3,000 volumes - 2,750 available for loan to staff, medical and nursing students; Not available for ILL.
Periodicals	130 titles - not available for loan or ILL; will photocopy.
A/V Stock	500 audio-cassettes, 100 video cassettes - available for loan; not available for ILL; 20 compact disks - not available for loan or ILL.
Catalogue	Filemaker Pro.
Classification	Dewey.
Computer Equipment	CD-Tower (running off SVH fileserver); Medline and "Knowledge Finder" runs on Apple and IBM; 4 Apples, 3 IBM PCs; Laser printer; Scanner; Slide-maker.
Other Equipment	Microfiche reader; Photocopier.

University College Cork,
Cork University Hospital,
Wilton,
Cork.
Tel: Cork (021) 343688/902976
Fax: Cork (021) 345826
E-mail: n.mcsweeney@ucc.ie or adcb8010@ucc.ie
Telnet: bureau.ucc.ie, Login: library

Librarian	Niall McSweeney
No. of Staff	5 (1 Professional, 4 Non-professional, 2 Part-time).
Branch	Branch of BOOLE LIBRARY.
Opening Hours	09.00 - 20.30 (Mon. - Fri.).
Services Offered	Issues and returns; ILL; Customer services; Instruction in Medline and other databases; Instruction in Internet; Word-processing; On-line searching; Medical Informatics Laboratory.
Bookstock	20,000 volumes - 9,000 available for loan (to hospital staff and students) and ILL.
Periodicals	390 titles - not available for loan; available for ILL; will photocopy.
A/V Stock	200 audio-cassettes, 250 video-cassettes - available for loan not ILL; 20 compact disks - not available for loan or ILL.
Catalogue	DOBIS-LIBIS.
Classification	Dewey.
Computer Equipment	25 PCs (with CD-ROM); 3 Apples; 2 OPACs; Word-processing; Medline networked (1966 to date); CINAHL; World Drug Index; Dental Programme; Serial needs; ADAM; Internet.
Other Equipment	Microfiche reader; 2 Photocopiers.

Segal House,
4, Annadale Avenue,
Belfast BT7 3JH.
Tel: Belfast (01232) 691351
Fax: Belfast (01232) 640121

MENCAP IN NORTHERN IRELAND continued

Librarian	Paschal McKeown.
No. of Staff	3 (1 Part-time person dedicated to library work).
Opening Hours	09.15 - 17.15.
Services Offered	Access to information on different matters which impact on the lives of individuals with a learning disability and their families; Information to be had on library premises; Also knowledge about other sources of information; Information is in the form of books, leaflets, journals, articles, videos and tapes.
Bookstock	250 volumes - not available for loan or ILL.
Periodicals	22 titles - not available for loan or ILL; no photocopying.
A/V Stock	8 audio-cassettes, 20 video-cassettes - not available for loan or ILL.

185   MIDLAND HEALTH BOARD
Central Office,
Arden Road,
Tullamore,
Co. Offaly.
Tel: Tullamore (0506) 46170
Fax: Tullamore (0506) 51204

Librarian	Sandra Keating
No. of Staff	1.5 (1 Professional, 0.5 Non-professional).
Opening Hours	10.00 - 17.00.
Services Offered	Reference; ILLs; Literature searching; Current awareness.
Bookstock	2,000 volumes - available for loan to MHB staff only; not available for ILL.
Periodicals	150 titles - not available for loan or ILL; will photocopy.
A/V Stock	Audio-cassettes; video-cassettes - not available for loan or ILL.
Catalogue	Card and PC (Union list).
Classification	Dewey, 19th Ed.
Computer Equipment	Medline, CINAHL - Networked.
Other Equipment	Microfiche reader; Photocopier.

LIBRARY & INFORMATION UNIT
Our Lady of Lourdes Hospital,
Drogheda,
Co. Louth.
Tel: Drogheda (041) 43696
Fax: Drogheda (041) 43626
E-mail: mmmlib@iol.ie

Librarian	Jean Harrison
No. of Staff	4 (1 Professional, 1 Non-professional, 2 Part-time).
Opening Hours	Sept. - June: 09.00 - 20.00 (Mon. - Thurs.), 09.00 - 17.00 (Fri.); July-Aug. inc.: 09.00 - 17.00 (Mon. - Fri.).
Services Offered	Lend books and videos; ILLs; Computerised searches on Medline, CINAHL, RCN Nurse, Cochrane databases; Internet Searches; Current awareness service; General information searches carried out in relation to Medical, Nursing, Paramedical Healthcare Management.
Special Collections	Nursing books and journals.
Subject Specialisation	Medical; Nursing; Midwifery; Healthcare and Management (general).
Bookstock	2,500 volumes - 2,400 available for loan (to NEHB staf and GPs) and ILL.
Periodicals	90+ titles - not available for loan or ILL; will photocopy.
A/V Stock	10 compact disks - not available for loan or ILL; 20 video-cassettes, 2 multimedia packs - available for loan and ILLs.
Other Materials	Leaflets and booklets on various voluntary and health organisations; Annual Reports of organisations including hospitals, health boards etc.
Catalogue	Bookshelf/Heritage Management System.
Classification	Dewey.
Computer Equipment	5 PCs; 3 CD-ROM drives; Medline (1966 to date); CINAHL (1982 to date); ADAM (Animated Dissection of Human Anatomy); RCN Nurse ROM; Clinical Surgery - Dr

MOTHER MARY MARTIN
LIBRARY & INFORMATION UNIT continued

| | Vincent Sheehan; Cochrane Database of Systematic Reviews; Cochrane Database of Pregnancy and Childbirth; New Grolier Encyclopaedia; Asthma Information Programme; Bioscience Programs; Internet; WordPerfect; Microsoft Word. |
| Other Equipment | Microform Reader; Photocopier; Binding. |

187 NATIONAL CHILDREN'S RESOURCE CENTRE
Barnardo's,
Christchurch Square,
Dublin 8.
Tel: Dublin (01) 454 9699
Fax: Dublin (01) 453 0300
E-mail: bernardo@iol.ie

Info. Services Co-ordinator	Angela Canavan
No. of Staff	8 (3 Professional, 5 Non-professional).
Opening Hours	09.30 - 13.00 (Mon. - Fri.). Opening hours extending to full office hours from Sept. 1996.
Services Offered	Information, training and advisory services on child-related subjects (including child development, health, education, bereavement, adoption, protection, health and safety, and childcare services).
Other Services	Newspaper cuttings service; Current awareness for members; Photocopying; Video viewing; Talks; Courses and activities.
Bookstock	5,000 volumes - available for loan (to members of NCRC) and ILL.
Periodicals	60 titles - not available for loan or ILL; will photocopy.
A/V Stock	350 video-cassettes - available for loan and ILL; small collection of multimedia packs - available for loan, but not ILL.
Catalogue	Computerised - InMagic.
Classification	Dewey and Subject categorisation.
Computer Equipment	Hardware:8 IBM Ps/2 Model 30-286

workstations; 1 Central fileserver IBM Ps/2 Model 65; Novell Advanced Netware LAN; CD-ROM drives. Software: InMagic; Microsoft Office; Access database; Catalogue of National Children's Bureau UK on CD-ROM.

Other Equipment — Photocopier available for public use; Video and audio recorders; TVs.

NATIONAL COUNCIL FOR THE BLIND OF IRELAND   188
PV Doyle House,
Whitworth Road,
Drumcondra,
Dublin 9.
Tel: Dublin (01) 830 7033
Fax: Dublin (01) 830 7787

Librarian — Siobhán Bermingham
No. of Staff — 3 (3 Non-professional, 2 Part-time).
Opening Hours — 09.00 - 13.00, 14.00 - 17.00 (Mon. - Fri.).
Services Offered — Comprehensive library service to blind and visually impaired individuals which includes a talking book library; Braille library; magazines on tape; Information and advice on libraries for the blind; ILL with other libraries for the blind; Supply and maintenance of special play-back equipment; Tape duplication and Braille transcription.
Special Collections — Four-track talking book library; Braille library; Reference library (Blindness and related topics only).
Bookstock — 100 volumes (approx.) - available for loan and ILL.
Periodicals — 13 titles - available for reference only and ILL; will photocopy.
A/V Stock — 1,800 audio-cassettes (4-track) - available for loan and ILL (special equipment needed); 1 compact disk - not available for loan or ILL.
Other Materials — Braille bookstock 1,000 (approx.) - available for loan and ILL.

NATIONAL COUNCIL FOR THE BLIND OF IRELAND
continued

Catalogue	Author/title Classified.
Classification	By category.
Computer Equipment	AST 4/5od PC with CD-ROM drive and Lunar Large print display.
Other Equipment	Microfiche reader; Kurzweil personal reader; Braille embosser; telex cassette duplicators; Photocopiers; Aladdin CCTV.

189 THE NATIONAL MICROELECTRONICS APPLICATION CENTRE (MAC) LTD.
UL Building,
The National Technological Park,
Plassey,
Limerick.
Tel: Limerick (061) 334699/202144
Fax: Limerick (061) 330316
E-mail: mac@ul.ie
Web site: Http://www.mac.ul.ie

Information Manager	Virginia Mulvihill
No. of Staff	14 (7 Professional, 5 Non-professional).
Opening Hours	09.00 - 17.30 (Mon. - Fri.).
Services Offered	Library, Internal use only, On-line searching service on new product development, technology, competitor analysis and brand names; Current awareness services; EC Research and Technology; Operation of Minitel host service VISTAR, including Dublin Public Libraries "Business Journals Index" - DPLNET; DIALOG agent in Ireland; EU Project Management; WWW Home Page maintenance.
Subject Specialisation	Electronic, Software, Telecommunications and Information Product Development and Process Applications; Design Engineering; Teleworking; Minitel services; ISDN; EU Contracts.
Special Collections	Electronic Product Information; EU Programme Reports

Bookstock	600 volumes (primarily manuals; data books; EU programme reports) - will distribute EU reports and extract and/or photocopy from data books.
Periodicals	75 titles - not available for loan or ILL; will photocopy.
A/V Stock	12 compact disks; 10 video-cassettes.
Other Materials	Software: more than 400 items - not available for loan or ILL.
Catalogue	3 systems of printed material management; Not automated.
Classification	Journals by alphabetical title order; Data books/Product manuals sorted by manufacturer and product type; EU reports listed by programme, project name and currency.
Computer Equipment	Novell LAN; PCs; Portables; Scanner; Laser Printer; CD-ROM drivers; Minitel Host; PAD; Internet server; Microsoft; Z39.50; Microbird; Bird; Dbase; HTML of text and images.
Other Equipment	2 Photocopiers; Picturetel Videoconferencing equipment; ISDN connection; H320 standard.

NATIONAL REHABILITATION BOARD (NRB)   190
25, Clyde Road,
Ballsbridge,
Dublin 4.
Tel: Dublin (01) 668 4181
Fax: Dublin (01) 660 9935

Librarian	Judy Cronin
No. of Staff	2 (1 Professional, 1 Non-professional).
Opening Hours	10.30 - 12.30, 14.00 - 16.30 (Mon. - Fri.).
Services Offered	Specialised information service provided by library; General information service provided by 18 NRB centres nation-wide.
Special Collections	Disability and rehabilitation; Health related information.
Bookstock	8,000 volumes - available for loan (except reference collection) and ILL.

Periodicals	200 titles - not available for loan, but available for ILL; will photocopy.
A/V Stock	Small collection of audio-cassettes, 260 video-cassettes - available for loan and ILL.
Catalogue	Computerised.
Classification	Dewey.
Computer Equipment	Viglen 486 (IBM compatible) hardware; InMagic for Windows (InMagic DB - Textworks) system is used for library database; Microsoft Word for Windows, version 2.0.
Other Equipment	Braille Reader and Printer; Laser Printer (Brother HL-8); Photocopier; Overhead Projector; Slide Projector.

191   NATIONAL SAFETY COUNCIL
[Entry as 1993 edition - no update received]
4, Northbrook Road,
Ranelagh,
Dublin 6.
Tel: Dublin (01) 496 3422
Fax: Dublin (01) 496 3306

Information Officer	Gavin Freeman
No. of Staff	14
Opening Hours	09.15 - 12.45, 14.00 - 17.30 (Mon. - Fri.).
Services Offered	Specialised enquiries for people doing projects or research, by appointment; Free distribution of leaflets.
Special Collections	Information files on road accident prevention, driving skills, fire prevention and water safety.
Subject Specialisation	Fire prevention; road accident prevention; water safety.
Periodicals	Complete sets of leaflets and posters on fire, road and water safety.
A/V Stock	Approximately 60 Film, VHS Video and Slide Sets on fire, road and water safety.

National Coaching and Training Centre,
University of Limerick,
Limerick.
Tel: Limerick (061) 202895
Fax: Limerick (061) 338174
E-mail: sportsinfo@ul.ie

Librarian	Gobnait O'Riordan
No. of Staff	2 (1 Professional, 1 Non-professional).
Opening Hours	09.00 - 17.00 by appointment.
Services Offered	Specialist sports information service; Enquiry service; ILL; Reference collection: texts, videos and journals; Current awareness.
Special Collections	Sports Science; Coaching.
Bookstock	600 volumes - not available for loan, but available for ILL.
Periodicals	50 titles - not available for loan, but available for ILL; will photocopy.
A/V Stock	100 video-cassettes - not available for loan or ILL.
Catalogue	In-house.
Classification	Dewey.
Computer Equipment	PCs and Microsoft software; LAN network; CD-ROM; databases; Printers.
Other Equipment	Photocopiers.

Medical Library,
General Hospital,
The Mall,
Sligo.
Tel: Sligo (071) 71111 ext. 4303
Fax: Sligo (071) 69095

Librarian	Catherine Breslin
No. of Staff	1 (Non-professional).
Opening Hours	09.00 - 17.00 (Mon. - Fri.).
Services Offered	Most Library services; ILLs; Searches.
Bookstock	3,200 volumes - not available for loan or ILL.

NORTH WESTERN HEALTH BOARD continued

Periodicals	240 titles - not available for loan or ILL; will photocopy.
A/V Stock	30 audio-cassettes, 80 video-cassettes - not available for loan or ILL.
Catalogue	Card; Author and Subject.
Classification	UDC.
Computer Equipment	2 PCs; Medline on CD-ROM; MultiMate; Lotus 123; WordPerfect; Windows; Slide Making Facilities; Language Tutorials; Harvard graphics.
Other Equipment	2 Microform readers; Photocopier; TV/video player.

194 NORTHERN IRELAND ASSOCIATION FOR MENTAL HEALTH
80, University Street,
Belfast BT7 1HE.
Tel: Belfast (01232) 328474
Fax Belfast (01232) 234940

Education Officer	Pauline Rainey
No. of Staff	4 (4 Non-professional).
Branches	Resource Beacon Centres in Armagh, Cookstown, Enniskillan, Limavady, Lisnashea, Londonderry, Magherafelt, Omaghand Twinbrook.
Opening Hours	09.15 - 16.30 (Mon. - Fri.).
Services Offered	Information/advice service on mental health available to personal callers or by telephone or post.
Subject Specialisation	Mental health.
Bookstock	300 volumes - not available for loan or ILL.
Periodicals	30 titles - not available for loan; will photocopy.
Computer Systems	Desk Top Publishing (Pagemaker 5); dBase III; WordPerfect.
Other Equipment	Photocopier.

ADVICE BUREAU
11, Upper Crescent,
Belfast BT7 1NT.
Tel: Belfast (01232) 231120
Fax: Belfast (01232) 231120

Information Officer	Mark Gavin
No. of Staff	3 (2 Professional; 1 Non-professional).
Services Offered	Information service for CABx; Consultancy service to bureaux workers.
Special Collections	Statutes (Northern Ireland); Legislation; Social Security Manuals; Housing Manuals.
Bookstock	500 volumes (approx.) - available for loan only to CABx.
Periodicals	30 titles (approx.) - not available for loan or ILL; will photocopy.
A/V Stock	Information service will be available in electronic format and Braille later this year.
Catalogue	Index to Information System.
Classification	Own system.
Computer Equipment	100+ PCs distributed in Wide Area Network over 29 offices; Lotus Notes (as text retrieval tool for information system); Lotus Smartsuite (for office tasks); and bespoke software for advice work, e.g., benefit calculation programs.
Other Equipment	1 Microform reader with Microfilm version of CAB information system; Photocopier.

COUNCIL
6, Murray Street,
Belfast BT1 6DN.
and
31, Castle Lane,
Belfast BT1 5DB.
Tel: Belfast (01232) 439953/311881
Fax: Belfast (01232) 235208/244364

NORTHERN IRELAND COMMUNITY RELATIONS COUNCIL
continued
E-mail: mark@nicrc.thegap.com

Information Officer	Ray Mullan
Information Centre Manager	Mark McCann
No. of Staff	5 (3 Professional; 1 Non-professional; 1 Part-time).
Opening Hours	Reference library (Murray Street) 09.00 - 17.00 (Mon. - Fri.); Information Centre (Castle Lane) 09.30 - 17.00 (Mon. - Sat.).
Services Offered	Reference library available at Murray Street (computer access for users shortly to be introduced); Information Centre holds wide range of Community Relations literature for sale; Also maintains a NI Newspaper database on community relations issues - available on computer; Original cuttings held on file; Computer printouts of summaries available.
Special Collections	Reference library contains literature on community relations themes in Northern Ireland primarily.
Bookstock	1,300 volumes - not available for loan or ILL.
Periodicals	168 titles - not available for loan or ILL.
A/V Stock	20 video-cassettes - not available for loan or ILL.

197 NORTHERN IRELAND COUNCIL FOR VOLUNTARY ACTION (NICVA)
127, Ormeau Road,
Belfast BT7 1SH.
Tel: Belfast (01232) 321224
Fax: Belfast (01232) 438350
E-mail: nicva@mcri.poptel.org.uk

Information Officer	Nadia Downing
No. of Staff	1 (Non-professional).
Opening Hours	14.00 - 17.00 (Mon. - Thurs.), 14.00 - 16.30 (Fri.).
Services Offered	Open to the public, students, academics but

	service primariliy aimed at voluntary and community groups; Photocopying; Reference only.
Special Collections	Complete collection of back issues of Scope - NICVA's Social Policy Journal.
Bookstock	5,000 items - not available for loan or ILL.
Periodicals	40 titles - not available for loan or ILL; will photocopy.
Catalogue	Computer listing of 14 subject areas.
Classification	Hierarchical.

NORTHERN IRELAND ECONOMIC RESEARCH CENTRE LIBRARY 198
48, University Road,
Belfast BT7 1NJ.
Tel: Belfast (01232) 325594
Fax: Belfast (01232) 439435
E-mail: e.moore@qub.ac.uk

Librarian	Ellen Moore
No. of Staff	1 (Professional).
Opening Hours	09.00 - 13.00, 14.00 - 17.00 (Mon. - Fri.).
Services Offered	Reference and information; Photocopying. The Northern Ireland Economic Research Centre is an Associate Centre of the Queen's University Belfast.
Special Collections	Economics; Northern Ireland/UK statistical material; Regional studies; Small firms.
Subject Specialisation	Economics, with particular reference to the economy of NI and regional development.
Bookstock	6,000 volumes - available for loan to NIERC staff only; not available for ILL.
Periodicals	70 titles (approx.) - not available for loan or ILL; limited photocopying.
Catalogue	Author/Title catalogue on dBase IV.
Classification	Library of Congress.
Computer Equipment	Internet Access: PC connected to LAN, connected to Queens University Belfast; WWW; Netscape; SuperJanet; Subscription to Blaise-Line (connection via SuperJanet); Software: Microsoft Office (Word, Excel,

NORTHERN IRELAND ECONOMIC RESEARCH CENTRE LIBRARY continued

PowerPoint).

Other Equipment | Microfiche reader; Photocopier

199 NURSE EDUCATION CENTRE, EHB
St. Brendan's Hospital,
Rathdown Road,
Dublin 7.
Tel: Dublin (01) 838 5844 ext.440

Librarian | Salah Mesallati
No. of Staff | 1 (Professional).
Opening Hours | 08.45 - 17.00 (Mon. - Fri.).
Services Offered | Source materials, e.g., Text books, Journals, etc.; CINAHL on CD-ROM; Reading area; Current awareness; Lending facilities; Photocopying service; ILL.
Special Collections | Core texts of Clinical Psychiatry, Psychiatric Nursing; Child Psychiatry; Psychotherapy and Counselling; Rehabilitation; Psychology; Behaviour therapy; Mental handicap; Challenging behaviour; Management; Forensic psychiatry.
Bookstock | c.2,500 volumes - c.1,500 available for loan (to EHB staff/students) and ILL.
Periodicals | 46 titles - not available for loan or ILL; will photocopy.
A/V Stock | 12 compact disks (CINAHL) - not available for loan or ILL.
Catalogue | Author/title/subject catalogue.
Classification | Dewey Decimal System.
Computer Equipment | 2 CD-ROM computers.
Other Equipment | Printer; Photocopier.

200 OUR LADY'S HOSPITAL FOR SICK CHILDREN
Medical Library,
Crumlin,
Dublin 12.
Tel: Dublin (01) 455 8111 ext. 2596
Fax: Dublin (01) 455 5307

Librarian	Suzanne Feeney
No. of Staff	3 (1 Professional, 2 Non-professional) 2 Part-time.
Opening Hours	09.30 - 20.00 (Mon. - Wed.), 09.30 - 17.00 (Thurs. - Fri.).
Services Offered	Loans; Search facilities; Current Awareness; Contents Pages; Accession Lists; SDI; ILL.
Bookstock	924 volumes - available for loan to hospital staff and students; limited ILL
Periodicals	89 titles - not available for loan or ILL; will photocopy.
A/V Stock	138 audio-cassettes - available for loan to hospital staff only.
Catalogue	Computerised - InMagic.
Classification	Dewey.
Computer Equipment	Medline on CD-ROM (1966 to date); CINAHL on CD-ROM; InMagic; Microsoft Works.
Other Equipment	Microfiche reader; Photocopier.

OVE ARUP AND PARTNERS IRELAND 201
[Entry as 1993 edition - no update received]
Consulting Engineers,
10, Wellington Road,
Ballsbridge,
Dublin 4.
Tel: Dublin (01) 668 3112
Fax: Dublin (01) 668 3169

Information Officer	Michael Walsh
No. of Staff	2 (1 Professional, 1 Non-professional) Part-time.
Opening Hours	09.00 - 17.30 (Mon. - Fri.).
Services Offered	In-house Library, Information, Archive Service.
Special Collections	Civil, Structural, Mechanical, Electrical Engineering Books; Trade Literature - Building Industry; Press Cuttings - relevant to consulting engineering practice; Professional Journals and Trade Magazines.

201 OVE ARUP AND PARTNERS IRELAND continued

Subject Specialisation	Engineering.
Bookstock	5,500 volumes (approx.) - available only for in-house use.
Periodicals	45 external and 5 internal titles - mostly for in-house use.
A/V Stock	120 video-cassettes (approx.) with access to large UK stock - mostly for use in-house or within the Industry.
Catalogue	Author/Subject/Class.
Classification	UDC for books; Alphabetical for Trade Literature.
Computer Equipment	Being considered.
Other Equipment	Microfilmed drawings; Reader and reproduction; Barbour Microform system with reader; Technica and Products; Photocopiers available.

202 THE PATENT OFFICE
45, Merrion Square,
Dublin 2.
Tel: Dublin (01) 661 4144 ext. 4104
Fax: Dublin (01) 676 0416

Librarian	Mary O'Rourke
No. of Staff	3 (Non-professional).
Opening Hours	09.45 - 16.15 (Mon. - Fri.).
Services Offered	Document delivery service; Trade mark and Patent Searching.
Special Collections	Legal and technical works of interest to inventors and those concerned with designs, trade marks and copyright; All International and European patent applications on CD-ROM; All GB patent applications (pre-1979 on paper, post-1979 on CD-ROM); Published Irish Patent applications on Microfilm (1978-); Access CD-ROM abstracts and cross references from 1978 to date of EP and PCT applications.

46, North Great Charles Street,
Dublin 1.
Tel: Dublin (01) 878 0255
Fax: Dublin (01) 874 2626
E-mail: pavee@aonad.iol.ie

Librarian	Nancy Collins
No. of Staff	1 (Part-time).
Opening Hours	09.30 - 17.00.
Services Offered	Information on travellers and related subjects; Photographic archive on view; Video archive on view; Press cuttings archive on view; Audio-visual shows on view; Workshops/seminars/guest speakers available; Traveller archive.
Bookstock	500 volumes (approx.) - not available for loan or ILL.
Periodicals	200 titles (approx.) - not available for loan or ILL; will photocopy.
A/V Stock	100 audio-cassettes; 100 video-cassettes, A/V shows (four).
Computer Equipment	Currently investigating options with the intention to computerise records this year.
Other Equipment	Photocopiers.

PHARMACEUTICAL SOCIETY OF IRELAND   204
[Entry as 1993 edition - no update received]
37, Northumberland Road,
Dublin 4.
Tel: Dublin (01) 660 0699/660 0551
Fax: Dublin (01) 668 1461

Librarian	Susan Payne
No. of Staff	1 (Professional).
Opening Hours	10.00 - 13.00, 14.00 - 16.00 (Mon. - Fri.).
Services Offered	Reading rights by prior appointment only.
Special Collections	Pharmacy and allied subjects.
Bookstock	60 volumes - not available for loan or ILL.
Periodicals	20 titles - not available for loan or ILL; will photocopy (small charge).
Other Equipment	Photocopier; Fax; Thermal Binder.

205 PRISON LIBRARY SERVICE
Library Office,
Wheatfield Detention Centre,
Clondalkin,
Dublin 22.
Tel: Dublin (01) 626 0011 ext. 307/251
Fax: Dublin (01) 623 1484

Librarians	Yvonne Desmond/Clare Scanlan/Brenda Ainsworth
No. of Staff	13 (3 Professional, 10 Non-professional).
Opening Hours	Varied.
Services Offered	Requests; Video viewing; Self-training computer packages; Literacy tutoring; Health education; Legal searching.
Bookstock	25,000 volumes - available for loan but not ILL.
Periodicals	20 titles - available for loan, but not ILL or photocopying.
A/V Stock	800 audio-cassettes, 150 video-cassettes - available for loan but not ILL.
Catalogue	Computerised Catalogue.
Classification	Dewey and Colour Code System.
Computer Equipment	18 PCs (3 PCs networked on Windows for Workgroups); CALM (catalogue); Clipper issue system and indexing; CD-ROM; WordPerfect; Pagemaker.
Other Equipment	1 Microfiche Reader; 1 Microfilm Reader; 4 InkJet wide carriage printers; 3 Laser printers; 4 dot matrix printers; 2 Photocopiers; Slide projector and screen.

206 PRISON SERVICE TRAINING CENTRE
Beladd House,
Portlaoise,
Co. Laoise.
Tel: Portlaoise (0502) 20240
Fax: Portlaoise (0502) 20946

Librarian	E. Kavanagh
Service Offered	The training centre is currently being re-organised, the library is the next step to

| | develop. |
| Bookstock | 1,000 volumes - available for reference only. |

RADIO TELEFÍS ÉIREANN   207
PROGRAMME LIBRARY
RTE,
Donnybrook,
Dublin 4.
Tel: Dublin (01) 208 2659
Fax: Dublin (01) 208 3096

Department	PROGRAMME TRAFFIC DEPT., (see above); General enquiries to ext. 2659.
Programme Traffic Executive	Linda Graves
No. of Staff	19 (Professional).
Opening Hours	09.15 - 19.00 (Mon. - Fri.); News Library: 10.00 - 22.00 (Mon. - Sun.).
Services Offered	Information retrieval, storage and movement relating to all current programmes; the News Library provides a complete library service for the RTE News Room, Research, Enquiries, etc.; the Sports Library provides complete library service for the RTE Sports Department, Research, Enquiries, etc.; Library Sales deals with enquiries from the public and other broadcasting organisations for copies of RTE programmes. Contact: Stephen D'arcy, Tel: 2083369 or Norma O'Connor, Tel: 2082786.
Department	PROGRAMME ARCHIVE, (see above); Tel: (01) 208 2361.
Archive Manager	Willie Murray
Librarian	Barbara Duvack/Pauline Goodwin
No. of Staff	7 (Professional).
Opening Hours	09.15 - 17.30 (Mon. - Fri.).
Services Offered	The archive is responsible for the information retrieval, storage and movement relating to archive film and videotapes. The archive also holds an archive collection on digital tape.

207 RADIO TELEFÍS ÉIREANN
PROGRAMME LIBRARY continued

Traffic and Archive Collections   Substantial collections of RTE news and television programmes, and inserts from 1962 to date. A collection of archive film (from c.1913) of Irish interest acquired from international agencies and local sources.

A/V Stock   155,000 video/film-cassettes (approx.) - not available for loan or ILL. Purchasing service available.

Computer Equipment   RTE computer system (TISY - Television Information System).

208 RADIO TELEFÍS ÉIREANN
REFERENCE AND ILLUSTRATIONS LIBRARY
New Television Building,
RTE,
Montrose,
Dublin 4.
Tel: Dublin (01) 208 3327
Fax: Dublin (01) 208 3031
E-mail: hallj@rte.ie or rterefli@iol.ie

Librarian   Jane Hall

No. of Staff   12 (2 Professional, 10 Non-professional).

Opening Hours   09.00 - 20.30 (Mon.- Fri.).

Services Offered   Reference: Information service and provision of written materials (printed and electronic) for programme makers. Also, some materials to support technical staff. Information on INIS (Irish News Information Service) on application to Librarian.
Illustrations: Provision of current and archive still pictures of broadcast quality for use by programme makers; Provision of electronic access to remote picture banks.

Special Services   PHOTOGRAPHIC ARCHIVE, RTE, Annexe 4 , Room 14, Montrose, Dublin 4; Tel: (01) 208 2815; (Jane Hall, Librarian).

Special Collections	Biographical files on Irish personalities; Archive photographs of the Cashman, Johnson and Murtagh Collections.
Bookstock	13,000 volumes - 10,500 available for loan (to RTE staff only) and ILL.
Periodicals	150 titles - not available for loan or ILL; will photocopy.
Other Materials	300,000 photographic prints and 36,000 slides not available for loan; 8 CD-ROMs not available for loan.
Catalogue	Computerised.
Classification	UDC and keywords.
Computer Equipment	Reference section has integrated system including `Techlib' library retrieval software; "PC-DOC" DIP system for newspaper cuttings; Jukebox holds 35 optical discs; "Sun spare" server runs Solaris 1-1 and TCP/IP protcol for network; Also 3 duel-drive CD-ROM changers to be networked 1996. Illustrations and Photographic Archive in process of selecting new system; 14 PCs; 1 Modem; 3 Printers; 2 Scanners.
Other Equipment	1 Microform reader/printer; 1 Photocopier; 2 Photo-CD viewers; 1 Photo-CD printer.

RADIO TELEFÍS ÉIREANN   209
SOUND LIBRARY
Radio Centre,
RTE,
Donnybrook,
Dublin 4.
Tel: Dublin (01) 208 2430/208 3326/208 2399
Fax: Dublin (01) 208 3304
E-mail: mbreen@rte.ie

Librarian	Don Kennedy
No. of Staff	15 (5 Professional, 10 Non-professional).
Departments	Main sound library; Sound archives; Radio news library; Radio tape traffic and repeat library; Cork studios.
Opening Hours	08.00 - 22.30 (Mon. - Fri.), 11.30 - 19.30

	(Sat.) .Public Holidays as Sat.
Services Offered	RTE Sound Library serves the recorded audio and related information needs of RTE radio and TV staff, orchestras, instrumental and vocal ensembles. Resources generally closed to all except RTE staff, but applications pertaining to advanced studies will be considered.
Special Collections	The Disc Collection covers all facets of music and the spoken arts, sound effects, mood music. The Sound Archive represents outstanding moments in Irish radio broadcasting, covering the social, political and cultural life of Ireland.
Special Services	RTE Irish Traditional Music field tapes are now available for consultation at the Irish Traditional Music Archive, 63, Merrion Square, Dublin 2; Tel: (01) 661 9699. RTE recorded Irish Art/Contemporary Music Centre, 95, Lower Baggot Street, Dublin 2; Tel: (01) 661 2105.
Subject Specialisation	Broadcasting; Irish history; Irish current affairs; Irish language; Irish social history; Irish art music; Irish traditional music; Music.
Bookstock	Small collection of specialised reference tools - not available for loan.
Periodicals	Small collection of Audio Trade and Disc Reviews - not available for loan; will photocopy.
A/V Stock	Commercial discs: 60,000 compact disks, 200,000 vinyl discs, 35,000 78s (over 2 million commercial tracks in total) - not available for loan. Radio Archives: 55,000 hours of ¼" audio tape, 2,000 DATs, 1,500 CD-Rs - not available for loan.
Catalogue	In-house developed computerised database.
Classification	In-house.
Computer Equipment	ICL Mainframe Super Dual SX 3900 40G storage; 13 terminals in Sound Library; PCs and various applications packages

	linked to WAN network and available throughout the organisation; New PC based LMS to become available in 1996; CD-ROMs: RED Musicmaster/Gramophone database; Newstar: on-line news information service.
Other Equipment	Gram decks; CD players; DAT players; 10" and 11" reel to reel players; Audio-cassette players; Multi format audio dubbing stacks; Access to audio enhancing desks and expertise; CD-ROM readers; CD-ROM recorders; PC based audio capturing system to CD-R (real time to compressed); PC driven audio juke boxes with down-loading facilities.

REDEMPTORIST COMMUNITY   210
Marianella,
75, Orwell Road,
Dublin 6.
Tel: Dublin (01) 492 2688

Librarian	Brendan McConvery
No. of Staff	1 (Non-professional).
Opening Hours	By appointment.
Subject Specialisation	Theology, with a concentration on Moral Theology.
Bookstock	20,000 volumes - not available for loan or ILL.
Periodicals	70 titles - not available for loan or ILL.
Catalogue	Author; subject (card).
Classification	Dewey.
Other Equipment	Photocopier.

REGIONAL MEDICAL LIBRARY   211
Regional Hospital,
Dooradoyle,
Limerick.
Tel: Limerick (061) 229288
Fax: Limerick (061) 229288
E-mail: mwhblib@iol.ie

211   REGIONAL MEDICAL LIBRARY continued

Librarian	Margaret Dillon
No. of Staff	5 (1 Professional, 4 Non-professional) all Part-time.
Opening Hours	09.00 - 21.00 (Mon. - Thurs.), 09.00 - 17.00 (Fri.).
Services Offered	Loans; Photocopying; ILL; Literature Searching : On-line, CD-ROM.
Bookstock	4,500 volumes - c.4,000 available for loan and ILL.
Periodicals	150 titles - not available for loan or ILL; will photocopy.
A/V Stock	60 audio-cassettes, 30 video-cassettes - available for loan, not available for ILL; 4 compact disks - not available for loan or ILL.
Catalogue	Integrated with University of Limerick on-line catalogue (URICA).
Classification	Dewey.
Computer Equipment	3 486 PCs; 2 single CD-ROM drives; 1 5-deck CD-ROM unit; MS Works; MS Office; Databases: Medline, CINAHL, CD Nurse ROM, Bookbank.
Other Equipment	1 Microfiche reader; 2 Photocopiers (1 public access, card-operated).

**212   RELIGIOUS SOCIETY OF FRIENDS IN IRELAND
HISTORICAL LIBRARY
Swanbrook House,
Bloomfield Avenue,
Morehampton Road,
Dublin 4.
Tel: Dublin (01) 668 7157**

Librarian	The Curator
No. of Staff	4 (Non-professional).
Opening Hours	11.00 - 13.00 (Thurs.)
Services Offered	Some genealogical work done.
Special Collections	12 volumes of manuscript material relating to Anthony Sharp; material dealing with Quakers in Ireland.
Bookstock	c.1,140 volumes.

Manuscripts	3,000 letters; over 1,700 other Mss.
Other Material	Maps; Wills; Marriage certificates; Minute books; Legal documents; Photographs.
Subject Specialisation	Quaker history
Equipment	1 Microfilm Reader; Photocopiers.

REPRESENTATIVE CHURCH BODY LIBRARY 213
Braemor Park,
Churchtown,
Dublin 14.
Tel: Dublin (01) 492 3979
Fax: Dublin (01) 492 4770

Librarian	Dr. Raymond Refaussé
No. of Staff	2.5 (1 Professional, 1 Non-professional, 0.5 Part-time).
Opening Hours	09.30 - 13.00, 13.45 - 17.00 (Mon. - Fri.).
Services Offered	Available for reading and reference to any interested person; Lending service to library members (membership by subscription to approved candidates).
Special Collections	Watson Collection of early prayer books; Church of Ireland archives and related Mss.
Subject Specialisation	Religion; Theology.
Bookstock	40,000 volumes - 30,000 available for loan (to members) and ILL.
Periodicals	75 titles - not available for loan or ILL; will photocopy.
A/V Stock	400 video-cassettes - available for loan and ILL.
Catalogue	Dictionary (card).
Classification	Dewey.
Computer Equipment	2 PCs (IBM PS/2); WordPerfect; Dataease.
Other Equipment	Microfiche reader; Microfilm reader/printer; Photocopier (not for public use - work done for readers).

214 RESEARCH GROUP ON CHEMICAL DEPENDENCY
Graham House,
1-5, Albert Square,
Belfast BT1 3EQ.
Tel: Belfast (01232) 240900
Fax: Belfast (01232) 331498

Librarian	Frank McGoldrick
No. of Staff	5 (1 Professional, 4 Part-time).
Opening Hours	09.00 - 17.00 (Mon. - Fri.).
Services Offered	Information on services in Northern Ireland in relation to drug and alcohol problems.

215 ROYAL DUBLIN SOCIETY
Ballsbridge,
Dublin 4.
Tel: Dublin (01) 668 0866
Fax: Dublin (01) 660 4014

Librarian	Mary Kelleher
Opening Hours	18.00 - 20.00 (Mon., during recital season), 10.00 - 17.00 (Tues., Fri.), 10.00 - 19.00 (Wed., Thurs.) (Thurs. until 20.00 on lecture evenings), 11.00 - 17.00 (Sat.).
Services Offered	Services to members of the R.D.S.; Available to non-members by appointment.
Subject Specialisation	Agriculture; Science and the Arts; Books on Ireland.
Bookstock	250,000 books and periodicals.
A/V Stock	110 audio-cassettes, small collection of video-cassettes - available for loan not available for ILL.
Catalogue	Author (Sheaf); Subject (Card).
Classification	Dewey.
Computer Equipment	IBM; LAN; Tinlib; CD-ROM.
Other Equipment	Microform reader/printer.

216 ROYAL IRISH ACADEMY
19, Dawson Street,
Dublin 2.
Tel: Dublin (01) 676 2570/676 4222
Fax: Dublin (01) 676 2346

Librarian	Siobhán O'Rafferty (Acting Librarian)
No. of Staff	4 (2 Professional, 2 Non-professional, 1 - 3 Part-time).
Opening Hours	10.30 - 17.30 (Mon. - Fri.). Closed first three weeks in August.
Services Offered	The Library is open to Members of the Academy, to members of the public who have obtained Members' permission to use the Library or who bring a letter of introduction from faculty or other library. Application forms available on request. Reader's Ticket fee: £10 p.a. Information leaflets available on some of the collections; Photography; Microfilming; Photocopying; Printouts from microfilms.
Special Collections	Manuscripts; Early printed books; Haliday Pamphlets and Tracts; Bergin and Moore Collections.
Bookstock	c.100,000 volumes - all, except pre-1800 items and items from special bequests, available for loan and ILL.
Periodicals	c.2,000 titles - available for loan and ILL; will photocopy.
AV Stock	1 compact disk - not available for loan or ILL.
Other Materials	c.2,500 manuscripts - not available for loan; c.300 microfilms (mainly of Irish manuscripts collection) - available for loan; Photographic collections including c.2,000 negatives - some available for loan; Antiquarian drawings collections - may be lent for exhibition purposes provided suitable environmental/security conditions obtain.
Catalogue	InMagic database, c.25,000 records; Author/title/subject card catalogue; Conversion of card catalogue in progress.
Classification	Fixed location.
Computer Equipment	Fileserver; 7 PCs; CD-ROM; Novell Netware; InMagic; WordPerfect 5.1.
Other Equipment	1 Microform reader/printer; Photocopier; Facility for readers to use laptop computers.

217 **ROYAL SOCIETY OF ANTIQUARIES OF IRELAND**
63, Merrion Square,
Dublin 2.
Tel: Dublin (01) 676 1749
Fax: Dublin (01) 676 1749

Assistant Librarian	Siobhán de hÓir
No. of Staff	2 (Professional).
Opening Hours	14.00 - 17.00 (Mon. - Fri.).
Special Collections	General archaeology; Irish archaeology; History; Local history.
Bookstock	c.2,000 volumes - c.500 available for loan to members only.
Periodicals	89 titles - not available for loan; will photocopy.
Catalogue	Author.
Classification	Subject.
Other Equipment	Photocopier

218 **SAVE THE CHILDREN (NI)**
UK Department,
Popper House,
15, Richmond Park,
Belfast BT10 0HB.
Tel: Belfast (01232) 431123
Fax: Belfast (01232) 431314

Information Officer	Gerard Duddy
No. of Staff	1.
Branches	Satellite sections in some projects for the benefit of users.
Opening Hours	09.00 - 16.30 (Mon. - Fri.).
Services Offered	Information Resource Files for use of staff and users in 30 subject categories related to the family, child care issues, social issues, women's issues and prisoners' families.
Subject Specialisation	Family and Children's rights and issues.
Bookstock	1,000 volumes (approx.) - available for loan to staff and users of our projects and other related statutory and voluntary organisations.
Periodicals	23 titles - not available for loan.

A/V Stock	50 audio-cassettes, 18 video-cassettes - available for loan to staff and users of our projects and other related statutory and voluntary organisations.
Computer Equipment	Tandon 386SX/20 PC used for word-processing; Databases; Desk top publishing.
Other Equipment	Photocopier; Overhead projector and screen; Video camcorder; Slide projector.

SHARE THE VISION 219
STV Office,
36, Circular Road,
Castlerock,
Co. Londonderry BT51 4XA.
Tel: Castlerock (01265) 848303
Fax: Castlerock (01265) 848003
E-mail: p.craddock@bbcnc.org.uk

Librarian	Peter Craddock.
No. of Staff	1 (Non-professional).
Opening Hours	Office Hours.
Services Offered	Consultancy and advice; Promotion of library and information service for print disabled people; Seminars; Workshops; Newsletter; Publications; Network development; Research programme.

SHORT BROTHERS PLC 220
PO Box 241,
Airport Road,
Belfast BT3 9DZ.
Tel: Belfast (01232) 458444
Fax: Belfast (01232) 733259

Librarian	J. McKane
Opening Hours	08.15 - 16.45 (Mon. - Thurs.); 08.15 - 12.30 (Fri.).
Services Offered	Essentially for members of the firm. Photocopying, ILL and other services to outside organisations by arrangement.

220 SHORT BROTHERS PLC continued

Bookstock	4,000 volumes.
Periodicals	200 titles.
A/V Stock	Standard Specifications on CD-ROM.
Catalogue	Author/title; classified (card).
Classification	UDC.
Computer Equipment	PCs.
Other Equipment	Microform reader.

**221 SIMON COMMUNITY NORTHERN IRELAND
57, Fitzroy Avenue,
Belfast BT7 1HT.
Tel: Belfast (01232) 232882
Fax: Belfast (01232) 326839**

Librarian	Kate O'Loughlin (until Oct. 1996)
No. of Staff	1 (Non-professional).
Opening Hours	The Simon Library is not a lending library open directly to the public, however the services outlined below are available during office hours 09.00 - 17.00 (Mon. - Fri.).
Services Offered	Information requests answered (phone, letter or in person); Reference access to library, library stock can be looked at in office (appointments should be made in advance).
Special Collections	The library consists of books, reports, periodicals and journals on the topics of Housing; Homelessness; Types of accommodation provision; Special needs groups; Social policy amongst others.
Bookstock	1,000 (approx.) - not available for loan or ILL.
Periodicals	40 titles - not available for loan or ILL.
Other Materials	Some leaflets/educational packs about housing/homelessness.
Catalogue	Author/title/subject, Card catalogue. In process of being computerised.
Classification	Alphanumeric.
Other Equipment	Photocopiers (charge).

SIPTU (SERVICES INDUSTRIAL PROFESSIONAL TECHNICAL UNION)
30, Parnell Square,
Dublin 1.
Tel: Dublin (01) 873 3977/872 6466
Fax: Dublin (01) 873 3062

Librarian	Jean Kennedy
No. of Staff	1.
Opening Hours	09.30 - 17.30 (by appointment only).
Services Offered	Photocopying; ILL by special arrangement.
Special Collections	Industrial relations and labour history material.
Bookstock	Limited number available for loan, strict lending criteria; not available for ILL.
Periodicals	Available for loan and ILL; will photocopy.

SOUTH EASTERN HEALTH BOARD - KILKENNY
Head Office,
Lacken,
Dublin Road,
Kilkenny.
Tel: Kilkenny (056) 51702
Fax: Kilkenny (056) 65270

Librarian	Ann Tierney
No. of Staff	2 (Non-professional).
Branches	WATERFORD REGIONAL HOSPITAL; Tel: (051) 73321, Fax: (051) 79495; (Marie O'Neill Maher, Librarian). WEXFORD GENERAL HOSPITAL, Tel: (053) 42233, Fax: (053) 41910; (Mary McDonald, Librarian).
Opening Hours	09.00 - 13.00, 14.00 - 17.00 (Mon. - Fri.).
Services Offered	Enquiry and reference service; Book loans; Computer searches and training; Photocopy supply; Journal contents bulletins; ILL; User education.
Bookstock	4,000 volumes - 3,800 available for loan and ILL.
Periodicals	80 titles - available for loan (after six

223   SOUTH EASTERN HEALTH BOARD - KILKENNY continued

	months) and ILL; will photocopy.
A/V Stock	12 audio-cassettes, 20 video-cassettes - available for loan and ILL; 14 compact disks - not available for loan or ILL.
Catalogue	Manual.
Classification	Bliss.
Computer Equipment	3 PCs with CD-ROM; Microsoft Office Pro; Medline; CINAHL; Healthplan; Justis Environmental Health; Nurse ROM; HELIOS Hanynet.
Other Equipment	Microfiche Reader; Photocopier.

224   SOUTH EASTERN HEALTH BOARD - TIPPERARY
St. Joseph's Hospital,
Clonmel.
Co. Tipperary.
Tel: Clonmel (052) 21900
Fax: Clonmel (052) 23975

Librarian	Dr S. Kingston
No. of Staff	1 clerical assistant for ½ day per week.
Opening Hours	Continuous.
Services Offered	Medical journals; Medical books.
Periodicals	21 titles - not available for loan or ILL.
A/V Stock	15 video-cassettes - available for loan but not available for ILL.

225   SPORTS COUNCIL FOR NORTHERN IRELAND
House of Sport,
Upper Malone Road,
Belfast BT9 5LA.
Tel: Belfast (01232) 381222
Fax: Belfast (01232) 682757

Information Officer	Patrick Murphy, BA.
Opening Hours	08.30 - 17.00 (Mon. - Thurs.), 08.30 - 16.30 (Fri.).
Services Offered	Reference facility open to staff, and public by appointment
Subject Specialisation	Sport; Physical recreation.

Bookstock	2,000 monographs.
Periodicals	20 titles covering sport and physical recreation.
A/V Stock	Some videos and tapes.

ST. LUKE'S INSTITUTE OF CANCER RESEARCH   226
St. Luke's Hospital,
Highfield Road,
Rathgar,
Dublin 6.
Tel: Dublin (01) 496 5692
Fax: Dublin (01) 497 4886
E-mail: gdoyle@iol.ie

Librarian	Gabrielle Doyle
No. of Staff	1 (Professional).
Opening Hours	09.00 - 13.00, 14.00 - 16.45 (Mon. - Fri.).
Services Offered	Reference, lending and information services for staff. Available to others by arrangement.
Special Collections	Science related to cancer research. Medicine, nursing and allied health subjects related to the treatment of cancer.
Bookstock	900 volumes - available for loan to staff.
Periodicals	74 titles - not available for loan or ILL; will photocopy.
Catalogue	Computerised Library Catalogue is on STATUS.
Classification	Dewey.
Computer Equipment	CD-ROM Databases: Cancerlit, CINAHL; On-line access to STN International; Internet.
Other Equipment	Microfiche Reader; Photocopier.

ST. VINCENT'S HOSPITAL   227
Richmond Road,
Fairview,
Dublin 3.
Tel: Dublin (01) 837 5101
Fax: Dublin (01) 837 0801

227 ST. VINCENT'S HOSPITAL continued

Librarian	Eimear Burke
No. of Staff	1 (Professional, Part-time).
Opening Hours	09.30 - 14.30 (Mon. - Fri.).
Services Offered	ILL through Irish Medical Libraries ILL network; CD-ROM searches on CINAHL database; ILL using BLDSC; Monthly current awareness bulletin; Subject information files; Careers and further education service.
Bookstock	c.3,000 - 2,700 available for loan (to hospital students and staff) not available for ILL.
Periodicals	33 titles - not available for loan or ILL; will photocopy.
A/V Stock	45 video-cassettes - available for loan, not available for ILL.
Catalogue	Card.
Classification	Dewey.
Computer Equipment	Viglen 486 DX-266 with internal CD-ROM drive; CINAHL.
Other Equipment	Photocopier.

228 TELECOM EIREANN
Technical Training Centre,
Wainsfort Road,
Terenure,
Dublin 6W.
Tel: Dublin (01) 490 2460
Fax: Dublin (01) 490 2596
E-mail: modowd@telecom.ie

Librarian	Mary O'Dowd
No. of Staff	4 (2 Professional, 2 Non-professional).
Opening Hours	09.30 - 17.30 (Mon. - Fri.).
Services Offered	Library offers a comprehensive range of services and facilities to all staff within Telecom Eireann including: Lending books, audio- and video-cassettes and computer-based training courses; Current Awareness: contents pages, weekly news clippings service; Information and

	Research Services: on-line searching, CD-ROMS and OPAC accessible over company wide area network, Internet searching; On-site Facilities: PCs for multimedia based training, video player and audio-cassette player; photocopying, study facilities.
Bookstock	3,000 (approx.) - 2,800 available for loan to Telecom Eireann staff only; ILL by special arrangement.
Periodicals	85 titles - not available for loan or ILL; will photocopy.
A/V Stock	77 audio-cassettes, 207 compact disks, 125 video-cassettes - available for loan to Telecom staff only; not available for ILL; 20 multimedia packs - not available for loan or ILL.
Catalogue	OASIS (automated) with OPAC.
Classification	Dewey, 20th edition.
Computer Systems	9 PCs (5 multimedia Siemens Nixdorf 486 (incl. CD-ROM drive and Sound card), 2 486 Siemens Nixdorf, 1 Dell 486 with CD-ROM drive and Internet, 1 AST 386); HP Laserjet 4 Plus/4M Plus Printer; Optical Server: Viglen 386 PC; 6 Toshiba CD-ROM Drives; Optinet Software; Library Management Software: OASIS (Catalogue, Circulation, OPAC modules); CD-ROMs: INSPEC, ABI Inform, DataPro, Standards Infodisc; Software: Word 6, Excel 5, PowerPoint, ccMail.
Other Equipment	Audio and video playback facilities; Rank Xerox 5047 Photocopier with auditron.

TRÓCAIRE   229
169, Booterstown Avenue,
Blackrock,
Co. Dublin.
Tel: Dublin (01) 288 5385
Fax: Dublin (01) 288 3577
E-mail: anne@trocaire.ie

229 **TRÓCAIRE continued**

Librarian	Anne Kinsella
No. of Staff	3 (1 Professional, 1 Non-professional, 1 Voluntary).
Opening Hours	09.30 - 13.00, 14.00 - 17.30 (Mon. - Fri.).
Services Offered	Subject Searches: computer printout; Journal index on database (Dataease); Photocopying; Recent additions list.
Special Collections	B&W photographs; Newspaper clippings.
Bookstock	Most (except reference collection) available for loan, not available for ILL.
Periodicals	141 titles - not available for loan or ILL; will photocopy.
A/V Stock	Video-cassettes - available through Trocaire Resource Centre, 12, Cathedral Street, Dublin 1.
Catalogue	Computerised - DataEase.
Classification	UDC.
Computer Equipment	DataEase; MS Works/Word; WWW; E-mail.
Other Equipment	1 TV/video; Photocopier.

230 **ULSTER-AMERICAN FOLK PARK**
Mellon Road,
Castletown,
Omagh,
Co. Tyrone BT78 5QY.
Tel: Omagh (01662) 243292
Fax: Omagh (01662) 242241
E-mail: uafp@iol.ie

Librarian	Christine McIvor, BA, ALA.
No. of Staff	3 (2 Professional, 1 Non-professional).
Opening Hours	09.30 - 16.30 (Mon. - Fri.).
Services Offered	Photocopying; Microfiche/film reader/printer; Letters and telephone queries also answered; Public welcome.
Special Collections	The Library of the Ulster-American folk park is primarily a Centre for Migration Studies. It also supports the Park's main activities by providing reference resources for the study of the history of both the

	United States and Ireland in the 18th and 19th centuries and the link between the two. Coverage includes traditional crafts, agriculture, ships and American published books, both antiquarian and new. Griffith's Valuation Records on microfiche and accompanying maps for 6 counties; Derry Journal on microfilm 1772-1887 (incomplete); US Land Records, wills, official papers microfilmed by Pennsylvania Historical and Museums Committee.
Bookstock	6,000 volumes (approx.) - available for loan (to staff only) and ILL.
Periodicals	43 titles - not available for loan or ILL; will photocopy.
A/V Stock	Small number of audio- and video-cassettes - available for loan (to staff only), not available for ILL.
Catalogue	Card Catalogue - Author and Classification Number.
Classification	Own faceted scheme.
Computer Systems	Emigration database held on MicroVAX 3100 (Emigration between Ireland and North America in the 18th and 19th centuries), primary source documents, e.g., passenger lists, newspaper articles, advertisements, family papers, diaries and journals being added continuously. Available via 4 terminals in Library.
Other Equipment	Microform reader/printer; Photocopier.

ULSTER CANCER FOUNDATION 231
40, Eglantine Avenue,
Belfast BT9 6DX.
Tel: Belfast (01232) 663281
Fax: Belfast (01232) 660081

Educ. & Care Services	Arlene Spiers
Cancer Information Officer	Ruth Campbell
Opening Hours	09.00 - 12.45, 14.00 - 17.00 (Mon. - Fri.).
Services Offered	Library facilities available to general

231   ULSTER CANCER FOUNDATION continued

	public; short-term loans arranged.
Subject Specialisation	Small collection of books and periodicals on cancer and smoking-related subjects, counselling and nursing care.

232   ULSTER FOLK AND TRANSPORT MUSEUM
Cultra,
Holywood,
Co. Down BT18 0EU.
Tel: Belfast (01232) 428428
Fax: Belfast (01232) 428728

Librarian	D. Roger Dixon
No. of Staff	2 (1 Professional, 1 Non-professional).
Opening Hours	09.00 - 17.00 (Mon. - Fri.).
Services Offered	Reference service to public.
Special Collections	Connell Collection; Irish Economic and Social History; Lloyds' Register of Shipping Collection.
Periodicals	200 titles - not available for loan or ILL; will photocopy.
A/V Stock	Audio-cassettes - responsibility of audio department, not library. Video-cassettes - responsibility of photographic department, not library.
Other Materials	Manuscript Archives; Questionnaires, etc.
Catalogue	Alphabetical Author/Subject (Card).
Classification	In-house.
Other Equipment	Microform reader/printer; Photocopiers.

233   ULSTER MUSEUM,
Botanic Gardens,
Belfast BT9 5AB
Tel: Belfast (01232) 383013 (Library)/(01232) 383090 (Registry)
Fax: Belfast (01232) 383003
E-mail: stf@belumreg.demon.co.uk

Registrar	Sylvia Frawley
Acting Librarian	Margaret Quine
No. of Staff	1 (Professional).

Opening Hours	09.00 - 12.45, 14.00 - 16.30 (Mon. - Fri.) Closed bank holidays.
Services Offered	Reference and lending for staff; Reference only for general public but items can, in certain cases, be lent to other libraries and accredited research workers; Photocopying.
Special Collections	Belfast printed books (1700 to c.1850); R.J. Welch Collection of photographic negatives; Alex. R. Hogg Collection of photographic negatives; Manuscripts; Small Document Archive; Various mss. collections relating to local naturalists.
Subject Specialisation	Archaeology; Art; Botany; Design; Geology; Industrial archaeology; Local history; Museology; Numismatics; Photography; Zoology.
Bookstock	30,000+ volumes - available for ILL.
Periodicals	180 titles - not available for ILL; will photocopy.
A/V Stock	15,000 Photographic negatives.
Catalogue	Author/title; Classified; Index (Card).
Classification	Dewey 16th edition; Own.
Other Equipment	Microfiche readers; Photocopier.

ULSTER ORCHESTRA SOCIETY LIMITED   234
Elmwood Hall at Queen's,
89, University Road,
Belfast BT7 1NF.
Tel: Belfast (01232) 664535
Fax: Belfast (01232) 662761

Librarian	Paul McKinley
No. of Staff	1 (Professional).
Opening Hours	09.00 - 17.00 (Mon. - Fri.) and at other times as required to service concerts and rehearsals.
Services Offered	Strictly limited to providing support and information to the UOS; However, outside enquiries re: publishers, etc. are dealt with.
Special Collections	Large holding of orchestral material. Number of items increases according to

ULSTER ORCHESTRA SOCIETY LIMITED continued
requirements of UOS.

Other Materials	Orchestral Catalogues: BBC orchestral catalogue; Orchestral Music in Print; Publishers Catalogues; BUCOS Catalogue.
Catalogue	Card Index.
Classification	By Card Index and Alphabetically.
Other Equipment	Photocopier.

235 VMRA CONSULTING ENGINEERS
Tramway House,
Dartry Road,
Dublin 6.
Tel: Dublin (01) 497 5716
Fax: Dublin (01) 497 5886
E-mail: library@tramway.ie

Librarians	Phil Comerford/Carol Lyons
No. of Staff	2 (1 Professional, 1 Non-professional).
Opening Hours	09.00 - 13.00; 14.00 - 17.30 (Mon. - Fri.).
Other Services	Services to members of firm; Others on application to Librarian; Photocopying; ILLs.
Special Collections	Material relating to building services, design, operation and maintenance; Barbour Index; Product catalogues.
Bookstock	800 books, 1000 product catalogues - available for loan and ILL.
Periodicals	70 titles - available for loan and ILL; will photocopy.
Other Materials	Barbour Index microfiche for Building Engineers.
Catalogue	Computerised; Idealist for Windows.
Classification	SFB.
Computer Equipment	Computer; Printers; CD-ROM; Idealist for Windows; Microsoft Office; Archivist International Building Services Abstracts.
Other Equipment	1 Scanner. Photocopier

WATERFORD CATHEDRAL LIBRARY   236
Christchurch Cathedral,
Waterford.
Tel: Waterford (051) 74119

Librarian	Julian Walton
No. of Staff	1 (Non-professional).
Opening Hours	By appointment only.
Services Offered	Reference only. Most of the works are currently stored in St. John's College, Waterford during cathedral restoration.
Bookstock	3,000 volumes - not available for loan or ILL.
Special Collections	Dobbyn Legal Collection (law books bequeathed in 1807).
Subject Specialisation	Theological and Legal.
Catalogue	Author
Classification	Own.

WOOD & ASSOCIATES   237
38, Arran Quay,
Dublin 7.
Tel: Dublin (01) 872 6088
Fax: Dublin (01) 872 6957

Information Officer	Cliona O'Neill
No. of Staff	9 (5 Professional, 2 Non-professional, 2 Part-time).
Opening Hours	08.30 - 17.30 (Mon. - Fri.).
Services Offered	In-house services; Photocopying.
Special Collections	Health and Safety literature; Motor; Occupational Safety; Road Accidents.
Bookstock	c.10,000 volumes (including papers) - not available for loan or ILL.
Periodicals	142 titles - not available for loan or ILL; will photocopy.
A/V Stock	17 video-cassettes - not available for loan or ILL; Barbour on microfiche.
Catalogue	Computerised on ASSASSIN.
Classification	Own.
Computer Equipment	486 PC; Windows for Workgroups; Barbour electronic index for Health and

237   WOOD & ASSOCIATES continued

	Safety.
Other Equipment	Microfiche reader; 2 Photocopiers; Laser printer; Electronic Typewriter; Fax.

238   YOUTH COUNCIL FOR NORTHERN IRELAND
Lamont House,
Purdys Lane,
Belfast BT8 4TA
Tel: Belfast (01232) 643882
Fax: Belfast (01232) 643874

Librarian	Clare Harvey/Patricia Mulhern
No. of Staff	2 (1 Professional, 1 Non-professional).
Opening Hours	09.00 - 17.00 (Mon. - Fri.).
Services Offered	Consultancy; Photocopying service.
Special Collections	Community Relations NI; Youth work and youth service related issues.
Bookstock	200-300 volumes - not available for loan or ILL.
Periodicals	2,000 titles - not available for loan or ILL; will photocopy.
A/V Stock	5 video-cassettes - not available for loan or ILL.
Computer Equipment	Microsoft Access database.
Other Equipment	Photocopier.

UNIVERSITY, COLLEGE AND SCHOOL LIBRARIES

ACCOUNTANCY & BUSINESS COLLEGE   239
13-14, Aungier Street,
Dublin 2.
Tel: Dublin (01) 475 1024
Fax: Dublin (01) 475 1043
E-mail: lib@abc.ie

Librarian	Catriona Sharkey
No. of Staff	3 (1 Professional, 2 Non-professional, 1 Part-time).
Opening Hours	Term: 09.00 - 21.30 (Mon. - Thurs.), 09.00 - 17.15 (Fri.), 10.00 - 16.00 (Sat.).
Services Offered	Induction services - user education; Issue desk information/reference service; Photocopying; ILL.
Special Collections	Company reports and information; Careers; Government publications.
Bookstock	6,700 volumes - 5,500 available for loan to College staff and students; available for ILL by arrangement.
Periodicals	95 titles - not available for loan or ILL; will photocopy.
A/V Stock	100 audio-cassettes - available for loan; 80 video-cassettes - not available for loan.
Catalogue	Computerised: search functions - title/author/keyword.
Classification	Dewey 20th edition.
Computer Equipment	ANBAR on CD-ROM; OPAC.
Other Equipment	Microfiche readers; 1 Photocopier; Video and TV available.

ALL HALLOWS COLLEGE   240
Gracepark Road,
Drumcondra,
Dublin 9.
Tel: Dublin (01) 837 3745 ext. 265
Fax: Dublin (01) 837 7642
E-mail: AHallows@iol.ie

240 ALL HALLOWS COLLEGE continued

Librarian	Miriam Flanagan
No. of Staff	1 (1 Professional, 3 FÁS Part-time).
Opening Hours	09.00 - 21.00 (Mon. - Wed.), 09.00 - 17.00 (Thurs., Fri.), 10.00 - 13.00 (Sat.).
Services Offered	ILL; Photocopying; Specialist Bibliographies.
Special Collections	No special collections as such but the library is theology/philosophy based and the stock reflects this.
Bookstock	20,000 volumes - 18,000 available for loan (to staff and students of the College) and ILL.
Periodicals	60 titles - not available for loan or ILL; will photocopy.
A/V Stock	24 audio-cassettes, 24 video-cassettes - available for loan and ILL. This section is in the process of development.
Catalogue	Author, Class, Title & Keyword (Card).
Classification	Dewey.
Computer Equipment	Computer facilities provided in the college for students (not in the library).
Other Equipment	Photocopier.

241 AMERICAN COLLEGE DUBLIN
2, Merrion Square,
Dublin 2.
Tel: Dublin (01) 676 8939
Fax: Dublin (01) 676 8941
E-mail: library@amcd.ie
Telnet: cela.seflin.lib.fl.us User Name: public

Librarian	Kathleen Clunan MS-LA (American Library Association)
No. of Staff	4 (2 Professional, 2 Non-professional).
Opening Hours	Term: 08.30 - 21.30 (Mon. - Thurs.), 08.30 - 18.00 (Fri.), 10.00 - 13.30 (Sat.).
Services Offered	Reference; Loan; ILL (through Lynn University, Florida (affiliated college) and through BLDSC); Photocopying; CD-ROM work stations; Internet (restricted access).

Central Office,
Park House,
87, Great Victoria Street,
Belfast BT2 7AG.
Department of Library and Resource Based Learning,
Room A16,
College Square East,
Belfast BT1 6DJ.
Tel: Belfast (01232) 265016
Fax: Belfast (01232) 265001
E-mail: alan.d@binst.dnet.co.uk

Head of Department	Alan Dummigan
Librarian	Fred Robb
No. of Staff	17 (4 Professional, 13 Non-professional).
Site Libraries	BRUNSWICK STREET, Brunswick Street, Belfast BT2 7GX; Tel: (01232) 265139, Fax: (01232) 265101; (Philip Peattie, Librarian). COLLEGE SQUARE EAST, College Square East, Belfast BT1 6DJ; Tel: (01232) 265072, Fax: (01232) 255001; (Jim Hanna, Librarian). MILLFIELD, Millfield, Belfast BT1 1HS; Tel: (01232) 265434, Fax: (01232) 265401; (David Fenton, Senior Library Assistant). ORMEAU, Ormeau Embankment, Belfast BT5 6PJ; Tel: (01232) 265334, Fax: (01232) 265301; (Donna Hyland, Senior Library Assistant). TOWER STREET, Tower Street, Belfast BT5 4FH; Tel: (01232) 265226, Fax: (01232) 265201; (Gerardine Mitchell, Librarian). WHITEROCK, 91, Whiterock Road, Belfast BT12 7PG; Tel: (01232) 265363, Fax: (01232) 265351; (Stephen Murray, Senior Library Assistant).
Opening Hours	3 main sites: 09.00 - 20.00 (Mon. - Thurs.), 09.00 - 16.30 (Fri.). 3 minor sites: 09.00 - 17.00 (Mon. - Thurs.), 09.00 - 16.30 (Fri.).
Services Offered	Full range of services to staff and students;

BELFAST INSTITUTE OF FURTHER AND HIGHER EDUCATION continued

	Loan; Reference: Consultation; Study; Help desk/Information queries; Induction; Referral; CD-ROM; Video viewing; Audio workstation; Open access IT (word-processing, spreadsheets, databases, etc.) on main sites; OPAC; ILL.
Special Collection	Small Local/Irish history (20th Century).
Bookstock	45,000 volumes - 42,000 available for loan (to staff and students) and ILL.
Periodicals	385 titles - not available for loan or ILL; will photocopy.
A/V Stock	200 audio-cassettes, 200 video-cassettes, 100 multimedia packs, 100 CD-ROMs - not available for loan or ILL.
Classification	Dewey 18th Edition (hoping to standardise to Dewey 20).
Computer Equipment	DYNIX Horizon system (Circulation, Cataloguing, OPAC currently - Acquisitions planned for August 1996) uses Institute network to run across 6 sites. Each site has stand-alone multimedia PC with CD-ROM; 30 PCs available; CD-ROM information service: titles taken: 5 papers (Times, Guardian, Independent, Daily Telegraph, Sunday Times), Selection of journals (Economist, New Scientist, etc.), Bookband, BNB, TES Bookfind, Reference titles.
Other Equipment	Microfiche reader (College Square East); Self-service photocopier in each site; Colour photocopier in Department Office.

243 BOOLE LIBRARY
UNIVERSITY COLLEGE CORK
Cork.
Tel: Cork (021) 902281
Fax: Cork (021) 273428
E-mail: library@ucc.ie

Librarian	John Fitzgerald
No. of Staff	87 (16 Professional, 71 Non-professional).

Departmental Libraries	MEDICAL LIBRARY, Cork University Hospital, Wilton, Cork; Tel: (021) 546400 ext. 2136/(021) 276871 ext. 2976, Fax: (021) 343688; (Niall McSweeney, Librarian).
Opening Hours	09.00 - 23.00 (Mon. - Fri.), 10.00 - 18.00 (Sat.). July to Sept.: 09.00 - 16.30 (Mon. - Fri.).
Special Collections	Friedlander; Senet; O'Riordin; Hawtin; Torna; St. Finbarre's Cathedral Library; Humour; Older printed books; Manuscripts.
Bookstock	600,000 volumes - except 4,000 reference, available for loan (to staff, students and registered external readers) and ILL.
Periodicals	3,000 titles - not available for loan or ILL; will photocopy.
A/V Stock	780 audio-cassettes, 41 compact disks, 47 CD-ROM, 913 video-cassettes - not available for loan or ILL.
Manuscripts	261 English mss., 176 Irish lamhscribhini - not available for loan.
Catalogue	On-line.
Classification	Dewey.
Computer Systems	DOBIS/LIBRIS Ver. 1.4, running on a dedicated IBM 9370 model 60; 46 dedicated terminals; Access to OPAC and to full system via the campus Ethernet; Network services (staff only); CD-ROM; Remote commercial databases; E-mail; HEANET; LANCASTER ILL system (Ver. 6.0); ISIS Serials Control system; LOGICRAFT CD Network; 47 CD-ROM titles; CD-ROM workstations (7 public access, 1 staff access).
Other Equipment	11 Microfiche readers; 3 Microfilm reader/printers (all public access); 1 Microfilm reader; 3 large display monitors for group viewing; 12 VHS & U-matic video-cassette players; 12 tape decks; 10 record players; 2 CD players; sound-slide projector; Photocopiers (14 public, 3 staff).

244 BURREN COLLEGE OF ART
Newtown Castle,
Ballyvaughan,
Co. Clare.
Tel: Clare (065) 77200
Fax: Clare (065) 77201
E-mail: burren@iol.ie

Librarian	Clare Kelly
No. of Staff	1 (Professional).
Opening Hours	09.30 - 17.30 (Mon. - Fri.).
Services Offered	ILLs; Reference; Photocopying; Printing.
Bookstock	1,500 volumes - 1,400 available for loan and ILL.
Periodicals	10 titles - not available for loan or ILL; will photocopy.
Other Materials	1,200 slides.
Catalogue	TinLib.
Classification	UDC.
Computer Equipment	2 PCs - Windows based; 1 CD-ROM; 1 Scanner - Photoshop; Modem; Printer.
Other Equipment	Photocopier.

245 CERT - STATE TOURISM TRAINING AGENCY
CERT House,
Amiens Street,
Dublin 1.
Tel: Dublin (01) 874 2555
Fax: Dublin (01) 874 2821
Telex: 90161 CERT EI

Librarian	Mary Penny
No. of Staff	2 (2 Professional).
Opening Hours	10.00 - 12.00, 14.00 - 16.00 (Mon. - Fri.).
Services Offered	Library service for staff of CERT; Reference library for public; Postal, telephone enquiries.
Bookstock	6,500 volumes - 6,200 available for loan (to staff) and ILL.
Periodicals	150 titles - not available for loan or ILL; will photocopy.
A/V Stock	150 audio-cassettes (mainly language

tapes), 170 video-cassettes - available for loan to staff only; not available for ILL.

Catalogue	Computerised using "Bookshelf" software.
Classification	UDC.
Computer Equipment	"Bookshelf" library system and accompanying hardware - Microcomputer version.
Other Equipment	Microfiche reader; Photocopier.

CHURCH OF IRELAND COLLEGE OF EDUCATION   246
96, Upper Rathmines Road,
Dublin 6.
Tel: Dublin (01) 491 0443
Fax: Dublin (01) 497 0878

Librarian	Valerie Coghlan
No. of Staff	4 (2 Professional, 2 Non-professional, 3 Part-time).
Opening Hours	Academic year: 10.00 - 13.00 (Mon. - Thur.), 15.00 - 18.00 (Tues. - Thurs.), 10.00 - 16.00 (Fri.), 19.00 - 21.30 (Mon. - Thurs.). Please check by telephone for out of term opening hours.
Services Offered	Library mainly available to CICE undergraduate students and postgraduates following a in-career development course attached to the college.
Special Collections	History of Irish Education; Children's Literature.
Subject Specialisation	Education.
Bookstock	27,000 volumes - 25,000 available for loan (to CICE students and in-career development students) and ILL (limited).
Periodicals	40 titles - restricted loan; not usually available for ILL; will photocopy.
A/V Stock	400 audio-cassettes, 50 compact disks - not available for loan or ILL; 300 video-cassettes - available for loan and limited ILL; 100 multimedia packs - available for loan (varies) not available for ILL.
Other Materials	2,000 Wall charts; 200 Slide packs; 100 Filmstrips; 100 Audio disks.

CHURCH OF IRELAND COLLEGE OF EDUCATION
continued

Catalogue	Automated: Softlink Alice; 2 OPACs.
Classification	Dewey.
Computer Equipment	CD-ROM; Internet terminal.
Other Equipment	1 Microform reader/printer; Photocopier; 2 Video recorders

247 CRAWFORD COLLEGE OF ART & DESIGN
Sharman Crawford Street,
Cork City.
Tel: Cork (021) 966777
Fax: Cork (021) 962267

Librarian	Patricia Keating
No. of Staff	1.5 (1 Professional, 1 Part-time).
Department	SLIDE LIBRARY (see above); (Madeleine Dunne, Librarian).
Branch Libraries	CORK SCHOOL OF MUSIC, Union Quay, Cork City; Tel: (021) 965583; (Aileen Farley, Librarian). CORK REGIONAL TECHNICAL COLLEGE, Rossa Avenue, Bishopstown, Cork; Tel: (021) 545222; (Derry Delaney, Librarian; Tadhg Coakley, Deputy).
Opening Hours	10.00 - 17.00 (Mon., Tues., Wed., Fri.), 14.00 - 20.00 (Thurs.).
Services Offered	Lending services; Reference facilities; Video and slide library; Photocopying; ILL.
Special Collections	Artists' Books; Art Books.
Bookstock	16,000 volumes - 15,000 available for loan (must be registered on CCAD Course) and ILL.
Periodicals	55 titles (15,000 issues in all) - not available for loan or ILL; will photocopy.
A/V Stock	87 video-cassettes - not available for loan or ILL.
Other Materials	30,000 Slides - reference only to other libraries.
Catalogue	Card Catalogue and Automated Catalogue.
Classification	Dewey.

Computer Equipment	Commencing automation: Using URICA information management programme; CD-ROMs: BNB, Whitakers, Baker & Taylor; Expect to buy Artsbibliographic Modern Shortly and LESH.
Other Equipment	Photocopier; Video monitor.

CURRICULUM DEVELOPMENT UNIT (CDVEC)   248
Sundrive Road,
Crumlin,
Dublin 12.
Tel: Dublin (01) 453 5487
Fax: Dublin (01) 453 7659

Librarian	Patricia Quigley
No. of Staff	1 (Professional).
Opening Hours	09.15 - 17.00 (Mon. - Fri.).
Services Offered	Library/Research service for City of Dublin VEC staff; Reference library for educational researchers; Postal/Telephone enquiries; Advice on School Librarianship; Translation (French-English); Proof-reading.
Special Collections	Curriculum studies (Post-primary); Development education; Political education; Lifeskills education; Adult education; Adult literacy; Environmental education.
Bookstock	10,000 volumes (approx.) - 9,500 available for loan (to CDVEC staff only) and ILL.
Periodicals	100 titles - not available for loan or ILL; will photocopy.
A/V Stock	10 CD-ROMs - not available for loan or ILL; 450 video-cassettes, 200 multimedia packs - available for loan to CDVEC staff only, not available for ILL.
Catalogue	Computerised.
Classification	DDC.
Computer Equipment	Hardware: DELL Pentium Multimedia PC; Hewlett Packard Deskjet 500 printer. Software: Cardbox Plus; Microsoft Office. Databases: Library catalogue; TES

248 CURRICULUM DEVELOPMENT UNIT (CDVEC) continued

	Bookfind. CD-ROMs: Encarta '95; Ancient Lands; Musical Instruments; Multimedia - Stravinsky & Beethoven.
Other Equipment	Photocopier

249 DEPARTMENT OF LIBRARY AND INFORMATION STUDIES
University College Dublin,
Belfield,
Dublin 4
Tel: Dublin (01) 706 7080
Fax: Dublin (01) 706 1161
E-mail: noreen.hayes@ucd.ie

Head of Department	Mary A. Burke, Ph.D.
No. of Staff	10 (6 Professional, 1 Non-professional) 10 Part-time.
Services Offered	Education and training for librarianship and information work; Research on theory and practice of library and information studies.

250 DUBLIN CITY UNIVERSITY LIBRARY
Dublin 9.
Tel: Dublin (01) 704 5212
Fax: Dublin (01) 704 5602
E-mail: infodesk@ccmail.dcu.ie
Telnet: library.dcu.ie Login: opac

Librarian	Dr. Alan MacDougall
No. of Staff	42 (14 Professional, 28 Non-professional) 21 Full-time, 21 Part-time.
Opening Hours	Term & Easter vacation: 08.30 - 22.00 (Mon. - Thurs.), 08.30 - 21.00 (Fri.), 09.30 - 17.00 (Sat.). Vacation: 08.30 - 21.00 (Mon. - Thurs.), 08.30 - 16.45 (Fri.).
Services Offered	Information/Reference service; Periodicals query service; Issue desk; User education; Information skills training; On-line searching; Services to the disabled; Photocopying; ILL.

Special Collections	EU Collection; Government Publications Collection; International and National Statistics Collection; Theses.
Subject Specialisation	Science, Business, Marketing, Languages and Communications.
Bookstock	135,500 volumes - 85,000 available for loan (to library members only) and ILL.
Periodicals	1,500 titles - not available for loan; available for ILL; will photocopy.
A/V Stock	500 audio-cassettes, 260 video-cassettes, 200 multimedia packs - available for loan and ILL; 20 compact disks - not available for loan or ILL.
Catalogue	DYNIX OPAC.
Classification	Dewey.
Computer Equipment	DYNIX integrated library system running on DEC system 5000 through Unix/Universe; Novell staff LAN; Novell student CD network; Lancaster ILL system; Library access system; 15 OPACs; 40 PCs (assorted models, including CD-ROM drives); 7 laser jet printers; 12 other printers; On-line databases: Dialog, ESA, STN and Itelis; Reuters and Datastream databases; 35 CD-ROM titles (11 networked).
Other Equipment	2 Microform reader/printer; Microfiche reader; 7 Rank Xerox photocopiers; 6 video-cassette recorders.

DUBLIN DIOCESAN LIBRARY 251
Clonliffe Road,
Dublin 3.
Tel: Dublin (01) 874 1680
Fax: Dublin (01) 836 8920

Librarian	Peter M. Folan
No. of Staff	5 (2 Professional, 3 Non-professional).
Opening Hours	Term: 10.30 - 21.30 (Mon. - Thurs.), 10.30 - 17.30 (Fri.), 10.30 - 13.00 (Sat.). Vacation: 10.30 - 17.30 (Mon. - Fri.).
Services Offered	Provides a centralised service to MATER

	DEI INSTITUTE OF EDUCATION and to HOLY CROSS COLLEGE, Clonliffe, Dublin 3.
Other Services	Photocopying; ILL; Second-hand book shop.
Special Collections	Archbishop McQuaid collection; Archbishop Ryan collection.
Bookstock	100,000 volumes - 60,000 (excluding reference stock and special collections) available for loan (to registered readers) and ILL.
Periodicals	750 titles (300 current, 450 ceased) - not available for loan or ILL; will photocopy.
Catalogue	Card Catalogue: Author, Classified and Subject Index
Classification	Dewey.
Other Equipment	Microfiche reader; 2 Microfilm Readers; 1 Self-service photocopier.

252   **DUBLIN INSTITUTE FOR ADVANCED STUDIES**
School of Celtic Studies,
10, Burlington Road,
Dublin 4.
Tel: Dublin (01) 668 0748
Fax: Dublin (01) 668 0561

Librarian	Siobhan Ní Laoire
No. of Staff	3 (3 Professional) 1 Part-time.
Services Offered	To School of Celtic Studies members, and research workers in specialised subject areas, by arrangement only.
Subject Specialisation	Celtic studies.
Bookstock	11,000 volumes - not available for loan; ILL by special arrangement only.
Periodicals	130 titles - not available for loan or ILL; photocopy by ILL to other libraries.
Other Materials	Microfilm
Catalogue	Computerised on Heritage; Card catalogue.
Classification	Dewey (modified).
Other Equipment	Microform reader/printer; Photocopier.

School of Cosmic Physics,
5, Merrion Square,
Dublin 2.
Tel: Dublin (01) 662 1333
Fax: Dublin (01) 662 1477
E-mail: ec@cp.dias.ie or ab@cp.dias.ie

Librarians	Anne Byrne (Geophysics); Eimhear Clifton (Cosmic Ray)
No. of Staff	2 (Non-professional).
Opening Hours	09.30 - 13.00, 14.00 - 17.30 (Mon. - Fri.). By appointment only.
Services Offered	Books not loaned; limited photocopying provided.
Subject Specialisation	Geology; Seismology; Palaeomagnetism and related subjects; Astronomy; Astrophysics; Nuclear physics.
Bookstock	5,000 volumes - not available for loan.
Periodicals	60 titles - not available for loan; both sections only oblige with photocopies University Libraries or individuals working in our respective fields.
Other Materials	Microfilm; Maps.
Catalogue	Author, Subject, Card and Computer index.
Classification	Own.

School of Theoretical Physics,
10, Burlington Road,
Dublin 4.
Tel: Dublin (01) 668 0748
Fax: Dublin (01) 668 0561
Telex: 31687
E-mail: goldsmit@stp.dias.ie

Librarian	Ann Goldsmith
No. of Staff	1 (Professional)
Opening Hours	10.00 - 16.30 (Mon. - Fri.).
Services Offered	Not willing to lend books; Photocopies supplied on request; On-line searching.

DUBLIN INSTITUTE FOR ADVANCED STUDIES continued

Special Collections	Small archival collection.
Subject Specialisation	Theoretical physics; Mathematics.
Bookstock	8,000 volumes - not available for loan or ILL.
Periodicals	300 titles (200 current, 100 non-current) - not available for loan, will photocopy.
Other Materials	Microforms.
Catalogue	Author; classified (Card).
Classification	Special (based on Dewey).
Computer Equipment	PC for administration only.
Other Equipment	Microform reader and reader/printer; Photocopier.

255   DUBLIN INSTITUTE OF TECHNOLOGY
Aungier Street,
Dublin 2.
Tel: Dublin (01) 402 3068
Fax: Dublin (01) 402 3003
E-mail: M.field@dit.ie
Telnet: ditlib.dit.ie

Librarian	Margaret Field
No. of Staff	8 (1 Professional, 3 Non-professional, 4 Part-time).
Opening Hours	Term: 10.00 - 21.00 (Mon. - Fri.), 10.00 - 13.00 (Sat.). Outside term: 10.00 - 17.15 (Mon. - Fri.).
Services Offered	To staff and students registered in the DIT: Reference; Research; Lending; Photocopying.
Subject Specialisation	Business studies; Commerce; Law.
Bookstock	28,000 volumes - 26,000 available for loan (to registered students and staff) and ILL.
Periodicals	410 titles - not available for loan, available for ILL; will photocopy.
A/V Stock	Small collection of audio-cassettes, video-cassettes and multimedia packs.
Catalogue	DYNIX.
Classification	Dewey.
Computer Equipment	Computers; DYNIX Library System; Lexis; Anbar; Fact Finder; FT McCarthy;

	ABI Inform; Humanities Index.
Other Equipment	Regma Microform reader/printer; 3
	Photocopiers; Scan jet printer.

DUBLIN INSTITUTE OF TECHNOLOGY 256
Bolton Street,
Dublin 1.
Tel: Dublin (01) 402 3681
Fax: Dublin (01) 402 3999
E-mail: pcahalane@dit.ie

Librarian	Peter Cahalane
No. of Staff	7 (3 Professional, 4 Non-professional).
Opening Hours	09.30 - 21.30 (Mon. - Thurs.), 09.30 - 17.30 (Fri.), 09.30 - 13.00 (Sat.). Final Term: 09.30 - 13.15, 14.00 - 17.00 (Sat.).
Services Offered	Lending stock; Journals; CD-ROM searching; Microfiche information systems; Photocopying; Slide viewers; Video players; ILL; Indexing and abstracting services.
Special Collections	Dissertations.
Subject Specialisation	Urban economics; Engineering; Architecture; Planning; Surveying; Printing.
Bookstock	40,000 volumes - 90% available for loan (to staff and students of the DIT) and ILL.
Periodicals	400 current titles - not available for loan or ILL; will photocopy.
A/V Stock	60 audio-cassettes, 250 video-cassettes - not available for loan or ILL.
Catalogue	OPAC (DYNIX library system).
Classification	Dewey.
Computer Equipment	DYNIX Library System: 5 OPACs and 5 system PCs; CD-ROM towers and network; 2 Multimedia PCs; CD-ROMs available: API on disc, Avery Index, Pina, Current Technology Index, ICONDA, Factfinder; Minitel.
Other Equipment	6 Microfiche readers; Microfiche printer; Microfilm reader; Microfilm reader; 6 Slide viewers; 5 VCRs; 3 Photocopiers.

DUBLIN INSTITUTE OF TECHNOLOGY
Cathal Brugha Street,
Dublin 1.
Tel: Dublin (01) 402 4423/402 4424/402 4361
Fax: Dublin (01) 402 4499
E-mail: ugavin@dit.ie
Telnet: library.dit.ie

Librarian	Ursula Gavin
No. of Staff	8 (2 Professional, 4 Non-professional, 2 Part-time).
Branch Library	RATHMINES HOUSE, 143-149, Lower Rathmines Road, Rathmines, Dublin 6; Tel: (01) 402 3461/402 3462, Fax: (01) 402 3499, E-mail: bgillespie@dit.ie; (Brian Gillespie, Librarian).
Opening Hours	10.00 - 21.00 (Mon. - Thurs.), 10.00 - 17.00 (Fri.), 10.00 - 13.00 (Sat. - Final term). Out of term: 10.00 - 17.00 (Mon. - Fri.). Rathmines House: same hours except 10.00 - 17.30 (Tues., Wed.).
Services Offered	Services to staff and students of the DIT; On-line searching on Dialog; Access to CD-ROMs; Access to Internet; Photocopying; ILL (some restrictions); Current contents; Reference.
Subject Specialisation	Catering; Tourism; Hotel Management; Environmental Health; Childcare (Rathmines House).
Bookstock	30,000 volumes - 25,000 available for loan (to staff and students) and ILL.
Periodicals	240 titles - not available for loan or ILL; will photocopy.
A/V Stock	100 audio-cassette packs - available for loan, not available for ILL; 250 video-cassettes - available for loan to staff only, not available for ILL; small quantity of multimedia packs - available for loan to staff only, not available for ILL.
Catalogue	DYNIX - OPAC.
Classification	Dewey.
Computer Equipment	DYNIX Library System; IBM PCs; Word; Excel systems processing; Database and

	Desk-top publishing; CD-ROMs: ABI Inform, Factfinder, Food Science and Technology Abstracts, Hospitality Index, Childdata*, ERIC*, Social Sciences Index*, Sociofile* (* in Rathmines House).
Other Equipment	Microform reader/printers; Photocopiers; TVs; Video players and recorders; Cassette players and recorders; Teletext.

DUBLIN INSTITUTE OF TECHNOLOGY 258
Chatham Row,
Dublin 2.
Tel: Dublin (01) 677 8820
Fax: Dublin (01) 677 8404
Telnet: ditlib.cc.dit.ie Login: opac

Librarian	Aoife O'Brien
No. of Staff	2 (1 Professional, 1 Non-professional).
Opening Hours	Term: 09.30 - 21.00 (Mon. - Thurs.), 09.30 - 17.30 (Fri.). Out of term: 09.30 - 13.00, 14.00 - 17.00 (Mon. - Fri.).
Services Offered	ILL (BLDSC) to staff and students only; Photocopier; Microform printing; Listening facilities; Video player; 3 Apple Macs (1 with music programs).
Special Collections	Opera Videos; Compact disks; Tapes; Records.
Subject Specialisation	Music.
Bookstock	c.5,000 volumes - 4,500 available for loan and ILL.
Periodicals	13 titles - not available for loan or ILL; will photocopy.
A/V Stock	150 audio-cassettes, 1,100 compact disks, 150 video-cassettes - available for loan to staff only, not available for ILL.
Catalogue	DYNIX.
Classification	DDC 20.
Computer Equipment	4 Siemens Nixdorf Pentiums with CD-ROM; 4 Apple Macs (2 with CD-ROM) (1 with Scanner); Microsoft Office; Finale; Cubase Score; Cubase Lite; Claire; Adobe Photoshop.

DUBLIN INSTITUTE OF TECHNOLOGY continued

Other Equipment — Microform reader/printer; Photocopier; TV/Video; 3 Audio-systems; 3 Keyboards.

259 DUBLIN INSTITUTE OF TECHNOLOGY
Kevin Street,
Dublin 8.
Tel: Dublin (01) 402 4894/402 4631 (voice-mail)
Fax: Dublin (01) 402 4999
E-mail: mdavis@dit.ie
Telnet: lib.dit.ie Login: opac

Librarian	Mary H. Davis, B.Sc. (Hons), Dip. Lib.
No. of Staff	5.5 (2 Professional, 3 Non-professional, 1 Part-time).
Opening Hours	Term: 09.30 - 21.00 (Mon. - Fri.), 09.30 - 12.45, 14.00 - 17.00 (Sat.). Vacation: 09.30 - 17.15 (Mon. - Fri.).
Services Offered	Limited access to: On-line databases searches: Dialog-Datastar/STN and Internet searching (Netscape); ILL; Photocopying.
Special Collections	Computer Science; Photography; Medical Physics.
Bookstock	42,000 volumes - 38,000 available for loan (to staff and students of DIT, and certain external readers) and ILL.
Periodicals	420 titles - not available for loan or ILL; will photocopy.
A/V Stock	30 audio-cassettes, 80 video-cassettes, 30 multimedia packs - available for loan but not available for ILL; 46 compact disks (11 databases) - not available for loan or ILL; 200 diskettes (to accompany texts).
Catalogue	DYNIX - OPAC.
Classification	DDC 20.
Computer Equipment	3 Pentiums (75mhz) with CD drive; 2 486s with 7-drive tower units; 7 386s for use with DYNIX system (4 OPACs); Internet access (Netscape) on 3 Pentiums, but access is restricted at the moment; Word-processing available on 5 of the above; HP Deskjet printers (510 or 660c) attached to 6

	of the above; Main CD-ROMs available: Medline, Inspec, Current Contents, Nature (full-text), BIP, Bookfind.
Other Equipment	1 Microfiche reader; 1 Reader/printer; 3 Photocopiers; TV & Video; Knogo Library Security System.

DUBLIN INSTITUTE OF TECHNOLOGY   **260**
40-45, Mountjoy Square,
Dublin 1.
Tel: Dublin (01) 402 4108
Fax: Dublin (01) 402 4299
E-mail: amcsweeny@dit.ie
Telnet: library.dit.ie Login: opac

Librarian	Ann McSweeney
No. of Staff	5.5 (1 Professional, 4 Non-professional, 2 Part-time).
Opening Hours	Term: 10.00 - 21.00 (Mon. - Thurs.), 10.00 - 17.00 (Fri., Sat.). Vacation: 10.00 - 17.00 (Mon. - Fri.).
Services Offered	Lending; Reference; Document Supply; ILL; CD-ROM databases; User education; Self service photocopying.
Subject Specialisation	Marketing; Art History; Design Studies.
Bookstock	28,000 volumes - 27,000 available for loan (to staff and students of DIT) and ILL (with some restrictions).
Periodicals	235 titles - not available for loan or ILL; will photocopy.
A/V Stock	50 compact disks, 25 video-cassettes, 12 multimedia packs - available for loan, not available for ILL.
Other Materials	7,000 Slides - available for loan, not available for ILL.
Catalogue	OPAC.
Classification	Dewey.
Computer Equipment	DYNIX Automated Library System; PCs; 4 CD-ROM workstations; 5 CD-ROM databases.
Other Equipment	Microform reader/printer; Microfiche reader; 2 Photocopiers; TV; Video-recorder; Slide viewer.

261   EARLSFORT TERRACE LIBRARY
University College Dublin,
Earlsfort Terrace,
Dublin 2.
Tel: Dublin (01) 706 7471
Fax: Dublin (01) 475 4568
Telnet: library.ucd.ie Login: opac

Librarian	Paul Murphy, (Sheila Murphy, Sub-Librarian).
No. of Staff	11 (4 Professional, 7 Non-professional, 6 Part-time).
Opening Hours	09.30 - 21.45 (Mon. - Fri.), 09.30 - 13.00 (Sat.).
Services Offered	The library is a branch of University College Dublin Library. Loans; ILL; Reference; Information; Networked CD-ROMs.
Bookstock	30,000 volumes - available for loan and ILL.
Periodicals	1000 current titles - not available for loan or ILL; will photocopy.
A/V Stock	20 compact disks, 30 video-cassettes - not available for loan or ILL.
Catalogue	On-line (1984 -), Card (- 1984)
Classification	Dewey (pre-1984 Engineering stock is UDC).
Computer Equipment	BLS integrated system; On-line hosts: Dialog, Datastar, ESA, Orbit; CD-ROMs: Medline, Psychlit, Current Contents, CAB Abstracts.
Other Equipment	2 Microform reader/printers; 2 Microform readers; 4 Photocopiers.

262   EDGEHILL THEOLOGICAL COLLEGE
9, Lennoxvale,
Belfast BT9 5BY.
Tel: Belfast (01232) 665870
Fax: Belfast (01232) 687204

Librarian	M. Gallagher
No. of Staff	1 (Non-professional).

Opening Hours	09.00 - 17.00 (Mon. - Fri.) excluding July and August.
Services Offered	ILL.
Special Collections	Coverdale Bible; Methodist Material.
Subject Specialisation	Methodism.
Bookstock	11,000 volumes - available for loan; not available for ILL.
Periodicals	12 titles - not available for loan or ILL, but will photocopy one article from any edition.
A/V Stock	15 audio-cassettes - available for loan, but not ILL; 5 video-cassettes - available for loan not ILL
Catalogue	Card; Computer.
Classification	Own.
Computer Equipment	1 486 PC; Catalogue operating on Microsoft Works.
Other Equipment	Photocopier.

EDUCATIONAL RESEARCH COLLEGE   **263**
St. Patrick's College,
Dublin 9.
Tel: Dublin (01) 837 3789
Fax: Dublin (01) 837 8997
E-mail: mary@erc.ie

Librarian	Mary Rohan
No. of Staff	2 Part-time.
Opening Hours	14.00 - 16.30 (Mon. - Fri.). Appointment necessary.
Services Offered	Access to periodicals and books.
Special Collections	Library has titles in Psychology, Education, Measurement and Statistics, and Evaluation.
Bookstock	15,000 volumes - generally not available for loan or ILL.
Periodicals	360 titles - not available for loan, but available for ILL; will photocopy.
Computer Equipment	ADLITE library software running on a LAN.
Other Equipment	Microform Reader/printer; Photocopier.

264 FREEMAN LIBRARY
Geography Department,
Trinity College,
Dublin 2.
Tel: Dublin (01) 608 1454
Fax: Dublin (01) 671 3397

Librarian	Richard Haworth
Opening Hours	09.00 - 13.00, 14.00 - 17.00 (Mon. - Fri.).
Services Offered	Photocopying.
Special Collections	Books and Papers of T.W. Freeman; Maps; Theses.
Subject Specialisation	Geography
Bookstock	4,000 volumes - available for loan to members of College only; ILL considered.
Periodicals	150 titles - not available for loan or ILL; will photocopy.
Other Materials	600 original theses - not available for loan.
Catalogue	Author (card).
Classification	Own.
Other Equipment	Photocopier.

265 FROEBEL COLLEGE OF EDUCATION
Sion Hill,
Blackrock,
Co. Dublin.
Tel: Dublin (01) 288 8520
Fax: Dublin (01) 288 8520

Librarian	Helen Delaney
No. of Staff	3 (1 Professional, 2 Part-time).
Opening Hours	09.30 - 17.30 (Mon., Thurs.), 09.00 - 20.30 (Tues.), 09.00 - 18.30 (Wed.), 09.00 - 16.00 (Fri.).
Services Offered	Loans; Reference; ILLs.
Subject Specialisation	Education.
Bookstock	11,000 volumes - available for loan and ILL.
Periodicals	22 titles - available for loan (to staff only) and ILL; will photocopy, within copyright law.
A/V Stock	Audio- and video-cassettes - available for

loan and ILL.

Catalogue	Computerised - ALICE.
Classification	Dewey.
Computer Equipment	3 PCs (Server, Client and Enquiry (with CD-ROM drive)); Laser printer; CD-ROMs; MS Word; MS Works.

GAMBLE LIBRARY 266
Union Theological College,
108, Botanic Avenue,
Belfast BT7 1JT.
Tel: Belfast (01232) 325374
Fax: Belfast (01232) 325397

Librarian	Doreen E. McDowell
No. of Staff	1 (Professional).
Opening Hours	Term: 10.00 - 16.00 (Mon. - Fri.).
Services Offered	To theological students, Ministers and members (membership on payment of fee).
Special Collections	Rare theological books.
Subject Specialisation	Theology.
Bookstock	50,000 volumes - all except rare books and reference books available for loan to members, not available for ILL.
Periodicals	200 titles - not available for loan or ILL; will photocopy.
A/V Stock	31 video-cassettes - available for loan; not available for ILL.
Catalogue	Author, Subject Card catalogue.
Classification	Own.
Other Equipment	Microform reader; Photocopier.

GARDA COLLEGE LIBRARY 267
Garda College,
Templemore,
Co. Tipperary.
Tel: Templemore (0504) 31522 ext. 2109
Fax: Templemore (0504) 32235
E-mail: tom.deegan@login.IEunet.ie

Librarian	Tom Deegan

267 GARDA COLLEGE LIBRARY continued

No. of Staff	2 (1 Professional, 1 Non-professional).
Opening Hours	09.00 - 13.00, 14.00 - 17.00, 18.00 - 21.00.
Services Offered	Loans and Reference (to students and staff); ILLs (staff); Card-operated photocopying machine; Information Enquiry Service to members not on college premises; Newspaper cuttings file from "Irish Independent"; INIS "Newspaper on Disk" (to staff).
Special Collections	Garda Commissioner's Annual Reports; Garda Siochana Information Annual; Police & Constabulary Almanac (Annual); Garda College Projects; Audit Commission Police Papers; CSPO papers; Cambridge University Institute of Criminology papers.
Bookstock	c.18,000 volumes - c.14,000 available for loan and ILL.
Periodicals	235 titles - not available for loan or ILL; will photocopy.
A/V Stock	5 audio-cassettes, 2 video-cassettes, 8 multimedia packs - not available for loan or ILL.
Other Materials	Prints for "Cops 'n' Robbers" type movies - not available for loan.
Catalogue	CALM CDS Ltd.
Classification	DDC 20.
Computer Equipment	CALM Library Catalogue; Word 6; GS Correspondence Register; CD-ROM; INIS.
Other Equipment	Microfiche Reader; Photocopier; OPAC (1 Terminal); 3 Video players.

**268 INFORMATION MANAGEMENT DIVISION
SCHOOL OF FINANCE AND INFORMATION,
The Queen's University of Belfast,
University Road,
Belfast BT7 1NN.
Tel: Belfast (01232) 245133 ext. 3621
Fax: Belfast (01232) 248372
E-mail: a.davies@qub.ac.uk**

| Services Offered | B.Sc. Information Management; B.Sc. Management; Diploma/M.Sc. in Information Management; Research for M.Phil. and Ph.D. |

JAMES HARDIMAN LIBRARY 269
University College,
Galway.
Tel: Galway (091) 524411
Fax: Galway (091) 522394
E-mail: marie.reddan@ucg.ie
Telnet: library.ucg.ie
Web site: Http://www.library.ucg.ie

Librarian	Marie Reddan
No. of Staff	53.96 Full Time Equivalents (14 Professional, 31 Non-professional, 27 Part-time).
Departmental Libraries	MEDICAL LIBRARY, Clinical Science Institute, University College Hospital, Galway; Tel: (091) 524222, ext. 2791, Fax: (091) 750517, E-mail: tim.colins@ucg.ie; (Tim Collins, Librarian). NURSING LIBRARY, University College Hospital, Galway; Tel: (091) 524222, Fax: (091) 527214, E-mail: marie.boran@ucg.ie; (Marie Boran, Librarian).
Opening Hours	09.00 - 22.00 (Mon. - Fri.), 09.00 - 13.00 (Sat.), with seasonal variations.
Services Offered	General Lending; Reference; CD-ROMs (networked); On-line Searching; Photocopying; ILL.
Special Collections	Main Collections (Books): Gregory Collection; Delargy Collection; Cairnes Collection. Main Collections (Manuscripts): Galway Civic Records 1485-1818, 1836-1839; Eyre Deeds; Hyde Mss.; Stiofan Bairéad Papers; Eoghan Ó Tuairisc Papers; Wilson-Lynch (Co. Clare) Estate papers, and collections of estate and

other papers relating to the West of Ireland; Druid and Taibhdhearc Theatre Archives; Ritchie-Pickow Archive (photographs and sound recordings of life and culture in 1950s Ireland).

Bookstock
247,571 volumes - c.110,000 available for loan and ILL.

Periodicals
1,927 titles - not available for loan, photocopies only available for ILL; will photocopy.

A/V Stock
800 audio-cassettes, 40 compact disks, 1,200 VHS standard video-cassettes, 80 multimedia packs - not available for loan or ILL.

Catalogue
OPAC and Card Catalogue.

Classification
Dewey.

Computer Equipment
Dec 5900; DYNIX software; In-house database on CD, external access; Access via HEANET to all external hosts and a variety of office software (Word, Excel, Powerpoint, etc.). A varied collection of CD-ROMs such as Medline, Science Citation Index, Social Science Citation Index, Arts and Humanities Citation Index, Current Contents, ABI, CITIS and MLA.

Other Equipment
Microform readers/printers; Microfilm readers; Microfiche readers; Micro-opaque reader; Kodak RD2 Microfilming unit; Carousel slide projectors; Sony TC FX210 Audio-cassette deck and headphones; Sanyo VTC-NX100 Video-cassette decks and headphones; Sony Trinitron Monitors; Sanyo TC190 Portable audio-cassette players; Photocopiers.

270 JESUIT LIBRARY
Milltown Park,
Dublin 6.
Tel: Dublin (01) 269 8411
Fax: Dublin (01) 260 0371
E-mail: bridjlmp@iol.ie

Librarian	Fergus O'Donoghue, S.J.
No. of Staff	5 (2 Professional, 3 Non-professional).
Opening Hours	All day to staff and students of the Milltown Institute. Others by arrangement.
Services Offered	Service to staff and students of the Milltown Institute and members of the Society of Jesus.
Special Collections	Materials relating to Ireland; Material relating to the Society of Jesus.
Subject Specialisation	Religion and philosophy.
Bookstock	100,000 volumes - 25,000 available for loan (to staff and students of the Milltown Institute); not available for ILL.
Periodicals	154 titles - not available for loan, ILL or photocopying.
Catalogue	Card; On-line catalogue from mid 1992.
Classification	Library of Congress.
Computer Equipment	1 CD-ROM - Cetedoc Library of Christian Latin texts; Gateway 2000 PS-60 with triple CD-ROM drive.

THE KIMMAGE MISSION INSTITUTE   271
Kimmage Manor,
Dublin 12.
Tel: Dublin (01) 455 7511/456 0057
Fax: Dublin (01) 455 7367

Librarian	James McDonnell
No. of Staff	3 (1 Professional, 3 Non-professional).
Opening Hours	09.30 - 17.00 (Mon. - Fri.) each semester.
Services Offered	Usual library services for faculty staff and students.
Bookstock	13,500 volumes - available for loan to residents only and by special arrangement to non-resident students of the faculty.
Periodicals	88 titles - not available for loan or ILL; will photocopy.
Catalogue	Computerised database.
Classification	Modified Dewey Decimal Classification.
Computer Equipment	2 Goldstar GT212 PCs, 30Mb HD, 320Kb RAM, 2 floppy disc drives (3.5" and 5.25"), Goldstar Colour Monitor 1425; 1

271 THE KIMMAGE MISSION INSTITUTE continued

	Viglen Plus PC incorporating 30Mb HD, 5.25" FD drive, 640Kb total memory, 640Kb base memory, monochrome monitor; Viglen 486 Pentium, 520 Mb HD, colour monitor, 1B 600 inkjet printer; Microsoft Office/Works; Word-processing - WordPerfect 5.1; Database - Cardbox Plus.
Other Equipment	1 Sharp SF 8570 Photocopier.

272 THE KING'S HOSPITAL HARDEN LIBRARY
The King's Hospital,
Palmerstown,
Dublin 20.
Tel: Dublin (01) 626 5933 ext. 245
Fax: Dublin (01) 626 5933
E-mail: kingshos@iol.ie

Librarian	Valerie Bond
No. of Staff	2 (1 Professional, 1 Non-professional).
Opening Hours	11.15 - 11.30, 13.00 - 14.00, 15.30 - 17.30.
Services Offered	School library and resource centre; Careers information centre; Computer access to CD-ROM, ECCTIS +, QUALIFAX, GAIRM, Internet (restricted access).
Special Collections	Careers and 3rd level education information.
Bookstock	6,000 volumes (approx.) - available for loan and ILL.
Periodicals	22 titles - available for loan and ILL.
A/V Stock	4 compact disks, 4 multimedia packs - not available for loan or ILL; 44 video-cassettes - available for loan.
Catalogue	Card, changing to ALICE software system.
Classification	Dewey.
Computer Equipment	Gateway 2000 PC with CD-ROM drive; 1 Samsung and modem; 1 other PC; ALICE database software.
Other Equipment	Photocopier; 2 Printers.

Henrietta Street,
Dublin 1.
Tel: Dublin (01) 874 7134
Fax: Dublin (01) 872 6048

Librarian	Jonathan N. Armstrong
No. of Staff	4 (2 Professional, 2 Non-professional).
Opening Hours	14.00 - 18.00 (Mon.), 11.00 - 18.00 (Tues.- Fri.), 10.00 - 13.00 (Sat.). Academic year: 14.30 - 18.00 (Mon.), 11.00 - 21.00 (Tues. - Thurs.), 11.00 - 18.00 (Fri.), 10.00 - 13.00 (Sat.). Library closed in July for annual vacation.
Services Offered	Reading room; Microfiche reading and printing; Computer database searching and printing; Photocopying.
Special Collections	Pamphlets (7,000 (approx.) dating from the 17th to the 19th centuries); Irish language manuscripts (15th to 19th centuries); Irish Appeals to the House of Lords; Private paper collection of John Patrick Prendergast (1808-1893); United States law materials.
Subject Specialisation	Law.
Bookstock	120,000 volumes (approx.) - Books printed after 1915 only are available for loan to Benchers of King's Inns or persons authorised by Benchers only, not available for ILL.
Periodicals	116 current titles (approx.) - available for loan to Benchers of King's Inns or to persons authorised by Benchers; not available for ILL; will photocopy if items are available only in King's Inns, and subject to age and condition.
Manuscripts	160 (approx.) excluding archival materials - not available for loan.
Catalogue	Card: Author and Subject. Guard book catalogues (author only) for earlier works.
Classification	Own.
Computer Equipment	386A PC with Microsoft Windows 3.0 and the Concord database from Textmaster

containing the judgements index of the Law Library (JILL) and an in-house database indexing Irish Legal Journals.

Other Equipment   Microfiche reader/printer; 2 Photocopiers.

274 **LIMAVADY COLLEGE OF FURTHER EDUCATION**
Main Street,
Limavady,
Co. Londonderry BT49 0EX.
Tel: Limavady (015047) 62334
Fax: Limavady (015047) 22229

Librarian	Jonathan Moore
No. of Staff	4 (1 Professional, 1 Non-professional, 2 Part-time).
Opening Hours	09.00 - 17.00, 19.00 - 21.00 (Mon.), 09.00 - 17.00 (Tues.), 09.00 - 17.00 (Wed. - Fri.).
Services Offered	Booklending; Reference; Guidance/Advice for students; Instruction on use of CD-ROM; Binding of assignments, etc.
Bookstock	2,500 volumes - available for loan to students and staff of college.
Periodicals	30 titles - not available for loan or ILL; will photocopy.
A/V Stock	8 compact disks - not available for loan or ILL; Video-cassettes - available for loan but not ILL.
Catalogue	Card
Classification	Dewey.
Computer Equipment	IPC - Microsoft Windows; CD-ROMs: Times/Sunday Times 1994, 1995; Encarta Encyclopaedia; Social Trends; Microsoft Bookshelf; Microsoft Art Gallery; Microsoft Ancient Lands.
Other Equipment	Printer with PC; Photocopier; Binding Machine.

LSB COLLEGE
6-9, Balfe Street,
Dublin 2.
Tel: Dublin (01) 6794844
Fax: Dublin (01) 679 4205

Librarian	Ritamary Bolton
No. of Staff	2 (1 Professional, 1 Non-professional).
Opening Hours	Term: 09.30 - 20.30 (Mon. - Thurs.), 09.30 - 17.30 (Fri.), 09.30 - 13.30 (Sat.). Outside term: 09.00 - 17.00.
Services Offered	To students and staff of college: Reading room; Induction for students; Current awareness for staff; ILL; General Circulations and Reference service; Internet connection pending.
Special Collections	Psycho-Analysis; Tourism.
Bookstock	6,500 volumes - 6,000 available for loan (to students and staff only) and ILL (apply to Librarian).
Periodicals	90 titles - not available for loan or ILL; will photocopy.
A/V Stock	500 audio-cassettes - not available for loan or ILL.
Catalogue	Author/title.
Classification	DDC 20.
Computer Equipment	PC; Windows; Printer; Computerised library system under consideration.

MARY IMMACULATE COLLEGE
South Circular Road,
Limerick.
Tel: Limerick (061) 314588
Fax: Limerick (061) 313632

Librarian	John Power
No. of Staff	8 (2 Professional, 6 Non-professional).
Opening Hours	Term: 09.00 - 22.00 (Mon. - Fri.), 14.00 - 18.00 (Sat.). Outside term: 09.00 - 17.00 (Mon. - Fri.).
Services Offered	Reference; Research; Lending; Periodicals; A/V; Children's Library; Primary School

Textbook Library; ILL; Photocopying. Above services to staff and students of the College and University of Limerick.

Special Collections — Education, Teaching Practice Library - 16,000 volumes; Primary School Textbook Library - 15,000 volumes.

Subject Specialisation — Education.

Bookstock — 180,000 volumes - 120,000 available for loan (to College and UL staff and students) and ILL.

Periodicals — 750 current titles - not available for loan or ILL; will photocopy.

A/V Stock — 2,500 audio-cassettes, 1,300 video-cassettes, 2,500 multimedia packs - available for loan to College and UL staff and students, but not available for ILL; 100 compact disks - not available for loan or ILL.

Catalogue — URICA/DYNIX Computerised library system.

Classification — Dewey.

Computer Equipment — URICA/DYNIX; 6 PCs; 7 OPACs.

Other Equipment — 2 Microform reader/printers, 5 Microfiche readers; 3 Microfilm readers; 3 Audio-cassette players, 1 Cassette copier, 1 Record/cassette copier, 6 Slide viewers, 6 Filmstrip viewers, 2 Radio cassette players; 2 Video players/recorders.

277 MULTI-DISCIPLINARY EDUCATION CENTRE
Altnagelvin Area Hospital,
Glenshane Road,
Londonderry BT47 1JB.
Tel: Londonderry (01504) 45171 ext. 3725
Fax: Londonderry (01504) 49334

Librarian — Frank A. O'Deorain

No. of Staff — 6 (2 Professional, 4 Non-professional, 1 Full-time, 3 Part-time).

Branch Libraries — An Outlier of the Northern Ireland Health and Social Services Library based at

	Queen's University Medical Library.
Opening Hours	09.00 - 17.30 (Mon.), 09.00 - 21.30 (Tues. - Thurs.), 09.00 - 17.00 (Fri.).
Special Collections	Post-graduate Medical; Nursing; Social Work and Community Care; Health Service Management.
Bookstock	7,500 volumes - 7,250 (approx.) available for loan to nursing students, tutors, Western Board employees; available to other libraries only if part of NI DHSS Library system.
Periodicals	126 titles - not available for loan or ILL; will photocopy.
A/V Stock	10 audio-cassettes, 70 video-cassettes, 30 multimedia packs - available for loan and ILL (only if in NI DHSS library system).
Catalogue	Currently a subset of Queen's University's BLCMP Microfiche. Local "Bookshelf" OPAC.
Classification	Library of Congress.
Computer Equipment	"Bookshelf" library catalogue and issue system; 5 terminals, 3 for OPACs; Cardbox - Plus Database for periodicals subscriptions; Medline; CINAHL; Oxford Text Book of Medicine on CD-ROM; On-line searching on Database Hosts: DATASTAR; Dialog; Blaise-line.
Other Equipment	Microfiche readers for catalogue; Video cassette recorder; TV for viewing VHS videos; Photocopier: £1 for 20 page token.

NATIONAL COLLEGE OF ART AND DESIGN 278
100, Thomas Street,
Dublin 8.
Tel: Dublin (01) 671 1377
Fax: Dublin (01) 671 1748
E-mail: murphye@ncad.ie

Librarian	Edward Murphy
No. of Staff	7 (2 Professional, 5 Non-professional).
Opening Hours	09.30 - 21.00 (Mon. - Thurs.), 09.30 - 17.00 (Fri.).

NATIONAL COLLEGE OF ART AND DESIGN continued

Services Offered	ILL; Photocopying including colour; Internet access; CD-ROM bibliographic access; ArtHouse access; Language Centre with audio, video and satellite access; External reader scheme.
Special Collections	Evie Hone Collection; College records; Student theses; Archive of material relating to Irish Art and Design, with particular emphasis on the 20th century.
Bookstock	46,000 volumes - majority available for loan (to staff, students, external scheme users) and ILL.
Periodicals	300 titles - some available for loan to staff only, not available for ILL; will photocopy.
A/V Stock	300 audio-cassettes, 300 video-cassettes - available for loan to staff only, not available for ILL; compact disks - not available for loan or ILL.
Catalogue	OCLC Author; Title; Subject.
Classification	Dewey (modified).
Computer Equipment	PCs for access to Internet, ArtHouse Database and CD-ROM databases.
Other Equipment	Microfiche readers; 3 Photocopiers (1 colour with ability to process Mac disks); Audio and video equipment for Language Centre.

279 NATIONAL COLLEGE OF INDUSTRIAL RELATIONS
Sandford Road,
Ranelagh,
Dublin 6.
Tel: Dublin (01) 497 2917
Fax: Dublin (01) 497 2200
E-mail: sosulliv@college.ncir.ie

Librarian	Sinead O'Sullivan
No. of Staff	5 (1 Professional, 4 Non-professional, 3 Part-time).
Opening Hours	Term: 09.30 - 21.00 (Mon. - Thurs.), 09.30 - 17.00 (Fri.), 09.30 - 13.00 (Sat.).

	Subject to variation during college holidays.
Services Offered	Lending service to staff, students and external members. Reference service to others on application.
Special Collections	Final year student theses - reference only; Labour Court recommendations.
Subject Specialisation	Industrial relations; Personnel management; Sociology of work.
Bookstock	16,000 volumes - 95% available for loan to students, staff and other members of the College; ILL by arrangement.
Periodicals	120 titles - not available for loan or ILL; will photocopy.
A/V Stock	100 compact disks - available on loan to staff only, not for ILL; 60 video-cassettes - some available for loan, but not ILL.
Catalogue	Computerised - InMagic Plus.
Classification	Dewey 20.
Computer Equipment	Software: InMagic Plus networked version; 2 OPACs on site and available throughout the organisation. CD-ROM: ABI-Inform, BookBank, TES Bookfind, ERIC, Accountancy, Institute of Management Databases Plus, McCarthy on CD-ROM; On-line: Dialog, BLAISE; Hardware: Dell 90t Pentium 90mhz 8MB RAM, ULTRA Pentium 100mhz 8MB RAM with CD-ROM (Pioneer DRW-624X 6 Disc interchangeable), WANG 461/255C 486 8MB RAM with CD-ROM (Panasonic Dualspeed), AST 3/25s 386 4MB RAM & Toshiba External SCS1 CD-ROM.
Other Equipment	Photocopiers;3M Security system Model.

NEWRY COLLEGE OF FURTHER & HIGHER EDUCATION   **280**
Patrick Street,
Newry,
Co. Down BT35 8DN.
Tel: Newry (01693) 61071
Fax: Newry (01693) 60684
E-mail: newryfurthhghedu@campus.bt.com

280 NEWRY COLLEGE OF FURTHER & HIGHER EDUCATION
continued

Librarian	Ursula McShane
No. of Staff	4 (1 Professional, 3 Non-professional, 2 Part-time).
Opening Hours	09.00 - 19.00 (Mon. - Fri.).
Services Offered	Split-site campus with a range of book covering most GNVQ courses, several HND courses; Small journal collection; Several CD-ROMs; Reference.
Bookstock	12,000 volumes - available for loan (staff and students at college) and ILL (restricted).
Periodicals	42 titles - not available for loan or ILL; will photocopy.
A/V Stock	76 audio-cassettes, 15 compact disks - not available for loan, or ILL; 175 video-cassettes - available for loan, but not ILL.
Catalogue	Computerised - Bookshelf OPACs.
Classification	Dewey.
Computer Equipment	Cataloguing, Circulation, OPAC system called Bookshelf: 7 terminals; 3 CD-ROMs; RM PC 466 Accelerater Multimedia.
Other Equipment	2 Photocopiers.

281 NORTHERN IRELAND HOTEL AND CATERING COLLEGE
Ballywillan Road,
Portrush,
Co. Antrim BT56 8JL.
Tel: Portrush (01265) 823768
Fax: Portrush (01265) 824733

Librarian	Helen M. White
No. of Staff	2 (1 Non-professional, 1 Part-time).
Opening Hours	09.00 - 17.30, 18.00 - 20.00 (Mon.), 09.00 - 17.30, 18.00 - 21.00 (Tues., Wed., Thurs.), 09.00 - 16.15 (Fri.).
Bookstock	2,954 volumes - 2,823 available for loan, not available for ILL.
Periodicals	70 titles - not available for loan or ILL; will photocopy.

A/V Stock	10 audio-cassettes, 38 video-cassettes, 10 multimedia packs - available for loan, but not ILL; 3 compact disks - not available for loan or ILL.
Catalogue	Classified (card), Computerised - Heritage.
Classification	Dewey.
Computer Equipment	CD-ROM reader: Times 1995,1996, WHATT, Food Safety Disk; Heritage Library Management System.
Other Equipment	Photocopier.

NORTH WEST INSTITUTE OF FURTHER & HIGHER EDUCATION

**Strand Road,
Londonderry BT48 7BY.
Tel: Londonderry (01504) 266711
Fax: Londonderry (01504) 260520
E-mail: lib@nwifhe.demon.co.uk**

Librarian	Madeleine Coyle
No. of Staff	4 (1 Professional, 2 Non-professional, 1 Part-time).
Branches	STRABANE CAMPUS, Derry Road, Strabane, Co. Tyrone; Tel: (01504) 382317, Fax: (01504) 383501; (Evelyn Canavan, Library Assistant).
Opening Hours	Term: 09.00 - 21.00 (Mon. - Thurs.), 09.00 - 16.30 (Fri.). Vacation: 09.00 - 13.00, 14.00 - 17.00 (Mon. - Thurs.), 09.00 - 13.00, 14.00 - 16.30 (Fri.).
Services Offered	Reference and Lending service to the staff and students of the Institute; Access to Word-processing, Spreadsheets, Desk-top Publishing and CD-ROM through open access PCs and laser printer.
Bookstock	13,760 volumes - 12,140 available for loan to staff, full-time and part-time students; occasionally available for ILL.
Periodicals	160 titles - not available for loan or ILL; will photocopy.
A/V Stock	42 compact disks - not available for loan or ILL; 70 video-cassettes - available for loan

282 NORTH WEST INSTITUTE OF FURTHER & HIGHER EDUCATION continued
to staff only; not available for ILL.

Catalogue	Computer-held catalogue.
Classification	Dewey Decimal.
Computer Equipment	OPUS 486 with CD-ROM players (4); Microsoft Office; Alous Pagemaker; variety of CD-ROM titles; OPUS 486 with tapestreamer; Library Management System - Heritage; TES Bookfind, Whitaker Bookbank.
Other Equipment	Hewlett-Packard 4m laser printer; Canon 1550 photocopier; Video presentation unit; Interactive Video unit Thorn 604.

283 QUEEN'S UNIVERSITY OF BELFAST
Main Library,
University Road,
Belfast BT7 1NN.
Tel: Belfast (01232) 335020
Fax: Belfast (01232) 323340
E-mail: n.russell@qub.ac.uk
Telnet: lib.qub.ac.uk

Librarian	N. Russell
No. of Staff	36 Professional; 38 Non-professional; 27 clerical and support.
Departmental Libraries.	AGRICULTURE LIBRARY, Newforge Lane, Belfast 9; Tel: (01232) 255226; MEDICAL LIBRARY, Institute of Clinical Science, Grosvenor Road, Belfast 12; Tel: (01232) 322043. SCIENCE LIBRARY, 19, Chlorine Gardens, Lennoxvale, Belfast BT9 5EQ; Tel: (01232) 335441, Fax: (01232) 382636, E-mail: science.library@qub.ac.uk; (Sheila Landy, Librarian). VETERINARY SCIENCE LIBRARY, Veterinary Research Laboratories, Stormont, Belfast BT4 3SD; Tel: (01232) 525622.
Opening Hours	09.00 - 22.00 (Academic year); 09.00 - 17.00 (Vacation).

Services Offered	Services to staff and students of the University; Associate membership scheme; Database searches; Photocopying; ILL.
Special Collections	Antrim Presbytery; Hibernica; Simms (early material of Irish interest published abroad); Thomas Percy (early English and Romance literature); Thomas Moore; Somerville & Ross papers; Hamilton Harty (music); McDouall (Sanskrit and Indo European); Sir Robert Hart; Queen's University Doctoral Theses; Architecture and Planning Irish database and slide collection.
Subject Specialisation	Humanities; Law; Economic and Social Sciences; Education; Science; Medicine; Agriculture; Engineering.
Bookstock	940,000 volumes - 900,000 available for loan and ILL.
Periodicals	6,000 titles - will photocopy.
A/V Stock	Video-cassettes, Multimedia packs.
Manuscripts	5,000 - not available for loan, but available for exhibitions.
Catalogue	All stock listed on on-line catalogue.
Classification	Library of Congress.
Computer Equipment	Campus and SuperJANET network; BLCMP BLS system; CD-ROM; BIDS; OCLC First Search.
Other Equipment	Microform readers/printers; Video players; Archival copier; Book detection systems; Admission monitoring system; Fax; PCs; Spine-labelling equipment; printers.

REGIONAL TECHNICAL COLLEGE - ATHLONE   284

Dublin Road,
Athlone,
Co. Westmeath.
Tel: Athlone (0902) 72647
Fax: Athlone (0902) 24417

Librarian	Jo Corkery
No. of Staff	6 (2 Professional, 4 Non-professional).
Opening Hours	Term: 09.15 - 21.45 (Mon. - Thurs.),

09.15 - 17.00 (Fri.), 09.15 - 13.00, 14.00 - 17.00 (Sat.). Vacation: 09.15 - 13.00, 14.00 - 17.00 (Mon. - Fri.).

Services Offered	On-line literature searching; ILL; CD-ROM Instruction.
Special Collections	Student Projects; College Exam Papers; Current Awareness files; Local Company Information.
Subject Specialisation	Polymer Science; Business studies; Science; Mineral science; Engineering.
Bookstock	22,000 volumes (approx.) - 21,600 available for loan and ILL.
Periodicals	150 titles - not available for loan or ILL; will photocopy.
A/V Stock	14 compact disks - not available for loan or ILL; 300 video-cassettes (Computing, Business Studies, Management) - available for loan to staff only, not available for ILL.
Catalogue	Accessible on OPAC - author, title, subject, keyword searches.
Classification	Dewey Decimal 20th edition.
Computer Equipment	URICA Library System; DIALOG and ESA-IRS; Minitel; On-line access to BLDSC via ARTTEL; CD-ROMs: Bookbank, ABI-Inform, McCarthy Disc, Social Work Abstracts, Chemistry Citation Index, Current Contents - Life Sciences, RAPRA Abstracts, Inside Information, Business Eye, WHATT (Hotel & Catering Information), Computer Select.
Other Equipment	Microfiche Reader; 2 Photocopiers.

285   **REGIONAL TECHNICAL COLLEGE - CARLOW**
Kilkenny Road,
Carlow.
Tel: Carlow (0503) 70400
Fax: Carlow (0503) 43787
E-mail: huttonl@novell1.rtc-carlow.ie

Librarian	Elizabeth Hutton

No. of Staff	6 (1 Professional, 5 Non-professional).
Opening Hours	09.00 - 22.00 (Mon. - Fri.), 09.00 - 13.00 (Sat.).
Services Offered	Library service to staff and students of the College; ILL and photocopying to outside organisations.
Special Collections	Tyndall Collection.
Subject Specialisation	Engineering; Science; Business studies.
Bookstock	22,000 volumes - 20,000 (approx.) available for loan and ILL (if title is not in heavy demand).
Periodicals	150 titles - not available for loan or ILL; will photocopy.
A/V Stock	300 video-cassettes (approx.).
Catalogue	On-line (In-house system)
Classification	Dewey, 18th, 19th and 20th editions.
Computer Equipment	Pentium Server and 6 workstations; In-house software for catalogue and circulation control; 2 printers; standalone PC and CD-ROM drive; ABI Inform; Medline; Biotechnology Abstracts; BNB; Bookbank.
Other Equipment	Microfilm reader/printer; 2 Microfiche readers; 2 Photocopiers.

REGIONAL TECHNICAL COLLEGE - CORK   286

Rossa Avenue,
Bishopstown,
Cork.
Tel: Cork (021) 545222
Fax: Cork (021) 545343
E-mail: ddelaney@rtc-cork.ie
Telnet: 157.190.241.10 Login: opac Password: opac123

Librarian	Derry Delaney
No. of Staff	3 Professional, 6 Non-professional, 5 Part-time, 2.25 FTE.
Departmental Libraries	CRAWFORD COLLEGE OF ART AND DESIGN, Sharman Crawford Street, Cork; Tel: (021) 966777, Fax: (021) 962267. (Patricia Keating, Librarian). CORK SCHOOL OF MUSIC, Union Quay, Cork;

Tel: (021) 270076, Fax: (021) 276595.

Opening Hours	09.15 - 21.45 (Mon. - Fri.); 09.15 - 17.00 (Sat.).
Services Offered	Loans to staff and students - others by arrangement; Photocopying; ILL; Networked PCs; Internet access.
Special Collections	Barbour Microfiles; Health and Safety; Building, Technical; Building, Product.
Bookstock	50,000 volumes - 45,000 available for loan (to staff and students - others by arrangement) and ILL.
Periodicals	560 titles - not available for loan or ILL; will photocopy.
A/V Stock	1,000 audio-cassettes (including records), 600 compact disks, 100 multimedia packs (mainly books and disks) - available for loan, not ILL; 105 video-cassettes - not available for loan or ILL.
Catalogue	Computerised catalogue at Bishopstown Campus. Art & Music catalogue records not yet converted from card.
Classification	Dewey 20.
Computer Equipment	Motorola XP1811; URICA (32 user license); 53 Networked PCs - 20 with integral CD-ROM drives; 7 Bay CD-ROM Towers; 3 Laser printers; 2 Scanners; 2 Dot Matrix printers; CD-ROMs: BNB, Inside Information, and a number of specialist bibliographical CD-ROMs.
Other Equipment	2 Microform reader/printers; 4 Photocopiers; 1 Apple Mac with laser printer (for use of those with Mac but no printer).

287 **REGIONAL TECHNICAL COLLEGE - DUNDALK**
Dublin Road,
Dundalk,
Co. Louth.
Tel: Dundalk (042) 70312
Fax: Dundalk (042) 38313
E-mail: queries@rtclib2.rtc-dundalk.ie

Librarian	Ann Cleary
No. of Staff	10 (3 Professional, 4 Non-professional, 3 Part-time).
Branches	ACQUISITIONS (see above); E-mail: frances@rtclib2.rtc-dundalk.ie; (Frances McKenna, Librarian). CATALOGUING (see above); E-mail: honora@rtclib2.rtc-dundalk.ie; (H. Faul, Librarian). EURO INFO POINT (see above); Tel: (042) 70492, Fax: (042) 38313, E-mail: eu-info@rtclib2.rtc-dundalk.ie.
Opening Hours	09.00 - 21.00 (Mon. - Thurs.), 09.00 - 17.00 (Fri.). Saturday opening during exams.
Services Offered	Document Access - loans; Document Delivery; Information Skills Training; Learner Support; Information Services to North East Border Region; Euro Information Point for East Border Region.
Special Collections	Architecture; Building Surveying; Food Science; Management.
Bookstock	31,491 - 30,000 available for loan (to members of college and external clients) and ILL.
Periodicals	314 titles - back issues only available for loan and ILL; will photocopy.
A/V Stock	100 audio-cassettes, 30 video-cassettes, 10 multimedia packs - available for loan; not available for ILL; 20 compact disks - not available for loan or ILL.
Catalogue	Datatrek Library System, OPAC searchable by author, title, subject, keyword.
Classification	Dewey 20.
Computer Equipment	6 PCs available for public use; 3 Multimedia workstations; 3 Printers for public use.
Other Equipment	4 Microform readers; Photocopiers; Video recorders; Cassette recorders.

REGIONAL TECHNICAL COLLEGE - GALWAY
Dublin Road,
Galway,
Tel: Galway (091) 753161/770555 ext. 2215/2113/2216/2121/2122
Fax: Galway (091) 751107
E-mail: ajoyce@aran.rtc-galway.ie
Telnet: library.rtc-galway.ie Login: opac

Librarian	Ann Joyce Walsh
No. of Staff	7 (3 Professional, 4 Non-professional).
Branch Libraries	GALWAY RTC - CASTLEBAR CAMPUS, St. Marys, Castlebar, Co. Mayo; Tel: (094) 25744, Fax: (094) 25757, E-mail: ann@crtcl.rtc-galway.ie; (Anne Walsh, Librarian). SCHOOL OF FINE WOODWORK AND DESIGN, Connemara West Centre, Letterfrack, Co. Galway; Tel: (095) 41047/41044, Fax: (095) 41112.
Opening Hours	09.30 - 17.30 (Mon. - Fri.), 18.30 - 21.30 (Mon. - Fri.) extended to 22.00. Last term: 18.30 - 21.00 (Fri.), 10.00 - 13.00 (Sat.).
Services Offered	Services to staff and students of college; Reference services to others on request; ILL; Photocopying.
Special Collections	Deposit Library for unreported Irish Law Reports since 1980; Diocesan Collection.
Bookstock	44,000 volumes - c.35,000 available for loan and ILL.
Periodicals	310 titles - not available for loan or ILL; will photocopy.
A/V Stock	Audio-cassettes, compact disks, video-cassettes, multimedia packs - not available for loan or ILL.
Catalogue	URICA on-line.
Classification	Dewey.
Computer Equipment	Motorola; PCs; Macs; CD-ROMs; Self-service Issue; Scanning Equipment; Multimedia PCs.
Other Equipment	Microform reader/printers; 3 Photocopiers; TVs/Videos; Cassette Recorders; Tape/slide machine.

Port Road,
Letterkenny,
Co. Donegal.
Tel: Letterkenny (074) 24888
Fax: Letterkenny(074) 24879
E-mail: jdevlin@janice.rtc-letterkenny.ie

Librarian	John Devlin
No. of Staff	6 (1 Professional, 2 Non-professional, 3 Part-time).
Opening Hours	09.00 - 13.00, 14.00 - 17.30, 18.00 - 22.00 (Mon. - Fri.), 10.00 - 13.00 (Sat.). Third Term: 10.00 - 13.00, 14.00 - 17.00 (Sat.).
Branches	ST. CONAL'S BUSINESS, DESIGN LIBRARY, High Road, Letterkenny, Co. Donegal; Tel: (074) 24888 ext. 4176, Fax: (074) 24879; (Seán O'Duibhilín, Librarian). ST. CONAL'S FINE ART, DESIGN, GRAPHICS LIBRARY, High Road, Letterkenny, Co. Donegal; Tel: (074) 24888 ext. 4176, Fax: (074) 25640. (Seán O'Duibhilín, Librarian).
Services Offered	On-line searching; Internet access; ILL; Microfilm and fiche access; Photocopying of O.S. maps, etc.; Access for local schools and industry.
Special Collections	Fine Art; Design/Graphics; Business Studies; Marketing; Food Technology; Russian Language and Culture; Irish Language; Donegal; Electronics; Computing; Chemistry; Biology.
Bookstock	30,000 volumes - 29,000 available for loan and ILL.
Periodicals	320 titles - not available for loan or ILL; will photocopy.
A/V Stock	250 audio-cassettes, 50 video-cassettes - available for loan and ILL; 10 compact disks - not available for loan or ILL; 100 multimedia packs - available for loan; not available for ILL.
Other Materials	Irish Times on Microfilm (1980 -);

Sunday Tribune on Microfilm (1980 -);
1,000 Fine Art Slides.

Catalogue	AACR2.
Classification	Dewey 20th Edition and supplements.
Computer Equipment	Bookshelf system to be upgraded to Heritage system, covers two campuses - 5 terminals; 4 CD Readers on two campuses.
Other Equipment	Microform reader/printer Minolta RP6072; 2 Photocopiers; 1 Bell & Microfiche reader.

290 REGIONAL TECHNICAL COLLEGE - LIMERICK
Moylish Park,
Limerick.
Tel: Limerick (061) 327688 ext. 265/266/267
Fax: Limerick (061) 327696
E-mail: jminihan@rsl.rtc-limerick.ie

Librarian	Joan M. Minihan
No. of Staff	7 (3 Professional, 3 Non-professional, 1 Part-time).
Departmental Libraries	ART LIBRARY, Clare Street, Limerick; Tel: (061) 327688 ext. 380/381 (Joan Minihan, Brid Foster, Librarians).
Opening Hours	Moylish: 09.30 - 21.00 (Mon. - Thurs.), 09.30 - 17.00 (Fri). Clare Street Campus: 09.30 - 13.00, 13.30 - 20.30 (Mon. - Wed.), 09.30 - 13.00, 13.30 - 17.30 (Thurs., Fri.).
Services Offered	Lending; Information and Reference; CD-ROM searching; Microfiche Information Systems; Video viewing; Language learning facilities; Photocopying; ILL; Binding; Scanning.
Special Collections	Building (7 Barbour Index Libraries on Microfiche - Technical, Engineering, Property and Estate Management, Product, Town Planning, Health/Safety and Environment, Water Quality); Art Collection including large slide collection;

	Product Data.
Bookstock	22,000 volumes - 95% available for loan (to students/staff of the college) and ILL.
Periodicals	150 titles - available for loan and ILL; will photocopy.
A/V Stock	100 audio-cassettes, 10 compact disks (networked), 600 video-cassettes (Art and English), 10 multimedia packs (mainly language course and Encarta, Art Gallery, Grolier Encyclopedia)- not available for loan or ILL.
Catalogue	Author, Title, Dewey class number.
Classification	Dewey
Computer Equipment	In-house system run on Wang 486 (standalone), programme written on dBase.
Other Equipment	TV/Video unit; 6 Microfiche readers; 2 Microfiche reader/printers; Photocopiers; 3 Language laboratories; 1 Laserprinter.

REGIONAL TECHNICAL COLLEGE - SLIGO   291
Ballinode,
Sligo.
Tel: Sligo (071) 55305/55246
Fax: Sligo (071) 44096
E-mail: jforan@54.rtc-sligo.ie

Librarian	Jim Foran
No. of Staff	7 (2 Professional, 5 Non-professional).
Opening Hours	10.00 - 17.00, 18.00 - 22.00 (Mon. - Thurs.), 10.00 - 17.00 (Fri.), 10.00 - 14.00 (Sat.).
Services Offered	Lending; Reference (including CD-ROM, Databases, Internet Access); ILL.
Special Collections	Business; Environmental Science; Engineering; Quality Assurance; Art and Design; Social Studies; Health and Safety; Irish Official Publications; Irish Language.
Bookstock	20,000 volumes - 17,000 available for loan (to staff, students and registered external readers) and ILL (using BLLD form).
Periodicals	150 titles - available for loan (to staff and students); not available for ILL; will

	photocopy.
A/V Stock	40 audio-cassettes, 20 video-cassettes - available for loan to staff and students, not available for ILL.
Other Materials	300 Art catalogues, 500 Slides - available for loan to staff and students; not available for ILL.
Catalogue	Author, Title, Subject, Classified.
Classification	Dewey 20th edition.
Computer Equipment	10 PCs; 7 CD-ROM drives on network; 1 HP Net Server; 2 Modems; CD-ROMs: ABI Inform; Poltox II, III; Art Index; CITIS; OSH-CD; Analytical Abstracts; Material Safety Data Sheets; DTI Manager Services; Word; Excel; Procomm.
Other Equipment	1 Microfiche reader/printer; 2 Photocopiers; 1 Datacard/Image Card System (Student ID generation).

292 REGIONAL TECHNICAL COLLEGE - TALLAGHT
Tallaght,
Dublin 24.
Tel: Dublin (01) 459 8888
Fax: Dublin (01) 459 8989
E-mail: library@staffmail.rtc-tallaght.ie

Librarian	Mary Orford
No. of Staff	7 (1 Professional, 2 Non-professional, 4 Part-time).
Opening Hours	Term: 09.00 - 21.00 (Mon. - Thurs.), 09.00 - 17.00 (Fri.), 10.00 - 13.00 (Sat.). Outside term : 09.00 - 17.00 (Mon. - Fri.).
Services Offered	Library service available to staff and students of RTC Tallaght; External members: application to librarian.
Special Collections	Business and social studies; Engineering; Agricultural engineering; Health science; Agribusiness; Boat building; Electronics; Computers.
Bookstock	c.13,000 volumes - available for loan (except reference/short loan) and ILL.

Periodicals	200 titles - available for loan to staff only, not available for ILL; will photocopy. Some back issues on microfiche.
A/V Stock	180 audio-cassettes, 10 compact disks, 150 video-cassettes - not available for loan or ILL.
Other Materials	Barbour Microfiles: Environmental Health, Fire and Safety.
Catalogue	Automated.
Classification	Dewey.
Computer Equipment	Horizon automated system (Circulation, Cataloguing and OPAC modules); CD-ROMs: BNB, Compton's Multimedia Encyclopaedia, Justis Celex, Applied Science, Medline, Current Contents, ILI Standards, Dictionary of Organic Compounds, Kirk-Othner Encyclopaedia; 5 PCs (Wang) and 2 CD-ROM drives Minitel.
Other Equipment	Microfiche reader/printer (Minolta); 1 Microfiche reader (Minolta); 2 Rank Xerox copiers; 2 TV/Video Monitors.

REGIONAL TECHNICAL COLLEGE - TRALEE 293
Clash,
Tralee,
Co. Kerry.
Tel: Tralee (066) 24666
Fax: Tralee (066) 25711
E-mail: jcooke@staffmail.rtc-tralee.ie

Librarian	John Cooke
No. of Staff	6 (5 Professional, 1 Part-time).
Opening Hours	Term: 09.00 - 21.30 (Mon. - Thurs.), 09.00 - 17.00 (Fri.).
Services Offered	Photocopying; ILL; Internet Searching; CD-ROM Searching.
Special Collections	Barbour Index: Construction and Engineering on microfiche.
Bookstock	27,000 volumes - 95% available for loan (to staff and students) and ILL.
Periodicals	250 titles - not available for loan or ILL;

293 REGIONAL TECHNICAL COLLEGE - TRALEE continued

	will photocopy.
A/V Stock	15 audio-cassettes, 10 video-cassettes, 5 multimedia packs - available for loan and ILL.
Catalogue	OPAC.
Classification	Dewey.
Computer Equipment	7 PCs; 1 Dell mainframe computer; Library System: DYNIX Horizon running on OS/2; Windows; Microsoft Word; Excel; Access; CD-ROMs: Current Contents (5 issues), Life Sciences, Eurocat, Information Finder, McCarthy, TES Bookfind, CITIS, ECCTIS, BNB.
Other Equipment	Microform reader/printer; 3 Microform readers; 2 Photocopiers with Copydex units; 3 Laserjet printers.

294 REGIONAL TECHNICAL COLLEGE - WATERFORD
Cork Road,
Waterford.
Tel: Waterford (051) 75934
Fax: Waterford (051) 78292
E-mail: library@rtc-waterford.ie

Librarian	Ted Lynch, MA, ATII, Dip. Lib.
No. of Staff	12 (3 Professional, 9 Non-professional, 3 Part-time).
Branch Libraries	ART COLLEGE, Newgate Street, Waterford; Tel: (051) 75934 ext. 2262, Fax and E-mail (see above). COLLEGE STREET CAMPUS LIBRARY, College Street, Waterford; Tel: (051) 75934 ext. 2262, Fax and E-mail (see above); (Jenny Maloney, BA ALA).
Opening Hours	09.15 - 21.00 (Mon. - Thurs.), 09.15 - 17.00 (Fri.), 09.00 - 13.00 (Sat.).
Services Offered	Normal lending services to staff and students; Others on application to librarian; Access to Networked resources for staff and students of the college; Photocopying; ILL.

Special Collections	Music; Art; Childcare; Nursing.
Bookstock	39,500 volumes - c.34,000 available for loan (to registered staff and students; external borrower in some circumstances) and ILL (E-mail: elynch@rtc-waterford.ie.
Periodicals	220 titles - not available for loan or ILL, will photocopy.
A/V Stock	390 audio-cassettes, 310 compact disks - - available for loan; not normally available for ILL; 300 video-cassettes - not normally available for loan or ILL; 154 multimedia packs - available for loan to staff; not available for ILL; 28 Music A/V sets - available for loan to students and staff.
Catalogue	Horizon Electronic Catalogue (8 OPACs).
Classification	Dewey - modified where appropriate.
Computer Equipment	Library Control System - Horizon; ILL - Minimil (Uni. Portsmouth); Acquisitions - In-house MS Access database; CD-ROMs: OCLC, Bookbank, Barbour Index, ABI Inform, Factfinder, Financial Times, Justis Weekly Law Reports, Justis Celex, Compuserve, Compuselect, McGraw Hill Encyclopaedia; CD-ROM Learning Resources (Business Science and Language), Library Multimedia Suite (30 multimedia workstations).
Other Equipment	Microform reader/printer for Music and Architecture; Microfiches; 3 Photocopiers. 10 A/V Work stations with access to satellite foreign language broadcasting.

ROYAL COLLEGE OF PHYSICIANS OF IRELAND   295
6, Kildare Street,
Dublin 2.
Tel: Dublin (01) 661 6677
Fax: Dublin (01) 676 3989

Librarian	Robert W. Mills
No. of Staff	1 (Professional).
Opening Hours	09.30 - 13.00, 14.00 - 17.00 (Mon. - Fri.).
Services Offered	Services to members of the medical

ROYAL COLLEGE OF PHYSICIANS OF IRELAND continued

	profession; Others at the Librarian's discretion; Photocopying; ILL.
Special Collections	Kirkpatrick Collection (Irish medical history); Churchill Collection (Obstetrics); Robert Travers Collection (Fine books); College and general Irish medical archives (17th Century to date).
Subject Specialisation	Medical History.
Bookstock	30,000 volumes.
Periodicals	25 current titles.
A/V Stock	Medical portraits.
Catalogue	Author; Part classified (card).
Classification	Own scheme.

296 ROYAL COLLEGE OF SURGEONS IN IRELAND
Mercer Street Lower,
Dublin 2.
Tel: Dublin (01) 402 2411
Fax: Dublin (01) 402 2457
E-mail: library@rcsi.ie
Telnet: Dublin (01) 478 2515 (8 bits, no parity)

Librarian	Beatrice M. Doran
No. of Staff	15 (5 Professional, 7 Non-professional 3 Part-time).
Departmental Libraries	BEAUMONT HOSPITAL LIBRARY, Beaumont Hospital, Dublin 9; Tel: (01) 837 7755 ext. 2531, Fax: (01) 836 7396, E-mail: library@rcsi.ie.
Opening Hours	Term: 09.00 - 22.15 (Mon. - Fri.), 09.00 - 17.00 (Sat.). Vacation: 09.00 - 17.00 (Mon. - Fri.).
Services Offered	Extensive collection of material on medicine, surgery and history of medicine; Reference enquiries welcomed by phone, post or in person; Document delivery; Photocopying; CD-ROM network; Internet access, On-line literature searching.
Special Collections	Arthur Jacob Library; Butcher-Wheeler Library; William Doolin Collection; Logan Collection on the History of Medicine;

	Bofin Collection on Forensic Medicine; Historical Medical and Surgical Instruments; Portraits, etc. Archives: Records of RCSI (1784 -); Records of many hospitals, including Mercer's Hospital (1734 - 1983); The House of Industry (1772 - 1871); Royal City of Dublin Hospital (1878 - 1965).
Subject Specialisation	Medicine, Surgery, Nursing and allied sciences.
Bookstock	75,000 volumes - 25,000 available for loan (to staff, students and graduates of RCSI, staff of Beaumont Hospital and registered external readers (fee payable)) and ILL.
Periodicals	650 titles - not available for loan or ILL; will photocopy.
A/V Stock	50 audio-cassettes - available for loan and ILL; 30 compact disks - not available for loan or ILL; 800 video-cassettes - available for loan; not available for ILL.
Other Materials	Medical portraits; Medical and Surgical Instruments.
Catalogue	OPAC - URICA.
Classification	DDC.
Computer Equipment	URICA Integrated Library System; Medline and other databases on CD-ROM (networked); Medical informatics laboratory with Macintosh computers; Internet access for students and staff; Hospital Information System (Beaumont Hospital Library).
Other Equipment	4 Microfiche readers; Microfiche reader/printer; 4 Photocopiers; Video players; Tape/slide players: Cassette players.

ST. ANGELA'S COLLEGE OF EDUCATION   297
Lough Gill,
Sligo.
Tel: Sligo (071) 43580/42785 ext. 215
Fax: Sligo (071) 44585

ST. ANGELA'S COLLEGE OF EDUCATION continued

Librarian	Evelyn Cooley
No. of Staff	3 (1 Professional, 1 Non-professional, 1 Part-time).
Opening Hours	09.00 - 13.00, 14.00 - 21.00 (Mon. - Fri.), 10.30 - 13.30 (Sat.).
Services Offered	Photocopying; ILL.
Special Collections	Home Economics; Religious Education; Education; Food Nutrition; Textiles.
Bookstock	15,000 volumes - available for loan (to staff and students) and ILL.
Periodicals	125 titles - not available for loan or ILL; will photocopy.
A/V Stock	210 video-cassettes - available for loan and ILL.
Other Materials	Charts; Educational resource materials; Dissertations from 1981 which are submitted by St. Angela's students as a requirement of the B.Ed.; Slides.
Catalogue	Card: Author, Title and Classified. In process of computerisation.
Classification	Dewey.
Computer Equipment	In process of computerisation; 1 PC and Laser Jet printer.
Other Equipment	1 Microfiche reader; 2 TVs; 2 Video recorders; 2 Photocopiers; Binder.

298 **ST. AUGUSTINE'S HOUSE OF STUDIES**
Taylor's Lane,
Ballyboden,
Dublin 16.
Tel: Dublin (01) 494 4966

Librarian	Nicole Marguerite Francoise Arnould
No. of Staff	1 (1 Professional, 1 Part-time).
Opening Hours	Not open to the public. Queries answered by telephone when the Librarian is there, usually Monday, Wednesday and Friday 09.30 -12.00.
Services Offered	Queries answered by telephone and letter; Photocopies provided of material essential to research.

Special Collections	The Library holds material on all aspects of Religion, especially its bearing on Irish History, and specially collects material relevant to the Augustinian Order world-wide.
Bookstock	7,000 volumes - available for loan to members of the Order only, not available for ILL.
Periodicals	c.30 titles - not available for loan or ILL; will photocopy.

ST. CATHERINE'S COLLEGE OF EDUCATION FOR HOME ECONOMICS
Sion Hill,
Blackrock,
Co. Dublin.
Tel: Dublin (01) 288 2342
Fax: Dublin (01) 283 4858
E-mail: library@sionhill.iol.ie

Librarian	Dara Breaden
No. of Staff	3 (1 Professional, 2 Non-professional, 2 Part-time).
Opening Hours	Term: 09.00 - 21.30 (Mon. - Thurs.), 09.00 - 17.00 (Fri.), 10.00 - 14.00 (Sat.). Vacation: 09.00 - 17.00 (Mon. - Fri.).
Services Offered	Current Awareness Service; Special services to Home Economics teachers; ILL; Photocopying; Reference.
Special Collections	Home Economics; Food Science; Fashion & Textiles; Education; Specialist School Library; Resource Centre.
Bookstock	18,500 volumes - 17,000 available for loan (to staff and students) and ILL.
Periodicals	170 titles - not available for loan; available for ILL; will photocopy.
A/V Stock	100 audio-cassettes, 450 video-cassettes - available for loan and ILL; compact disks - not available for loan or ILL.
Other Materials	600 Posters; Computer Software; Slides; Realia.
Catalogue	Card: author/title/classified.

299 ST. CATHERINE'S COLLEGE OF EDUCATION FOR HOME ECONOMICS continued

Classification	Dewey.
Computer Equipment	Apple Mac; CD-ROM.
Other Equipment	Microfiche Reader; TV/VCR; Photocopiers.

300 ST. COLUMBAN'S LIBRARY
Dalgan Park,
Navan,
Co. Meath.
Tel: Navan (046) 21525
Fax: Navan (046) 22799

Librarian	Teresa Caldwell
No. of Staff	1 (Professional).
Opening Hours	09.00 - 13.00, 13.30 - 16.30 (Mon. - Fri.) subject to staff availability.
Special Collections	Core collection: Mission studies, special focus on Third World issues, justice and peace. Older collection: Irish interest; General literature; Traditional seminary subjects. Periodical Collection: Number of periodicals on China. Audio Visual Collection: number of 16mm films and VHS videos on mission.
Bookstock	3 volumes (professional/vocational interests) - available for loan and ILL.
Periodicals	93 titles - not available for loan or ILL; will photocopy.
A/V Stock	225 video-cassettes - available for loan and ILL.
Catalogue	Core collection: Computer Book Catalogue. Older collection: Card Catalogue.
Classification	Dewey Decimal
Computer Equipment	1 Commodore PC 486 sx-25; Smartware II, Microsoft Windows 3.1 and Gofer - text finder utility from microlytics.
Other Equipment	Photocopier.

ST. MARY'S COLLEGE
191, Falls Road,
Belfast BT12 6FE.
Tel: Belfast (01232) 327678
Fax: Belfast (01232) 333719
Telnet: 143 117 22 167

Librarian	Sarah Fitzpatrick
No. of Staff	9 (4 Professional, 5 Non-professional, 2 Part-time).
Departmental Libraries	TRENCH HOUSE SITE, Stewartstown Road, Belfast BT11 9GA; Tel: (01232) 617631; (J. Morrissey, Deputy Librarian).
Opening Hours	09.00 - 21.00 (Mon. - Thurs.), 09.00 - 17.00 (Fri.). Vacation: 09.00 - 13.00, 14.00 - 17.00 (Mon. - Fri.).
Services Offered	On-line searching; CD-ROMs; ILL; Word-processing facilities; Photocopying.
Special Collections	Irish literature; Irish history; Education; Children's literature.
Bookstock	100,000 volumes - 90,000 available for loan (to students) and ILL.
Periodicals	404 titles - not available for loan; available for ILL; will photocopy.
A/V Stock	2,000 audio-cassettes, 75 compact disks, 140 video-cassettes, 4,000 multimedia packs - available for loan and ILL.
Catalogue	OPAC.
Classification	Dewey 20th edition.
Computer Equipment	Nimbus Computers with 20mb hard disks; Apple Macintosh; Word Processing; Database; Spreadsheet; CD-ROM workstations.
Other Equipment	Microform reader/printer; Photocopiers.

ST. PATRICK'S COLLEGE
Drumcondra,
Dublin 9
Tel: Dublin (01) 837 6191
Fax: Dublin (01) 837 6197

Librarian	Evan J. Salholm

302 **ST. PATRICK'S COLLEGE** continued

No. of Staff	7 (2 Professional, 5 Non-professional).
Opening Hours	Term: 10.00 - 22.00 (Mon. - Thur.), 10.00 - 17.30 (Fri.), 10.00 - 13.00 (Sat.). Vacations: 10.00 - 13.00, 14.00 - 17.00 (Mon. - Fri.).
Services Offered	Service to staff and students of the college; Access to others for study purposes by arrangement with the Librarian.
Special Collections	Irish school text-books; Children's books.
Subject Specialisation	Education
Bookstock	120,000 volumes - 115,000 available for loan (to registered students and staff) and ILL.
Periodicals	400 titles - not available for loan or ILL; will photocopy.
A/V Stock	All items held in College Resource Centre and A/V department.
Catalogue	COM Catalogue (OCLC).
Classification	Dewey 20th.
Computer Equipment	2 Digital Dec PCs; Use of OCLC database for current cataloguing and retrospective conversion.
Other Equipment	5 Microfiche readers; 1 Microfilm reader, 1 Microform reader/printer; 4 photocopiers (3 for student use; 1 for staff use).

303 **ST. PATRICK'S COLLEGE**
Maynooth,
Co. Kildare.
Tel: Maynooth (01) 628 5222
Fax: Maynooth (01) 628 6008

Librarian	Thomas Kabdebo, PhD, FLA
No. of Staff	40 (including part-timers, security men and contract workers).
Opening Hours	Term: 09.00 - 21.30. Vacation: 10.00 - 17.00.
Services Offered	Photocopying; Photography; Loans; Self-service typewriting; CD-ROMs.
Special Collections	RUSSELL RARE BOOKS, Library comprising all materials up to 1850

	(strengths: Irish Mss., Irish History, Irish Colleges); Bible collection; Arthur Griffith Archive; JOHN PAUL II LIBRARY: College Collection; Feminist Theology; Translations of literary classics.
Subject Specialisation	Theology; Arts; Sciences; Social Sciences.
Bookstock	180,000 volumes (including pamphlets) - 100,000 available for loan and ILL (except books which are either rare, pre-1850 or unique). Including documents and microfilms the physical total is 250,000.
Periodicals	3,000 titles (1,050 subscriptions, 100 exchange and donations) - similar loan facility as for books; will photocopy. Note: the volume total is over 20,000. Office documents: Careda, Ireland, EDC.
A/V Stock	500 audio-cassettes, 100 video-cassettes, records, 8,000 slides, films - not available for loan.
Other Materials	Games; 400 maps.
Manuscripts	500 sets of manuscripts which include Salamanca with 40,000 items - not available for loan.
Catalogue	Name, Title, Classified, Subject headings catalogue on-line from 1982.
Classification	Dewey, 19th edition and 20th edition in certain areas.
Computer Systems	URICA System; OCLC; ILL Lancaster System; First Search; Internet; CD-ROM, 7 databases, 2 stations.
Other Equipment	A/V viewers; Epidiascope; Video; PCs; Printers; Microform readers and reader/printers; Rapid binder; Photographic equipment; Guillotine; Binding presses; Temperature and hydro meters; Driller and other small binding tools.

ST. PATRICK'S COLLEGE   304
Thurles,
Co. Tipperary.
Tel: Thurles (0504) 21822
Fax: Thurles (0504) 23735

304   **ST. PATRICK'S COLLEGE** continued

Librarian	Martin Hayes
No. of Staff	3 (1 Non-professional, 2 Part-time).
Opening Hours	09.00 - 22.00 (Mon. - Fri.).
Services Offered	Reading and Reference facilities; Photocopies.
Special Collections	Theology; Philosophy; Irish History; General Church History; Pamphlet Collection - 18th and 19th centuries; Periodical Library.
Bookstock	23,000 volumes - available for loan to staff and students of College; not available for ILL
Periodicals	72 titles - not available for loan or ILL; will photocopy.
A/V Stock	120 audio-cassettes, 50 video-cassettes - not available for loan or ILL.
Catalogue	Card - Author, Subject, Title.
Classification	Own.
Other Equipment	Photocopier; Video viewer.

305   **STRANMILLIS COLLEGE**
Belfast BT9 5DY
Tel: Belfast (01232) 384309
Fax: Belfast (01232) 663682
E-mail: library@stran-ni.ac.uk

Librarian	E.J.W. McCann
No. of Staff	10 (4 Professional, 6 Non-professional).
Opening Hours	Term: 09.00 - 21.00 (Mon. - Thurs.), 09.00 - 16.30 (Fri.). Vacation: 09.00 - 17.00 (Mon. - Thur.), 09.00 - 16.30 (Fri.).
Services Offered	To staff and students, extern borrowers and others at librarian's discretion.
Special Collections	Ulster Collection; Early school text books.
Subject Specialisation	Education; Local history.
Bookstock	120,000 volumes - 110,000 available for loan (to staff, students and registered borrowers) and ILL (BLDSC forms).
Periodicals	500 titles - not available for loan; available for ILL per BLDSC forms; will photocopy subject to copyright.

A/V Stock	200 audio-cassettes, 200 video-cassettes, 200 multimedia packs - available for loan and ILL; compact disks - not available for loan.
Other Materials	Illustrations; Slides.
Catalogue	BLCMP member library; OPAC.
Classification	Dewey.
Computer Systems	Blaise, Dialog, Various CD-ROMs.
Other Equipment	Microform readers/printers; Photocopiers; Video; Sound recorders; Slide projectors.

TRINITY COLLEGE LIBRARY 306
College Street,
Dublin 2.
Tel: Dublin (01) 677 2941
Fax: Dublin (01) 671 9003
E-mail: radams@tcd.ie
Telex: 93782
Telnet: library.tcd.ie Login: opacg
EIRPAC/IPSS: 272 4360 5600134
Europanet: 20437250000504
Direct Dial: Dublin (01) 671 2322

Librarian	William G. Simpson
No. of Staff	120 (43 Professional, 73 Non-professional, 3.5 FTE).
Departmental Libraries	EARLY PRINTED BOOKS, Trinity College Library, College Street, Dublin 2, Tel: (01) 608 1172, Fax: (01) 671 9003, E-mail: cbenson@tcd.ie; (Charles Benson, Librarian). JOHN STEARNE MEDICAL LIBRARY, St. James's Hospital, Dublin 8; Tel: (01) 608 2474, Fax: (01) 453 6087, E-mail: catherine.whitney@tcd.ie; (Catherine Whitney, Librarian). MANUSCRIPTS DEPARTMENT, Trinity College Library, College Street, Dublin 2, Tel: (01) 608 1189, Fax: (01) 671 9003, E-mail: bmeehan@tcd.ie; (Dr. Bernard Meehan, Librarian). SCHOOL OF OCCUPATIONAL THERAPY, Rochestown Avenue, Dun Laoghaire, Co.

	Dublin; Tel: (01) 608 5126, E-mail: tpope@tcd.ie; (Thelma Pope, Librarian).
Opening Hours	Term: 09.00 - 22.00 (Mon. - Fri.), 09.30 - 16.00 (Sat.). Vacation: 09.30 - 17.00 (Mon. - Fri.), 09.00 - 13.00 (Sat.).
Services Offered	Circulation facilities; Reference Services; Reprographic and Microfilming Services: V. Morrow, Tel: (01) 608 1660.
Special Collections	Manuscripts; Early printed books; Maps; British & Irish Legal Deposit (1801 -); EU and UN publications.
Special Services	INFORMATION SERVICE, Berkeley Library, Trinity College, College Street, Dublin 2; Tel: (01) 677 2125, Fax: (01) 671 9003, E-mail: elizabeth.mcnamara@tcd.ie; (E. McNamara, Librarian) The Information Service is a commercial service for private and Government sectors.
Bookstock	3,200,000 volumes - 3,000,000 are available for loan (to academic staff from main collection; separate undergraduate lending collection) and ILL through ICLS/BLDSC.
Periodicals	12,368 titles - not available for loan or ILL; but will photocopy.
A/V Stock	47 compact disks - not available for loan or ILL.
Catalogue	OPAC (Author, title, subject, series); also printed and card catalogues.
Classification	Dewey.
Computer Equipment	Mainframe: DEC System 5000 Model 240; Library System Software: DYNIX (Geac from Oct. 1996); Networked CD-ROM services.
Other Equipment	8 Microfilm readers; 2 readers/printers; 11 public photocopiers; 1 risograph printer.

307   UNIVERSITY COLLEGE DUBLIN
Belfield,
Dublin 4

Tel: Dublin (01) 706 7583
Fax: Dublin (01) 283 7667
Telnet: library.ucd.ie (no password required)

Librarian	S. Phillips
No. of Staff	120 (40 Professional, 50 Non-professional, 30 Full Time Equivalent).
Departmental Libraries	ARCHITECTURE LIBRARY, University College Dublin, Richview, Clonskeagh, Dublin 14; Tel: (01) 706 2741, Fax: (01) 283 0329, E-mail: jbarrett@acadamh.ucd.ie; (J. Barrett, Librarian). BLACKROCK CAMPUS LIBRARY, Michael Smurfit Graduate School of Business, University College Dublin, Carysfort Avenue, Blackrock, Co. Dublin; Tel: (01) 706 8920, Fax: (01) 283 1991, E-mail: steele_j@blackrock. ucd.ie; (J. Steele, Librarian). EARLSFORT TERRACE LIBRARY, University College Dublin, Earlsfort Terrace, Dublin 2; Tel: (01) 706 7471, Fax: (01) 475 4568, E-mail: smurphy@iveagh.ucd.ie; (S. Murphy, Librarian). VETERINARY MEDICINE LIBRARY, University College Dublin, Shelbourne Road, Dublin 4; Tel: (01) 668 7988, Fax: (01) 668 9732, E-mail: angela.hastings@ucd.ie; (A. Hastings, Librarian).
Opening Hours	Term: 09.30 - 22.00 (Mon. - Fri.), 09.30 - 13.00 (Sat.). Hours vary in vacations.
Services Offered	Lending; Information, reference services; On-line retrieval; ILL; Document supply; Self-service photocopying.
Special Services	ARCHINFO - INFORMATION FOR ARCHITECTS, Architecture Library, University College Dublin, Richview, Clonskeagh, Dublin 14; Tel: (01) 706 2777, Fax: (01) 283 0329, janes@acadamh.ucd.ie; (J. Nolan, Librarian). DEVELOPMENT STUDIES INFORMATION CENTRE, Library, University College Dublin, Belfield,

Dublin 4; Tel: (01) 706 7560, Fax: (01) 283 7667, E-mail: salcor@ollamh.ucd.ie; (S. Corcoran, Librarian). SERVICES FOR STUDENTS WITH DISABILITIES, Library, University College Dublin, Belfield, Dublin 4; Tel: (01) 706 7636, Fax: (01) 283 7667, E-mail: dstokes@acadamh. ucd.ie; (D. Stokes, Librarian).

Special Collections   40,000 volumes of pre-1850 printings, and collections of special provenance, including the Library of the Catholic University of Ireland, Zimmer Collection (Celtica), Baron Palles Collection (Law), O'Lochlainn and O'Kelley Collections (Irish printings), Curran Collection (Irish literature), Kavanagh papers. SPECIAL COLLECTIONS, Library, University College Dublin, Belfield, Dublin 4; Tel: (01) 706 7686, Fax: (01) 283 7667, E-mail: jessop@acadamh. ucd.ie; (N. Jessop, Librarian).

Bookstock   950,000 volumes (including periodical volumes) - 425,000 available for loan (to registered users) and ILL.

Periodicals   5,000 titles - not available for loan or ILL; will photocopy.

A/V Stock   Substantial number of audio-cassettes, compact disks, video-cassettes, multimedia packs - available for loan but not ILL.

Other Materials   Gramophone records.

Manuscripts   100 (approx.) - not available for loan

Catalogue   OPAC; Card catalogues (closed).

Classification   Dewey.

Computer Equipment   BLS Library system on a Data-General MV9500 supports 60 processing terminals, 50 OPAC terminals and 16 concurrent network connections; 70 desktop PCs provide a range of office applications and are networked for access to E-mail, Internet and networked information services; A wide range of CD-ROM

	products is provided on 8 networked and 12 standalone CD-ROM workstations.
Other Equipment	15 Microform readers, reader/printers; 12 Photocopiers; Equipment for visually disabled readers; Video playback machines; Tape-slide players.

UNIVERSITY OF LIMERICK 308
Limerick
Tel: Limerick (061) 333644
Fax: Limerick (061) 338044
Telnet: lib@ul.ie Login: opac
Web site: Http://www.ul.ie/services/library/welcome.html

Librarian	Patrick J. Kelly
No. of Staff	54 (11 Professional, 43 Non-professional).
Opening Hours	Term: 08.30 - 21.00 (Mon. - Fri.), 09.00 - 12.45 (Sat.). Vacation: 09.00 - 17.00.
Services Offered	Information service (extensive use of electronic information sources); Current awareness service; Circulation; Self-service photocopying; ILL; Business & Technical Information Service (BTiS) for external users.
Special Collections	Irish and European statistics; Irish companies information; Irish, British and ASTM standards; European Documentation Centre.
Bookstock	145,000 volumes - 95% available for loan (to registered users) and ILL.
Periodicals	2,256 titles - not available for loan or ILL; will photocopy individual articles.
A/V Stock	1,600 Audio-cassettes; 500 Video-cassettes; 1,500 multimedia packs (including tape slides, teaching kits, language courses) - all available for loan and ILL; 50 compact disks - not available for loan or ILL.
Other Materials	6,000 other items (including Slide sets, Microform sets, Maps, Posters, Transparencies; Software programs.
Catalogue	OPAC (also available externally).

308 UNIVERSITY OF LIMERICK continued

Classification	Dewey 20.
Computer Equipment	URICA Integrated Library System (Acquisitions, Cataloguing, Circulation, OPAC, Serials) on McDonnell Douglas 19150 S with 45 ports (6 for external OPAC access); Lancaster ILL package on DELL 483; 26 dumb terminals; 22 PCs (Wang and Dell); 1 Apple Mac; 34 printers (including laser printer); Access via LAN to office system for Word-processing, E-mail; Networked products including CD-ROMs, Programming Languages, Word-processing, Spreadsheet and other software products; 22 networked CD-ROM drives, 6 non-networked CD-ROM drives; Minitel.
Other Equipment	4 Microfilm readers; 4 Microfilm reader/printers; Photocopiers (10 Public, 2 Office); Fax; Answering machines; Video players; Slide viewer.

309 UNIVERSITY OF ULSTER LIBRARY

Cromore Road,
Coleraine,
Co. Londonderry BT52 1SA
Tel: Coleraine (01265) 44141
Fax: Coleraine (01265) 324928
E-mail: n.gardner@ulst.ac.uk
Telnet: library.ulst.ac.uk
Web site: Http://library.ulst.ac.uk

Director of Educ. Services	N. Gardner
No. of Staff	148 (96 Professional, 92 Non-professional, 51 Part-time).
Campus Libraries	COLRAINE CAMPUS, (see above); E-mail: ee.urquhart@ulst.ac.uk; (E.E. Urquhart, Librarian). JORDANSTOWN CAMPUS, Shore Road, Newtownabbey, Co. Antrim BT37 0QP; Tel: (01232) 365131, Fax: (01232) 366849, E-mail: dc.shorley@ulst.ac.uk; (Debbie Shorley.

Librarian). MAGEE COLLEGE, University of Ulster, Magee College, Northland Road, Londonderry BT48 7JL; Tel: (01504) 371371, Fax: (01504) 325626, E-mail: pd.teskey@ulst.ac.uk; (Patrick Teskey, Librarian). BELFAST CAMPUS, University of Ulster at Belfast, York Street, Belfast BT15 1CD; Tel: (01232) 328515, Fax: (01232) 327278, E-mail: o.fitzpatrick@ulst.ac.uk (Olivia Fitzpatrick, Librarian).

Opening Hours	Term: 09.00 - 22.00 (Mon. - Fri.), 10.00 - 17.00 (Sat.) (also 10.00 - 17.00 for two Sundays at exam time). Vacation: 09.00 - 17.00 (Mon. - Fri.).
Services Offered	To staff and students of the Colleges; others by arrangement with the Librarian; Photocopying; ILL.
Special Collections	At Coleraine: Henry Davis gift of rare books and incunabula; Stelfox Natural History Collection; Denis Johnston Mss.; Henry Morris Irish Collection; Headlam-Morley Collection (World War I); Paul Ricard Collection (World War II); John Hewitt's library and manuscripts. At Magee College: Spalding Collection on Eastern Civilisations; Londonderry local collection; Irish Presbyterianism; Steward, Deuchanel and Witherow Mss. Collections.
Subject Specialisation	American and women's studies.
Bookstock	646,808 volumes - 638,451 available for loan (to staff and students) and ILL.
Periodicals	5,,396 titles - not available for loan or ILL; will photocopy.
A/V Stock	Audio-cassettes, video-cassettes; multimedia packs.
Catalogue	OPAC.
Classification	Dewey at Belfast and Jordanstown; Library of Congress at Coleraine and Magee.
Computer Equipment	BLCMP (Library Services Ltd.) Talis system currently running Circulation's Control and OPAC modules and soon to run Acquisitions, Cataloguing and ILL;

309 **UNIVERSITY OF ULSTER LIBRARY continued**

Access via UU network to OPAC, BIDs, First Search, Internet, Networked CD-ROMs. Each campus also has stand-alone CD-ROMs.

Other Equipment: Microform readers and reader/printers; Card operated self-service photocopiers.

310 **UPPER BANN INSTITUTE OF FURTHER & HIGHER EDUCATION**
Portadown Campus,
26-44, Lurgan Road,
Portadown,
Co. Armagh.
Tel: Portadown (01762) 337111
Fax: Portadown (01762) 350490

Librarian	Janice Scott
No. of Staff	4 (1 Professional, 3 Part-time).
Opening Hours	09.00 - 20.00 (Mon. - Fri.), 09.00 - 16.45 (Sat.).
Services Offered	Normal lending services for all staff and students; Reference; Short-loans for popular material; Requests; ILL; CD-ROMs; Access to PCs and Apple Macs; Photocopier; Facilities for group and private study; Induction sessions for all students.
Bookstock	8,500 volumes - 8,000 available for loan and ILL.
Periodicals	35 titles - not available for loan or ILL; will photocopy.
A/V Stock	20 compact disks, 10 video-cassettes - not available for loan or ILL.
Catalogue	Automated.
Classification	Dewey.
Computer Equipment	4 PCs (Multimedia); 4 Apple Macs.
Other Equipment	Photocopiers.

ROYAL COLLEGE OF NURSING OF THE UK - NI BOARD
17, Windsor Avenue,
Belfast BT9 6EE
Tel: Belfast (01232) 668236
Fax: Belfast (01232) 382188

Librarian	Rae Gould/Maureen Dwyer
No. of Staff	2 (2 Professional, 1 Part-time).
Opening Hours	Term: 09.00 - 19.00 (Mon. - Wed.), 09.00 - 16.45 (Thurs., Fri.). Vacation: 09.00 - 16.45 (Mon. - Fri.).
Services Offered	Loan service to those engaged in RCN courses. Reading and Reference Services to all RCN members. Others only on written application to librarian.
Special Collections	Nursing.
Bookstock	7,000 volumes - 6,700 available for loan to those engaged in RCN course; Not available for ILL.
Periodicals	50 titles - not available for loan or ILL; will photocopy at 5p per copy.
A/V Stock	Video-cassettes - available for loan (short-term only) and ILL.
Catalogue	Author; Classified (card). Changes and development imminent.
Classification	Dewey.
Computer Equipment	Changes and Development imminent.
Other Equipment	Microform reader/printer, Photocopier.

COLICO DIRECTORY OF ASSOCIATIONS AND ORGANISATIONS

312 AN CHOMHAIRLE LEABHARLANNA (THE LIBRARY COUNCIL)

Director	Norma McDermott
Address	53/54, Upper Mount Street, Dublin 2.
Tel:	Dublin (01) 676 1167/676 1963
Fax:	Dublin (01) 676 6721
E-mail:	libcounc@iol.ie
Web site:	http://dallas.ucd.ie/ ~ library

Constitution   An Chomhairle Leabharlanna was established by the Public Libraries Act, 1947. The Local Government Act 1994, in section 34 provides for the continued operation of An Chomhairle Leabharlanna as prescribed in the 1947 Act and allows the Minister for the Environment to make regulations for the purposes of the continued establishment and operation of the Council.

Functions   An Chomhairle advises local authorities and the Minister for the Environment on the development of public library services; establishing, maintaining and operating a central library; assisting and advising local authorities on the improvement of their library services; making recommendations to the Minister for the Environment in relation to such services.

Membership   The Chairman is appointed by the Minister for the Environment after consultation with the Minister for Education. Twelve members are appointed by the Minister for the Environment on the nomination of the following Bodies: Governing Body of University College, Cork (1); Governing Body of University College, Dublin (1); Governing Body of University College, Galway (1); Board of Trinity College,

	Dublin (2); Council of Trustees of the National Library of Ireland (1); County Councils' General Council (3); Association of Municipal Authorities of Ireland (2); Library Association of Ireland (1).
Activities	Provides an Information and Current Awareness service for libraries. Collects and publishes Public Library statistics. Operates a Small Research Grants Scheme. Provides the Secretariat for the Committee on Library Co-operation in Ireland. Administers the Irish Joint Fiction Reserve Scheme. Provides the secretariat for the Euro-Focus on Libraries. Provides accommodation for the secretariat of the Library Association of Ireland and facilities for meetings of library interest groups.
Publications	*Annual Report of An Chomhairle Leabharlanna 1947 -Irish Library News:* a monthly newsletter containing information on libraries and librarianship in Ireland. *ISBN Region K (Ireland) List:* a locations list using ISBNs of the holdings of Irish Libraries and the BLDSC; it is produced on a cumulative basis and is issued 4 times per year. *Serials Information News:* a monthly publication containing information on serial acquisitions, cancellation and retention policies of libraries; facilitates co-operation between libraries in the management of serial collections. *Tips:* a current awareness service for public library staff based on the contents page listings of 25 library related serials; photocopies of the articles listed are supplied on request.

ARLIS UK & EIRE 313

Administrator	Sonia French
Address	ARLIS/UK & Ireland 18 College Road Bromsgrove Worcs B60 2NE England.

313   ARLIS UK & EIRE continued

Tel:	(01527) 579298
Fax:	(01527) 579298
E-mail:	sfrench@arlis.demon.co.uk

Constitution	ARLIS/UK & Ireland is an independent body founded in 1969, which became an educational charity in 1995.
Functions	It aims to promote all aspects of the librarianship of the visual arts, including architecture and design.
Membership	The Society welcomes as members all those involved in the documentation of these fields and represents the profession to the outside world open to individuals and institutions.

314   ASSISTANT LIBRARIANS' SECTION OF THE LIBRARY ASSOCIATION OF IRELAND

Chairman	Pat Lonergan, Kildare County Library
Secretary	Jess Codd
Address	Tipperary Joint Library Committee County Library Castle Avenue Thurles Co. Tipperary
Tel:	(0504) 21555
Fax:	(0504) 23442
E-mail:	tipplibs@iol.ie

Constitution	The Assistant Librarians Section is a section of the Library Association of Ireland consisting of a committee and members drawn from the membership of the Library Association of Ireland.
Functions	To provide information, training, education for all grades in the Library Service below rank of county librarians.
Membership	Drawn from the Library Association of Ireland excluding county librarians (senior management) who have their own section.
Activities	Seminars; Annual weekend conferences;

occasional surveys on specific topics
related to library matters.

ASSOCIATION OF ASSISTANT LIBRARIANS, 315
NORTHERN IRELAND DIVISION

Chairperson	Ms. Irene Knox
Tel:	(0232) 381188
Secretary	Ms. Linda Clarke
Address	Reference Library
	Area Headquarters
	Demense Avenue
	Ballymenta BT42 7BG
Tel:	(0266) 41531
Constitution	The Association of Assistant Librarians, Northern Ireland Division is a sub-group of Association of Assistant Librarians - a group of The Library Association.
Functions	The main function is that of training for all types of librarianship. The Association is particularly concerned with the interests of students and younger members of the profession.
Membership	There are approximately 300 members
Activities	Training courses; annual weekend school; committee meetings; fund raising. The Association also operates a register of unemployed librarians for would-be employers.
Publications	*Link* - four issues per year.

ASSOCIATION OF CHIEF LIBRARIANS OF EDUCATION 316
AND LIBRARY BOARDS

Secretary	J.N. Montgomery
Address	c/o Belfast Public Libraries,
	Central Library
	Royal Avenue
	Belfast BT1 1EA
	Northern Ireland.
Tel:	0801 232 243233
Fax:	0801 232 332819

316 ASSOCIATION OF CHIEF LIBRARIANS OF EDUCATION AND LIBRARY BOARDS continued

Functions   To consider and recommend, or take
                             appropriate action on matters of mutual
                             interest or concern to the five Education
                             and Library Boards. To liaise with the
                             Department of Education (N.I.), Library
                             and Information Services Council (N.I.),
                             Association of Education and Library
                             Boards, Association of Chief Executives of
                             Education and Library Boards; to receive
                             reports from (a) representatives directly or
                             indirectly appointed on inter-board working
                             parties and committees (b) working parties
                             established to co-ordinate inter-board
                             library activities such as *Public Service
                             Information Bulletin, the Northern Ireland
                             Local Study List,* computerisation.

Membership   Consists of the Chief Librarians of the five
                             Education and Library Boards.

317 AVIT- AUDIO-VISUAL AND INFORMATION TECHNOLOGY SECTION OF THE LIBRARY ASSOCIATION OF IRELAND

Secretary   Tara Doyle
Address   Reference and Illustrations Library
                             RTE
                             Donnybrook
                             Dublin 4.
Tel: 2083357
Fax: 2083031
E-mail: doylet@rte.ie

Constitution   AVIT is a special interest section of the
                             Library
                             association of Ireland in existence since
                             1982.
Functions   AVIT aims to provide its members and
                             others with a forum for discussion and
                             information on topics of interest in the
                             audio visual and information technology
                             fields. It is particularly concerned with the
                             development and impact of audio visual

and information technologies within the library and information environment.

Membership	280
Activities	Seminars, Workshops, Conferences, Visits, Occasional publications.

BRITISH AND IRISH ASSOCIATION OF LAW LIBRARIANS (BIALL) 318

Administrator	Susan Frost
Address	11 Lamintone Drive
	Lemmington Spa
	Warwickshire
	CV32 6SJ
Tel:	(0044) 1926 430000
Fax:	(0044) 1926 430000
Constitution	The British and Irish Association of Law Librarians was formed in 1969. It is governed by a Council which consists of four annually elected officers assisted by an annually elected committee of five.
Functions	To promote the better administration and exploitation of law libraries and legal units, by further education and training, through the organisation of meetings and conferences, publication of useful information, encouragement of bibliographical study and research in law and librarianship, and co-operation with other organisations and societies.
Membership	Open to individuals and institutions. Approximately 600 members.
Activities	Courses and lectures in law librarianship; visits; education and training; committee meetings; annual conference.
Publications	*The Law Librarian* - 4 issues per year. Moys, E.M. (ed.) *Manual of Law Librarianship* 2nd edition. Miskin, C. (ed.) *Directory of Law Libraries in the British Isles* 3rd edition. *BIALL Newsletter* - 4 issues per year.

319   CATALOGUING AND INDEXING GROUP OF THE LIBRARY ASSOCIATION OF IRELAND

Chairman	Mr. Peter Guilding
Secretary	Ms. Barbara McDonald
Address	Cataloguing Department
	Trinity College Library
	College Street
	Dublin 2.
Tel:	(01) 608 1659
Fax:	(01) 671 9003

Constitution — The Cataloguing and Indexing Group was set up in March 1981 as a group within the Library Association of Ireland to represent the interest of cataloguers and indexers.

Functions — To provide a forum to discuss matters of common interest in cataloguing, classification and indexing.

Membership — Membership is confined to members of the Library Association of Ireland. Non LAI members may become affiliated members of the group.

Activities — Seminars; workshops and lectures for members; liaising with other professional bodies at national and international level; disseminating information among members.

Publications — Seminar papers.

320   COMMITTEE ON LIBRARY CO-OPERATION IN IRELAND

Chairman	Mr. R.T.A. Farrow
Secretariat	Public Relations Officer: Mr. Kirby Porter
Address	An Chomhairle Leabharlanna
	53/54 Upper Mount Street
	Dublin 2.
Tel:	Dublin (01) 6761167 / 6761963
Fax:	Dublin (01) 6766721

Constitution — The Committee on Library Co-operation in Ireland was established in January 1977, succeeding the Steering Committee on Irish Library Co-operation. The Committee meets three times a year.

Functions
To promote inter-library co-operation and the exchange of information between libraries; to examine all aspect of library co-operation in Ireland and formulate proposals for action where necessary; to co-ordinate co-operative activities between libraries, ensuring as far as possible that co-operative arrangements between different types of libraries in Northern Ireland and the Republic are compatible; to monitor the Irish Joint Fiction Reserve Scheme operated by An Chomhairle Leabharlanna on the Committee's behalf; to provide liaison between Irish Libraries, the British Library and other similar bodies.

Membership
(a) Five representatives appointed by the Library and Information Services Council, Northern Ireland. (b) One representative appointed by the Library Association, Northern Ireland Branch. (c) Seven representatives appointed by An Chomhairle Leabharlanna (The Library Council) as follows:- two representatives of An Chomhairle Leabharlanna, of whom one shall be the Director, three representatives of Public Libraries in the Republic, two representatives of Special Libraries in the Republic. (d) Two representatives appointed by the Committee of National and University Librarians, of whom one shall be from the National Library of Ireland. (e) One representative appointed by the Library Association of Ireland. (f) One representative appointed by the British Library Document Supply Centre.

Activities
It acts as a formal advisory body to An Chomhairle Leabharlanna and the Library and Information Services Council, Northern Ireland on all matters relating to library co-operation and interlending. The

320   **COMMITTEE ON LIBRARY CO-OPERATION IN IRELAND**
continued

Committee monitors the ISBN Region K (Ireland) List; Serials Information News; Irish Joint Fiction Reserve Scheme. Establishes subcommittees from time to time e.g. Newsplan Steering Committee. The Committee collects and publishes the annual inter-library loan statistics of Ireland.

Publications   Annual Report.

321   **CONSORTIUM OF NATIONAL AND UNIVERSITY LIBRARIES (CONUL)**

Chairman	Ms. Beatrice Doran
Secretary	Dr. Alan MacDougall
Address	Director of Library Services
	Dublin City University
	Dublin 9.
Tel:	7045212
Fax:	7045602

Constitution   The Consortium of National and University Librarians (CONUL) was established in 1972.

Functions   To promote co-operation among the member libraries in furtherance of their objectives; to provide a forum for discussion for all matters of mutual interest and concern; to represent the collective view of the membership.

Membership   The librarians or library directors of:- Dublin City University, National Library of Ireland, Royal College of Surgeons in Ireland, St. Patrick's College Maynooth, Trinity College Dublin, University College Cork, University College Dublin, University College Galway, University of Limerick.

Activities   Meetings; collection and exchange of statistical and other information; working groups are established, as required, to address specific problems, to propose recommendations for action, or to share experience in particular areas of library activity.

COUNCIL OF R.T.C. LIBRARIANS 322

Chairman	Ms. Anne Walsh, Galway R.T.C.
Secretary	Ms. Joan Minihan
Address	The Library
	Limerick CoACT
	Moylish
	Limerick
Tel:	Limerick (061) 451344
Fax:	Limerick (061) 451707

Functions   To promote efficient organisation and management of technical libraries; to provide a forum for discussion and to consider the development of R.T.C.s as regional technical information centres.

Membership   Librarians of the Regional Technical Colleges are eligible for full membership of the Council. The admission of Librarians of analogous institutions is at the discretion of the Council.

Activities   Annual general meeting and other meetings as necessary.

COUNTY AND CITY LIBRARIANS SECTION OF THE 323
LIBRARY ASSOCIATION OF IRELAND

Chairman	Miss Ann Coughlan
Address	Offaly County Library
	O'Connor Square
	Tullamore
	Co. Offaly
Tel:	Offaly (0506) 21419
Secretary	Mr. Damien Brady
Address	Limerick County Library
	58 O'Connell Street
	Limerick
Tel:	Limerick (061) 318477

323 COUNTY AND CITY LIBRARIANS SECTION OF THE LIBRARY ASSOCIATION OF IRELAND continued

Constitution	The County and City Librarians Section is a special interest section of the Library Association of Ireland.
Functions	To act as a forum for County and City Librarians to discuss problems in the public library service and to advise and make recommendations to the relevant authorities.
Membership	Practising city and county librarians
Activities	Organise an annual autumn seminar; conducts surveys; monitors bookfunds; makes recommendations to the Library Association of Ireland on relevant issues.

324 EURO-FOCUS ON LIBRARIES

Chairman	Mr. S. Phillips
Secretary	Ms. Annette Kelly
Address	An Chomhairle Leabharlanna 53/54 Upper Mount Street Dublin 2.
Tel:	Dublin (01) 6761167 / 6761963
Fax:	Dublin (01) 6766721
Functions	Euro-Focus disseminates information on European initiatives relevant to the Library and Information sector in Ireland. The Secretariat for Euro-Focus on Libraries is provided by An Chomhairle Leabharlanna.
Membership	Representatives of (a) Government Departments:- Environment, Enterprise & Employment; (b) Library and Information Sector:- An Chomhairle Leabharlanna, Committee of National and University Librarians, Department of Library and Information Studies UCD, Forbairt (the Irish Science and Technology Agency), Higher Education Authority, Library Association of Ireland, Local Government Computer Services Board, National Library of Ireland and Trinity College Dublin.

Chairperson	Mary Doyle
Secretary	Mrs. Lisa Shields
	Librarian
Address	Met Eireann
	Glasnevin Hill
	Dublin 9.
Tel:	(01) 806 4235
Fax:	(01) 806 4247

Constitution	The Government Libraries Section was formed in 1984 as the Government Libraries Group. In 1995, it changed its name to the Government Libraries Section of the Library Association of Ireland.
Functions	To promote and develop the role of libraries in the Civil Service and to promote co-operation between Government Libraries.
Membership	Membership is drawn from staff in government libraries and others interested in the area (58 members).
Activities	Monthly committee meetings; visits to libraries; seminars.
Publications	*Government Libraries Information Newsletter* - (GLINT).

HEALTH SCIENCES LIBRARIES GROUP OF THE LIBRARY ASSOCIATION OF IRELAND 326

Secretary	Ms. Margaret Dillon
Address	Regional Medical Library
	Regional Hospital
	Dooradoyle
	Limerick
Tel:	(061) 229288

Constitution	This is a special interest group within the Library Association of Ireland, set up in 1987. It is affiliated to the European Association for Health Information and Libraries.

326 HEALTH SCIENCES LIBRARIES GROUP OF THE LIBRARY ASSOCIATION OF IRELAND continued

Functions	To provide a forum for members working in medical or health services libraries.
Membership	Open to members of the Library Association of Ireland with an interest in medical or health service librarianship.
Activities	Meetings, courses, seminars.

327 INSTITUTE OF INFORMATION SCIENTISTS (IRISH BRANCH)

Chairman	Michael Flanagan
Secretary	Barry Harrington
Address	Information Services Department Forbairt Glasnevin Dublin 9.
Tel:	(01) 8082000
Fax:	(01) 8082008
E-mail:	harringtonb@forbairt.ie

Constitution	The Institute of Information Scientists (founded in 1958) is the major professional organisation for information staff. The Irish Branch, founded in 1972 is one of four geographic divisions of the institute.
Functions	The Institute of Information Scientists provides a wide variety of services. Through the *Journal of Information Science* and the Institute newsletter *Inform* members are kept up to date with advances and developments in all aspects of information science and technology. The book publishing programme includes the proceedings of conferences organised by the Institute. Occasional publications include a members salary survey and a membership list.
Membership	Membership is open to suitably qualified personnel in the information profession. The Irish Branch has approximately eighty members.

Activities	The Irish Branch organises an Annual General Meeting in addition to 4-5 Branch Meetings per year. Strong links have been maintained with the Financial and Business Information group., which was established in 1994. Joint meetings have covered such topics as *"The impact of Internet on the information business"*, *"An overview of teleworking developments in Ireland"*, and *"IT strategies for public libraries"*.
Publications	The proceedings of the Joint Annual Seminar with the Library Association of Ireland (Universities and Special Libraries Group) are published each year.

IRISH SOCIETY FOR ARCHIVES   328

Secretary	Ms. Rena Lohan
Address	National Archives
	Bishop Street
	Dublin 8.
Tel:	(01) 4783711
Fax:	(01) 4783650

Constitution	The Irish Society for Archives was established in 1970 and is a voluntary organisation.
Functions	To promote awareness among the public of archives and archival matters and to promote the preservation of and availability of archives.
Membership	Membership is open to any individual, institution or society interested in archives or in the aims of the society. 150 members.
Activities	Meetings; visits; lectures
Publications	*Irish Archives* (Spring and Autumn publication).

LIBRARY AND INFORMATION SERVICES COUNCIL   329
(NORTHERN IRELAND)

Executive officer	Post Vacant

329 LIBRARY AND INFORMATION SERVICES COUNCIL (NORTHERN IRELAND) continued

Hon. Secretary	Mr. R.T.A. Farrow
Address	Library Headquarters
	1 Spillars Place
	Omagh
	BT78 1HL
Tel:	(01662) 244821
Fax:	(01662) 246716

Constitution   The Council is under the management of an Executive Committee. Following a structural review in 1996 there will be 4 Panels: (1)Government Libraries Panel (2)Training and Research Panel (3)Specialist Libraries and Information Services Forum, and (4)Local History Panel

Functions   To seek to achieve the highest standard in library services for all the people of Northern Ireland, and to co-ordinate the efforts of all Library Authorities towards this end; to promote and encourage the interchange of ideas on questions relating to the library services and to provide a forum for debate on such matters; to supply information and advice on library matters; to exercise vigilance in relation to all proposed legislation, regulations and administrative arrangements affecting library services and to take action, where deemed necessary, for the safeguarding or improvement of standards in the services affected; to provide a collective voice on library matters.

Membership   Organisations which, in the opinion of the Council make a contribution to library provision in Northern Ireland, shall be entitled to membership and be invited to nominate two members. Where organisations have non-librarians on their management committees, it is suggested that one of the nominees be a non-librarian.

| Publication | *Annual Report; Libraries in Primary Schools: Guidelines for good practice, Libraries in Post-primary Schools: Guidelines for good practice.* |

LIBRARY AND INFORMATION SERVICES COUNCIL 330
(NORTHERN IRELAND) - GOVERNMENT LIBRARIES PANEL

| Functions | To seek to achieve the highest standards of library services for the users of Government libraries and to co-ordinate the efforts of all the panel members towards this end; to promote and encourage the interchange of ideas on questions relating to the library services and to provide a forum for debate on such matters; to supply information and advice to users and managements relating to libraries in Government Departments; to advise on matters relating to proposed legislation regulations and administrative arrangements affecting Government Libraries and to take action where necessary for the safeguarding and improvement of standards the services affected. |
| Membership | Consists of:- (1) two representatives from each Northern Ireland Government Department and from other such organisations as the Panel consider would benefit from membership; (2) one representative nominated by the Executive Committee of LISC (NI); (3) not more than three additional co-opted members. |

LIBRARY AND INFORMATION SERVICES COUNCIL 331
(NORTHERN IRELAND) - LOCAL HISTORY PANEL

| Functions | To improve services to the public in the field of local history by communicating and disseminating information to all resource |

331 LIBRARY AND INFORMATION SERVICES COUNCIL (NORTHERN IRELAND) - LOCAL HISTORY PANEL continued

	providers, producing finding aids and information on resources and promoting good practice and developing standards.
Membership	Consists of representatives of public and academic libraries, the Public Record Office Northern Ireland, major museums and other related bodies.

332 LIBRARY AND INFORMATION SERVICES COUNCIL (NORTHERN IRELAND) - SPECIALIST LIBRARIES AND INFORMATION SERVICES FORUM

Function	To act as a point of contact between librarians with similar responsibilities and interests to eliminate the feeling of isolation; to provide a forum for relating experiences and exchanging views; to increase co-operation and aid problem solving.
Membership	Consists of:- (1) those librarians employed in libraries/information services other than public, academic or government departments (2) a member nominated by the Executive Committee of LISC (NI) (3) up to 3 co-opted members.

333 LIBRARY AND INFORMATION SERVICES COUNCIL (NORTHERN IRELAND) - TRAINING AND RESEARCH PANEL

Functions	To analyse training needs and identify and consult with providers. To identify areas where research is needed and present proposals to LISC (NI).
Membership	To be determined by LISC (NI) Executive Committee.

LIBRARY ASSOCIATION, NORTHERN IRELAND BRANCH

Chairman	Dr. J. Warner
Secretary	Ms. Elga Lague
Address	Central Library
	Foyle Street
	Derry BT48 1AL
Tel:	(0044) 1504 266888

Constitution	Branch of The Library Association (UK)
Functions	Professional liaison and development
Membership	450 members (approx.), drawn from all types of library and information services
Activities	Public relations; correspondence and lobbying of public officials; communication with members; organisation of conferences, courses, awards and social events; co-ordination of professional activities outside workplaces; participation in North/South activities, including joint LAI/LANI Annual conference.
Publications	Annual Report, *An Leabharlann, The Irish library* (jointly with the LAI).

LIBRARY ASSOCIATION OF IRELAND

Hon. Secretary	Mr. Brendan Teeling
Address	53 Upper Mount Street
	Dublin 2.
Tel:	(01) 6619000
Fax:	(01) 6761628

Constitution	The Association was formed in 1928 and incorporated as a limited liability company in 1952. It is governed by an Executive Board consisting of the Honorary Officers (President, Hon. Secretary and Hon. Treasurer) and 21 members elected annually. Twelve interest groups or sections operate within the Association:- Academic and Special Libraries Section; Assistant Librarians Section; Audio Visual and Information Technology Section;

335 LIBRARY ASSOCIATION OF IRELAND continued

Cataloguing and Indexing Section; County & City Librarians' Section; Government Libraries Section; Health Sciences Libraries Section; Meitheal Oibre (Irish Language Section); Munster Regional Section; Rare Books Group; Western Regional Section; Youth Library Group.

Functions
The objects for which the Association is established are:- (1) to represent the profession of librarianship in Ireland, to promote the educational and professional interests of members and to maintain the status of the profession (2) to promote and develop high standards of librarianship and of library and information services in Ireland.

Membership
Personal membership is open to persons employed in the profession of librarianship, or to persons with an interest in the work, welfare and progress of libraries. Institutional membership is open to libraries, corporate bodies, institutions or societies which have an interest in library or information services. Personal members may apply for Associateship.

Activities
Annual Joint Conference with the Library Association, Northern Ireland Branch; Annual and General Meetings; seminars; study tours.

Publications
An Leabharlann, The Irish Library - quarterly journal; *Directory of Libraries in Ireland* (both publications jointly with the Library Association, Northern Ireland Branch); Annual report; Professional register and membership list; Occasional other directory and conference proceedings publications.

336 MUNSTER REGIONAL SECTION - LIBRARY ASSOCIATION OF IRELAND

Secretary   Kate Coveney

Address	Old Mill Library
	Kent Street
	Clonakilty
	Co. Cork
Tel:	(023) 34275
Fax:	(023) 34315
Constitution	This organisation is a regional section of The Library Association of Ireland.
Functions	To encourage participation in library education and development and to act as a social forum for library staff in the Munster area.
Membership	Open to all members of the Association within the Munster area - public, academic and special and those with an interest in this region.
Activities	Annual one day seminar, evening lectures and demonstrations, tours and social evenings.

NORTH/SOUTH LIAISON COMMITTEE 337

Address	c/o Library Association of Ireland
	53 Upper Mount Street
	Dublin 2.
Constitution	The North/South Liaison Committee was established in 1962 as a joint committee of the Library Association of Ireland and the Library Association, Northern Ireland Branch.
Functions	To act as a liaison between the two Associations, and to promote co-operative activities within the library profession.
Membership	Members are nominated by the Executive Board of the Library Association of Ireland and the Committee of the Library Association, Northern Ireland Branch. The offices of Chairman and Secretary alternate on a yearly basis between these two organisations.
Activities	Annual joint conferences; meetings

337 NORTH/SOUTH LIAISON COMMITTEE continued

Publications   *An Leabharlann, The Irish Library* -
quarterly journal; *Directory of Library and
Information Services in Ireland* and
Conferences Proceedings.

**338 RARE BOOKS GROUP OF THE LIBRARY ASSOCIATION OF
IRELAND**

Secretary   Dr. Lydia Ferguson
Department of Early Printed Books
The Library
Trinity College
College Street
Dublin 2.

Constitution   The Rare Books Group was established in
1985 as a special interest group of the
Library Association of Ireland.

Functions   The promotion of the care and preservation
of early printed books in Ireland. The
cultivation of an awareness of the
importance of early books and special
collections.

Membership   Open to members of the Library
Association of Ireland. Non LAI members
also welcome as associate members

Activities   Seminars and informal talks on aspects of
early printed books and historical
bibliography. Visits to libraries and
collections of interest to the Group's
members.

339 READING ASSOCIATION OF IRELAND

Secretary   Patricia Hayden
Address   c/o Educational Research Centre
St. Patrick's College
Drumcondra
Dublin 9.
Tel: (01) 8373789
Fax: (01) 8378997

Constitution	The Reading Association of Ireland was established in 1975. It is a national affiliate of the International Reading Association.
Functions	To stimulate and promote interest in literacy; to sponsor conferences and workshops related to literacy development; and to disseminate knowledge helpful in the solution of literacy problems.
Membership	Membership is open to all persons interested in the functions of the Association. 150 members.
Activities	Meetings; seminars; annual conference; summer course; RAI Children's Books Awards (biennial); support of research.
Publications	*Reading News* (3 issues per year); pamphlets for teachers and parents; Conference Proceedings.

SCHOOL LIBRARY ASSOCIATION - REPUBLIC OF IRELAND BRANCH - SLARI 340

Honorary Secretary	Ms. Vivien Bond
Address	SLARI c/o The Library The King's Hospital Palmerstown Dublin 20.
Tel:	(01) 626 5933
Fax:	(01) 626 5933
Constitution	SLARI is a branch of the School Library Association.
Functions	It specifically reflects the interests and requirements of all those involved with and interested in school libraries in the Republic of Ireland by providing members with contact with others involved in school libraries at primary and second level; up-to-date sources of information provision; ideas for encouraging reading throughout the school and a focus for working towards better library provision in Irish schools.

340   SCHOOL LIBRARY ASSOCIATION - REPUBLIC OF IRELAND BRANCH - SLARI continued

Membership   Open to all with an interest in school libraries

Activities   Conference and seminars on many aspects of school library organisation; annual weekend training course.

Publications   Quarterly publication *The School Librarian*, newsletters.

341   ULSTER SOCIETY FOR BIBLIOGRAPHICAL STUDIES

Secretary   Mr. Wesley McCann

Address   c/o The Library
                            Stranmillis College
                            Belfast BT9 5DY.

Tel: (0801 232) 384312

Fax: (0801 232) 663682

Constitution   The Society was formed in 1989. The members annually elect an Hon. Secretary, Hon. Treasurer and Committee, who in turn invite a member to act as Chairman for the year.

Functions   To promote the study of bibliography in all its branches.

Membership   Open to all those who support the aims of the Society. There is an annual membership subscription - currently £5.00.

Activities   Monthly meetings are held from October to May (excluding December) on the third Thursday of the month. The Society also arranges visits to places and events of bibliographic interest. The Society meets in the Linen Hall Library, Belfast.

342   UNIVERSITY AND SPECIAL LIBRARIES SECTION OF THE LIBRARY ASSOCIATION OF IRELAND

Secretary   Ms. Catherine Watters

Address   c/o Tax Library
                            Coopers & Lybrand
                            George's Quay,

Dublin 2.

Tel: (01) 6610333

Fax: (01) 7048600

Constitution   The University and Special Libraries Section is a special interest section of the Library Association of Ireland. The business of the Section is managed by the Honorary officers and committee elected at the Section's Annual General meeting.

Functions   To facilitate communication and information exchange among members; to encourage appropriate education, development and training activities for library and information workers; to represent the needs and interests of members to the Library Association of Ireland Executive Board and other bodies as appropriate.

Membership   Corporate and individual members of the Library Association of Ireland who choose to opt for membership of the Section.

Activities   Meetings; seminars; workshops; visits; publications.

Publications   Various seminar proceedings.

WESTERN REGIONAL SECTION OF THE LIBRARY ASSOCIATION OF IRELAND   343

Chairman   Ms. Patricia Ffrench

Secretary   Ms. Bernie Lally
Library
Regional Technical College
Dublin Road
Galway.

Tel: (091) 753161 ext. 2215

Fax: (091) 751107

Constitution   A Regional Section of the Library Association of Ireland, the Western Regional Section is bound by the Memorandum and Articles of Association of the L.A.I..

343   WESTERN REGIONAL SECTION OF THE LIBRARY ASSOCIATION OF IRELAND continued

Functions	To promote librarianship among County, R.T.C. and University library staff in the West of Ireland.
Membership	County Library staff in Galway, Mayo, Donegal, Sligo and Roscommon; R.T.C. staff in Sligo, Galway, Letterkenny and Castlebar; staff in U.C.G.
Activities	Annual lecture at AGM; Study day trip; Annual one-day seminar.

344   YOUTH LIBRARY GROUP OF THE LIBRARY ASSOCIATION OF IRELAND

Chairman	Ms. Rosemary Walton
Secretary	Ms. Breid Ryan
Address	c/o South Dublin County Libraries 2nd Floor Cumberland House Fenian Street Dublin 2.
Tel:	(01) 661 9000
Fax:	(01) 676 1628
Constitution	The Youth Library Group is a special interest group of the Library Association of Ireland.
Functions	To serve the interest of all members concerned with library work with young people, through public libraries, schools and the community.
Membership	Membership is open to members of the Library Association of Ireland with special interest in Youth Libraries and literature.
Activities	Committee meetings; day courses, workshops and seminars on topics of interest to members; talks to outside interest groups.
Publications	Newsletter to members; booklists.

NAME INDEX
LIBRARIES,
INFORMATION SERVICES,
SPECIAL COLLECTIONS, ASSOCIATIONS

315

317

SUBJECT INDEX

INDEX OF DATABASES, SOFTWARE AND SYSTEMS

340

SOFTWARE

SYSTEMS AND
NETWORKS